W/D

THE NATIONALISTS

Volume XI of The Australians

Also by Vivian Stuart

THE EXILES Volume I of The Australians
THE SETTLERS Volume II of The Australians
THE TRAITORS Volume III of The Australians
THE EXPLORERS Volume IV of The Australians
THE ADVENTURERS Volume V of The Australians
THE COLONISTS Volume VI of The Australians
THE GOLDSEEKERS Volume VII of The Australians
THE PATRIOTS Volume VIII of The Australians
THE EMPIRE BUILDERS Volume IX of The Australians
THE SEAFARERS Volume X of The Australians

THE NATIONALISTS

Volume XI of The Australians

Vivian Stuart

(William Stuart Long)

AIDAN ELLIS

First published in the United Kingdom by Aidan Ellis Publishing Ltd.,
Cobb House, Nuffield, Henley-on-Thames, Oxon RG9 5RT

Copyright © 1989 by Book Creations, Inc NY 12029, USA.
Produced by George Engel & published in the USA under the title The
Nationalists

First published 1989

British Library cataloging data:

Long, William Stuart.
  The Nationalists.
  I. Title   II. Series
  823'.914[F]

ISBN 0-85628-176-X

Printed and bound in Great Britain by Redwood Burn Limited,
Trowbridge, Wiltshire

Phototypeset in Great Britain by AKM Associates (UK) Limited,
Ajmal House, Hayes Road, Southall, London

ACKNOWLEDGMENTS

I was assisted by many publications in the writing of this book, notably the following: *Omdurman* by Philip Ziegler (New York: Dorset Press, 1973); *Good-bye Dolly Gray: The Story of the Boer War* by Rayne Kruger (Philadelphia: J. B. Lippincott., 1960); *The Boer War* by Eversly Belfield (London: Leo Cooper, 1975); *Kitchener: Portrait of an Imperialist* by Philip Magnus (New York: E. P. Dutton & Co., 1959); and *A History of Australia* by C. M. H. Clark, Volume 5, *The People Make Laws*, (Melbourne: Melbourne University Press, 1981).

I would like to acknowledge with thanks the contribution of Eugene Janes of Darwin, Australia, who supplied information about the Aborigines.

Having adapted material from all sources to suit the story, I should say that any deviations from the historical record are my own. They are, I hope, pardonable in a work of fiction.

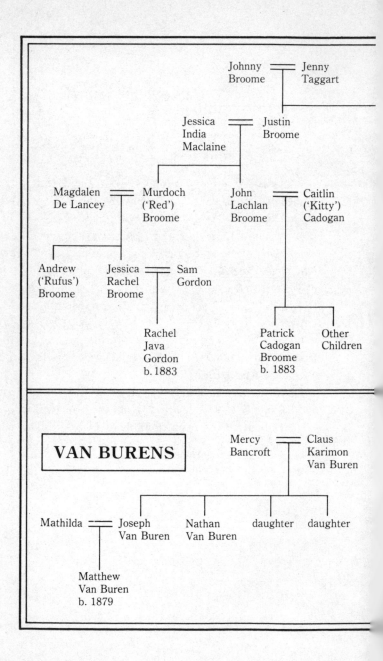

Johnny Broome ══ Jenny Taggart

Jessica India Maclaine ══ Justin Broome

Magdalen De Lancey ══ Murdoch ('Red') Broome

John Lachlan Broome ══ Caitlin ('Kitty') Cadogan

Andrew ('Rufus') Broome

Jessica Rachel Broome ══ Sam Gordon

Rachel Java Gordon b. 1883

Patrick Cadogan Broome b. 1883

Other Children

VAN BURENS

Mercy Bancroft ══ Claus Karimon Van Buren

Mathilda ══ Joseph Van Buren

Nathan Van Buren

daughter

daughter

Matthew Van Buren b. 1879

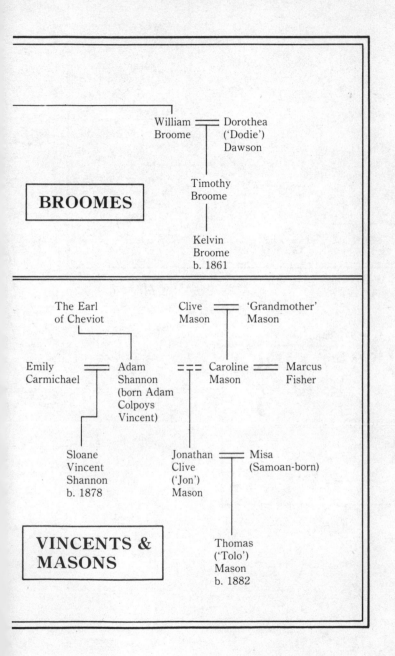

William Broome ══ Dorothea ('Dodie') Dawson

BROOMES

Timothy Broome

Kelvin Broome b. 1861

The Earl of Cheviot

Clive Mason ══ 'Grandmother' Mason

Emily Carmichael ══ Adam Shannon (born Adam Colpoys Vincent)

═══ Caroline Mason ══ Marcus Fisher

Sloane Vincent Shannon b. 1878

Jonathan Clive ('Jon') Mason ══ Misa (Samoan-born)

VINCENTS & MASONS

Thomas ('Tolo') Mason b. 1882

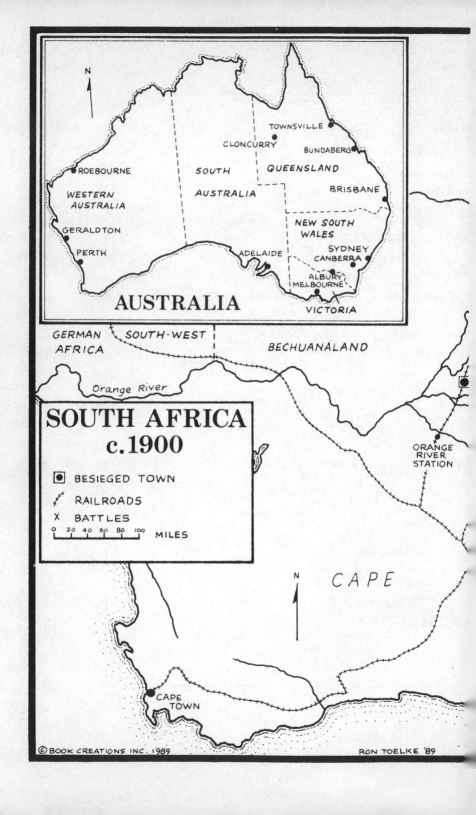

AUSTRALIA

N

ROEBOURNE

WESTERN
AUSTRALIA

GERALDTON

PERTH

SOUTH
AUSTRALIA

CLONCURRY

TOWNSVILLE

QUEENSLAND

BUNDABERG

BRISBANE

NEW SOUTH
WALES

ADELAIDE

SYDNEY
CANBERRA

ALBURY
MELBOURNE

VICTORIA

GERMAN
AFRICA

SOUTH-WEST

BECHUANALAND

Orange River

SOUTH AFRICA
c.1900

⊡ BESIEGED TOWN

⋇ RAILROADS

X BATTLES

0 20 40 60 80 100 MILES

ORANGE
RIVER
STATION

N

CAPE

CAPE
TOWN

© BOOK CREATIONS INC. 1989

RON TOELKE '89

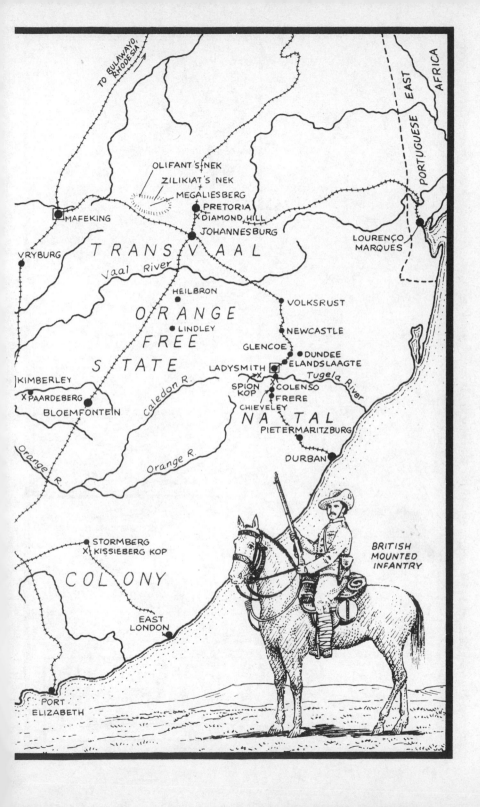

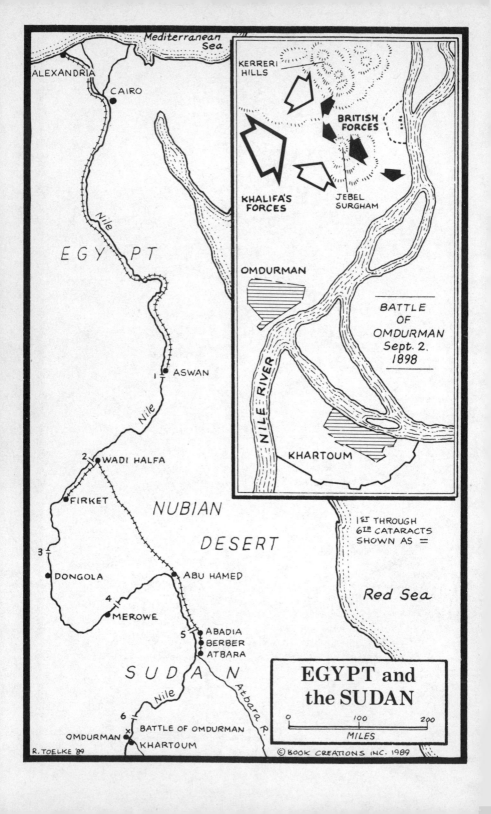

Mediterranean
Sea

ALEXANDRIA

CAIRO

EGYPT

KERRERI
HILLS

BRITISH
FORCES

KHALIFA'S
FORCES

JEBEL
SURGHAM

OMDURMAN

BATTLE
OF
OMDURMAN
Sept. 2.
1898

NILE RIVER

KHARTOUM

1 ASWAN

Nile

2 WADI HALFA

FIRKET

NUBIAN

DESERT

1ST THROUGH
6TH CATARACTS
SHOWN AS ═

3

DONGOLA   ABU HAMED

4

MEROWE

5   ABADIA
       BERBER
       ATBARA

Red Sea

SUDAN

Nile

Atbara R.

6

OMDURMAN   BATTLE OF OMDURMAN

×

KHARTOUM

R. TOELKE '89

EGYPT and
the SUDAN

0   100   200

MILES

© BOOK CREATIONS INC. 1989

PART ONE
1896 – 1899

CHAPTER I

In a grove of trees not far from the main house of a cattle station in Victoria owned by Jon Mason, a campfire flickered, alternating light and shadow across the faces of a half-dozen of the Aboriginal station workers.

An old man, a wise man, was speaking, his voice cast low in respect for the spirits of the night. His eyes were lifted towards the glowing heavens and the Southern Cross.

"In the Dream Time," the old man was saying, "no blackfellow. Only kangaroo, iguana, the birds. All bin walk like blackfellow. Him all the same blackfellow after he bin turn into Kangaroo, iguana, bird."

Jon Mason's son, Thomas, a serious youth of fourteen whose large brown eyes were glued to the face of the white-bearded old Aboriginal, had heard the story before, but he never tired of the tales spun so willingly by the old man. Beside him sat his mother, Misa.

From Misa, Thomas—called Tolo by all—had taken the grace and some of the darkness of her Samoan skin; from Jon, his English father, had come a face of sharp lines, a nose of assertive character.

Misa had her arm across her son's shoulders. She had matured in mind and body in the years since Jon had married her in Samoa and brought her back to his country. More shapely of hip and breast now, she remained thin of waist. She wore her ebony hair long, so that it brushed her shoulders, hanging in a loose cascade which smelled of flowers. Her features were not as broad as were those of most Samoans. Her lips were large but well shaped, her eyes huge, her smile a white blaze of pure happiness, especially when it was directed at Jon Mason.

With her husband away to attend to business in Melbourne and then to travel up to Sydney, Misa was free to pursue her special interest, the legends of the Aborigines. She herself was devoutly Christian, having been reared in a misson on the Samoan island of Apia, but she respected the old beliefs of the native Australians, just as she respected the beliefs of her own people.

The Aboriginal religion was totemic, based on the belief that all in the universe was a oneness. The ancient man's story about animals that walked like men was leading to the statement that the spirits of the men of the Dream Time had become the animals of the present day and, thus, were akin to men in spirit.

Misa glanced at her son, saw a look of puzzled concentration on his face, then lifted her own face to stare at the stars, letting the words flow past her. The Aboriginal explained that there is more of the sacred, the good in life than the profane, or evil. All things form a unity. Man is fused with nature in art, belief, life, death, past, present and future.

"I don't quite understand," Tolo whispered to Misa.

"Just listen," she whispered back.

A man begins his life as the spirit-child of an animal, or a pool of water, or even a rock. He is incarnated by his mother.

The old man did not speak specifically of it, but Misa had learned, somewhat to her bemusement, that the Aborigines believed sexual intercourse had only an incidental role in the conception of a child. Sometimes, she knew, native girls were a bit too casual about sex. She had watched carefully a relationship that had grown up between her son and a girl on the station, Daringa, who was, Misa guessed, about sixteen.

Until a few months ago, Tolo, when not at his lessons under his tutor, had spent his time with the Aboriginal boys, practising the native art of killing birds and rabbits with accurately thrown rocks or with the boomerang. But now Daringa occupied his attention. It had been her brightness and curiosity that started their relationship. Daringa had asked Tolo what magic was held by a book that he was reading, and he had tried to explain, then had ended up by beginning the process of teaching her how to read. When she showed aptitude for the lessons, Tolo had asked his mother for help, and thus Misa, too, developed a special interest in the bright young girl who was so eager to please.

Daringa's father was an intelligent man named Colbee, a valued and expert worker whom Jon had made his head stockman. Colbee was, however, a product of the old traditions, and his looks were dark and threatening whenever he saw his daughter reading from one of the white man's books. He had told Misa that he did not know what spirits were contained in the book, but he knew that they could not be of the land, because they had been brought in by the white man, to this ancient place the white man had renamed "Australia".

"You must not be so old-fashioned, Colbee," Misa had replied.

"But why does she read the white man's book?" Colbee had persisted. "She will never be white."

For that Misa had no answer. Indeed, the question had forced her to look back to her own trials since first arriving in Australia . . .

It had not taken long after Jon had brought her from Samoa for Misa to realize that her initial fears about marrying into white Australian society had not been groundless. Jon and she had discussed the European settlers' attitude that Australia was for people with white skin only, and he had assured her that he would allow no one to insult her. He had been true to his word. No man, no woman dared insult Misa—to her face, at least.

Jon Mason was one of Victoria's richest men, and consequently one of the state's most powerful citizens. Ironically most of his wealth had come from his stepfather, Marcus Fisher, whom he had despised so much that he had changed his name to that of his maternal grandfather. Fisher had perished in Samoa during a great hurricane in 1889, shortly before Jon's marriage to Misa.

That Jon and Misa had married at all was an act of a loving God. Years earlier, Misa had been one of many Polynesians, known as Kanakas, who were indentured workers in the Queensland canefields, lured there under false pretences by white Australians. She had given herself to Jon in exchange for his help in liberating her people and setting them on their homeword journey to Samoa. Out of that union had come Tolo. It was only years later, shortly after the hurricane, that Jon found Misa again—and was introduced to his son for the first time.

When Jon and Misa had returned to Australia from their honeymoon voyage, accompanied of course by Tolo, they learned that Marcus Fisher's body had been recovered on Apia and legally identified. By law all of Fisher's vast holdings now belonged to the stepson whom Fisher had formally adopted when Jon was a boy. The properties included a fine manor outside Melbourne, a town house and business property in the city, including a shipping company, cattle and sheep stations in both Victoria and New South Wales, and sugarcane plantations in Queensland.

Jon at first wanted nothing to do with Fisher's wealth. The man had so mistreated his mother, Caroline, while she was alive that she had been driven to drink and nearly to madness. "Misa," he declared when he received the list of Fisher's holdings, "I don't want that man's money or properties. I've been doing all right with my own trading activities. We're by no means rich, but I'll be able to provide for you and Tolo very well on my own, thank you."

Misa, however, had tactfully pointed out that Jon had inherited not only riches but obligations. "Don't they still use indentured Kanakas on those sugarcane plantations?" she asked. "I wonder if there are men with whips driving them to work harder. As owner, Jon, you could see that the Kanakas are treated fairly, along with the Aboriginal stockmen who are on the stations."

Jon, who had quickly come to respect his bride's surprisingly practical mind, listened attentively.

"Consider this, too," Misa went on. "Tolo, who is half-Samoan, will one day be alone in this country. I think that he will find less prejudice if he is very rich, don't you agree? So look upon the wealth that you have inherited from Marcus Fisher as security for your son."

Jon had accepted his wife's logic, for prejudice there surely was. Though he had been aware that he was going against Australian custom by marrying a woman of dark skin, nevertheless the virulence and extent of the hatred for her shocked him.

He would have been less surprised had Misa been a true blackfellow, a full Aboriginal. It was an accepted theory among white Australians that the unique Aboriginal population was a dying race, a subhuman species destined to wither away before the competition from the fully developed white race. And he had known that some of this same prejudice extended to any race of brown-skinned people, including Samoans and all of the peoples of Asia.

Nevertheless, he had not expected his own friends to shun his family. Living in the great house by the lake—where his poor drunken mother had imagined that white swans swam on the waters before the house—Jon had attempted to introduce his wife and his son to Melbourne society. He had met with so little success that he often wished he could take a gun and blast the smug, tight little smiles off the faces of the people who spoke to him in public—and ignored his invitations.

It was when Thomas began school and found himself taunted as a half-breed that Jon gave up on Melbourne society altogether. He took the boy out of school and hired tutors for him, a solution that suited the youth very well, since it gave him more time to be with his father and explore the outdoors. He especially loved the lake in front of the house, which his father now stocked with swans, in memory of Caroline.

Then Jon decided to abandon Melbourne altogether. He took his family to the most pleasant of his cattle stations, a move that pleased his wife and son. The station was close enough to Melbourne for Jon to make regular trips to town to attend to his prospering businesses there; seeing that his wife and son were happily situated, he soon began to make regular trips farther afield, to Sydney and Queensland.

He also began to raise his voice in the growing debates centering on the efforts to unify the separate Australian states into one commonwealth. It was a matter that would have consequences for the entire subcontinent and, indeed, throughout the entire British Empire. Jon felt it was odd that his opinions on such a public matter were given careful attention when, by contrast, the very men who listened to him in debate would not have him and his family home to dinner. He was getting a bitter lesson in both the power of wealth and the irrationality of bigotry.

On the night that Tolo and his mother were sitting under the stars with the station's stockmen and their families, listening to old Abo myths and watching the campfire flicker, Jon was in Sydney preparing for a convention of the Australian Federation Leagues, to be held at Bathurst, not far from Sydney, in November 1896.

At Caroline Station—Jon and Misa had renamed the large land holding northwest of Melbourne in honour of Jon's mother—

Misa had long since established her authority with a calm certainty, leaving no doubt in anyone's mind that with the master away one had best obey the mistress. For matters having to do with the cattle and sheep, the head stockman Colbee had primary responsibility, and Misa rarely ventured into his arena of expertise except as an interested observer—and then usually at the insistence of Tolo.

It was a beautiful life for a boy not long past puberty. Tolo was content, and as far as he was concerned, Melbourne could rot. There was water for skimming rocks and for swimming, and horses, and interesting stretches of grazing land that merged into the woodlands. There were several varieties of lizards to chase and catch. Now and then he would join in a spirited hunt when a morning outing showed eager boys the diggings and furrows of a night-feeding wombat. He also searched the woodlands for tiger snakes, whose venom was so virulent that one milking produced enough poison to kill one hundred and eighteen sheep. He had gleaned this information from a book in his father's library and had imparted it to his Aboriginal friends, only to meet blank stares. If anything, the Aborigines would have said that the tiger snake could kill many times more than one hundred and eighteen sheep.

Tolo got along all right with his present tutor, an Englishman named Dane de Lausenette. Born into an impoverished family, Dane proudly claimed that his French-sounding name had come to England with William the Conqueror in 1066 and had continued in an unbroken line since. He was a slim, handsome man in his mid-twenties, and in the early days, when he had discovered that Jon Mason was to be absent frequently from Caroline Station, he had envisioned intimate moments with the beautiful brown-skinned mistress of the house. But his one attempt at flirtation with Misa had been so coldly and finally rebuffed that he never dared try again.

Dane did not, however, let his rejection by Misa as a would-be lover depress him. Other females lived on the station, women of darker skin and coarser features, to be sure, but female nonetheless. Recently he had narrowed his attentions to Daringa, not because she was younger and more attractive in his eyes, but because she was close at hand. Tolo had made it easy for the tutor when he asked Dane to assist him in teaching Daringa how to read.

There were those who said that the Aboriginal proved his inferiority and demonstrated his less-than-civilized status by the fact that he had never invented any form of alcohol. Learned men wrote that civilization began when hunter-gatherer clans learned to ferment grain to make alcoholic beverages and settled in one spot to grow grain in order to have a constant supply of beer. Accordingly, the Abo was not civilized. Being unaccustomed to alcohol, he was easy victim to the white man's liquor.

It cost Dane de Lausenette only a bit of wine to make Daringa giggle and beg for more, and only a bit more to get her to agree to undress. After the first time Daringa was always willing to lie with Dane, in exchange for a glass or two of the tasty wine that made her feel so happy and full of ghosts. Her trysts were limited by opportunity to no more than one a week, and those became more and more risky when others began to notice a change in Daringa's actions and attitudes.

The first to become suspicious was a young stockman named Bennelong, to whom Daringa was promised. No longer was Daringa willing to walk into the forest with him, there to play the games that were allowed to man and woman so promised. In fact, Daringa now showed Bennelong nothing but scorn, an attitude that caused the young stockman puzzlement and anger.

Tolo, too, was spending less time with Daringa, and one day Misa asked him, "Why are you no longer giving Daringa reading lessons?"

"She says she has learned enough," Tolo replied. "She claims she's not interested in reading about white people who live far away."

On the morning after Jon and his mother had sat by the fire, listening to the old man's tales, Daringa was in the loft of a cattle shed, lying contentedly on loose straw, hands behind her head, a stem of dry grass in her mouth. Soon Dane would be with her, and the sensations would begin. She felt no guilt, only some regret that it was necessary to hide in a loft to enjoy love with the man of her choice.

She tensed in anticipation as sounds came from below. She raised herself on one elbow and was smiling when the tutor's face showed above the floor level as he climbed the ladder.

There were few preliminaries, and that suited Daringa well, for her body was more than ready to receive the strong Englishman when he lay down beside her on the straw.

The giving was mutual and strenuous, so that both were breathing hard when it was over. Dane lay on his back beside her.

"A spirit has entered me," Daringa said.

De Lausenette had not become as familiar with Aboriginal ways as had Misa and Tolo. "What I put into you was not a spirit," he said, grinning lustily.

"What I am saying," she told him carefully, "is that a spirit has entered me to become incarnate as a child. So you see, you will have to marry me now."

"Bloody hell," Dane said, sitting up and tugging at his clothing.

"But this is for the good," she said. "I wonder if our child is a spirit of the water, or perhaps of the kangaroo."

De Lausenette, recovering his composure, laughed. "Look, girl," he said. "How many blackfellows can also be father of your child?"

Daringa's thick-featured face pouted in puzzlement. "No blackfellows. Only you."

"Not on your bloody life," Dane said. "Look, Daringa, you know that what you're saying is bloody nonsense. I, marry you? Impossible!"

For the first time Daringa was feeling fright. It was fine, the way of nature, of the great oneness, to have a child growing inside her belly. It was the way of her people to accept the will of the spirits. Now it was time to marry, for the spirit-child in her had been aided by this white man, and his responsibility was clear.

"But I will be in disgrace," she said, "unless you, who aided me in calling the spirits, become the father."

"Look, Daringa," Dane said. "There's a very simple solution to this little problem. You say you haven't been doing the old slap and tickle with blackfellows."

"No," she said crossly.

"Then go to that young buck, what's his name? Bennelong? He has desire for you. This you have told me. Give yourself to him, and then the child will be his. Do you see how simple it is?"

Daringa frowned. "I will not lie to the spirits."

"You won't be lying to the spirits, only to Bennelong."

"The spirits would curse me, and the child." She lifted her chin and said firmly, "When I tell Mistress and my father they will see to it that you do as the spirits have willed."

"Now look, you," Dane said, in sudden anger, "you will not speak of this, not to anyone. We both agreed. You said that you would keep it a secret, for to tell would bring displeasure from your father."

"That was before the spirit-child entered me," she said. "You will not marry me?"

"No, damn it," Dane said. "Listen to reason, girl."

She leapt to her feet, pulling down her dress. "I will go now and tell Mistress," she said.

Dane caught her by the leg and pulled her down beside him. "You will do no such thing," he hissed.

She was surprisingly strong. She wriggled out of his grasp and scrambled to her feet. She was running towards the edge of the hay loft, for the ladder. He jumped to his feet and made a grab for her, but his feet slipped on the loose straw and he fell heavily, his weight striking the back of her legs. She was propelled forward off the edge. She gave one cry of alarm as she fell head first. There was a solid thud followed by a silence. De Lausenette looked down from the loft. Daringa lay on her side, her neck twisted oddly. Her legs jerked for a few moments, moving spasmodically as a chicken moves when its neck is broken, and then she was still.

Dane's only thought in the face of this sure knowledge of Daringa's death was to get out of the barn before someone came. He was not, at that moment, even sorry that she was dead. Her death, he calculated coldly, in fact cleared up a troublesome situation. He considered himself fortunate to have come into the employment of one of the richest men in Australia, and he had ambitions to be more than a tutor. He had worked hard to establish a good relationship with Jon Mason, and Daringa's announcement that she was with child had posed a threat to that relationship and the potential for future advancement in Mason's employment. Now all he had to do was get out of the shed and pretend that he had not seen Daringa since the last time he had helped Tolo give her a reading lesson.

He scurried down the ladder. He had to step over Daringa's bare black legs. Her simple shift was hiked up to show her thighs. He moved around her and started towards the door, then changed his mind and looked to the back of the shed, where a smaller door led into a cattle pen. And there, standing in the door, was an Abo boy of about ten years, his wide eyes fixed on the still body of Daringa.

"She fell," Dane said. "It was an accident. I was just coming into the shed when she fell."

The boy's eyes shifted to Dane's face, and Dane saw there a look of contempt that told him the boy knew all—that he had seen Daringa fall and then had seen Dane climb down from the loft. Dane turned and ran to the front door. The space outside was empty, and he ran to the house and entered his quarters.

He knew now that he had said good-bye to all his hopes of becoming an important man in Jon Mason's business empire. He had only one choice now: to flee, to leave Australia behind. First he would have to reach Melbourne, then board a ship. Fortunately he had plenty of time before Mason was to return from Sydney, and the overland trek to Melbourne would not be all that difficult. He considered taking a horse, but decided that to go back to the stock sheds would be too risky. Already the Abo boy was probably spreading the news of Daringa's suspicious death.

Dane took only bare necessities. He left most of his clothes and his collection of Australian rocks, but packed all of his savings into his small bag. He slipped out of the house unseen, he thought, leaving by a back door. Bending over so as to be less visible, he ran to the cover of a copse of trees and then crossed the stream to the dense woods. He would go cross-country for a while, for to take the Melbourne road would be too risky: on the highway the Abos from Caroline Station could easily run him down on horseback.

What Dane did not know was that Tolo had seen him hurry into the house, and the boy had gone to the tutor's room to see if he wanted to go swimming in the creek. Puzzled and curious when he saw the tutor packing in haste and leaving quickly, Tolo followed him.

The bush held no terrors for the youth, who had often travelled through it for miles, either alone or in the company of Abo boys. He took the strange affair to be a game, pretending that he was an

Abo tracker on the trail of an escaping criminal. He could not imagine that Dane, who was by no means a bushman, would go far into the woods.

When night overtook them and the tutor settled down to sleep with his back against a large tree, Tolo found a suitable tree, nearby but out of de Lausenette's unsuspecting view. Then he climbed it, propped himself into a comfortable fork, and was asleep almost immediately.

For Colbee, Daringa had been the last of several children by three different wives. Since she was the last blessing given to him by the spirits of the Dream Time, she had been of special value. To see her lying in the dirt of the shed, her neck twisted like a bird killed for Sunday dinner, was a deep sadness to him. He turned to the boy who had fetched him, signalling him to leave; then he stood alone and motionless over the lifeless body for long minutes. Finally he sat down, legs crossed, his knees almost touching Daringa's body.

The pained look on Colbee's face relaxed so that his expression was unreadable. His eyes squinted and seemed to glaze over, and he could no longer hear the sounds from outside, the lowing of a cow, the crow of a rooster. He sank deep, deep, and was transformed into pure spirit of grief, and in a place of blackness and warmth he sought answers.

The boy who had summoned Colbee could not keep still about what he had seen. He next sought out Bennelong, Daringa's betrothed, and ran after him as the young man hurried to the shed. Bennelong paused at the half-open door and looked in at Daringa's body and then at Colbee, who was still in deep meditation.

Bennelong yearned to go to Daringa's side, but from childhood he had been trained to respect the meditation of an old man. When an old man sat motionless by himself, he was never to be disturbed, for he was focusing his own thoughts to call on the *miwi*, the power. The *miwi* was located in the pit of the stomach, and with *miwi* the *wiringin*, the "clever man," could leave his own body to envisage things that were far away.

For the better part of an hour Bennelong stood in the open door while Colbee sat motionless. Meanwhile flies had taken the moisture from the lips of the dead girl, and the stench of her death-spasm excrement had filled the shed. When at last Colbee stirred and came back into his body from far away, Bennelong moved forward and knelt beside Daringa. He used his fingertips to close her eyes. Then he looked at Colbee.

"Do you see?" Bennelong asked.

"He flees through the bush," Colbee said. He pointed towards far Melbourne. "There."

"It is to be mine," Bennelong said.

Colbee nodded.

"Shall I help you carry her?" Bennelong asked.

"No. She is my daughter," Colbee answered.

Bennelong left the father to bend and lift the dead weight. He walked with his head erect, his eyes seeing into distances, to the cabin that was his, and had been intended for Daringa as well. He had the special things hidden in the bottom of an old trunk, carefully protected: emu feathers and hanks of human hair. He placed them on a table and, sitting down, took his knife and made a careful, shallow cut in the inside of his elbow. He let his rich, copper-smelling blood run into a dish. Before he had enough, he felt a bit dizzy, but he took that to be a sign that the spirits were talking.

He used the human hair to link together the emu feathers, cementing the union with human blood, which dried into a glue. There took shape two almost identical objects, circular, cupped. They were *kadaitcha* shoes, spirit shoes—more anklets really than shoes, having no soles to leave a distinct print in the dust.

Only Bennelong, in his tribe, knew the secret of fashioning the shoes. Only he had been appointed by the elders and the spirits to be the *kadaitcha* man—the man chosen to deal with anyone who broke the tribal law. As *kadaitcha*, Bennelong had one duty, to punish offenders. If the offence were serious enough, the punishment could be death.

He worked on the magic shoes far into the night. There was no hurry. The spirits—and the almost uncanny ability of the Aboriginal to follow a trail—would guide him surely to the man who had killed Daringa. The shoes would protect him against the white man's law, for they would leave no tracks, no trace of

Bennelong's vengeance. He was gone with the first light of morning, the shoes on his feet.

Colbee knew of Bennelong's departure without having seen it with his eyes. He had spent the night sitting beside his daughter's body, in communion with the spirits. During the long night it had seemed just and right that Bennelong was fashioning the *kadaitcha* shoes.

But with the dawn the spirits of anger and loss gave way to the spirits of caution. To kill a white man was a serious thing. Even if Bennelong had been made invisible and trackless by the *kadaitcha* shoes, the white man was not stupid. Suspicion would fall first on Daringa's male relatives, and then on the man to whom she was promised. If Bennelong killed the white tutor, there would be serious repercussions for all of the Aborigines who worked on Caroline Station. Jon Mason was a good man, a fair man, but not even he could accept the killing of a white man by blackfellows.

Dane de Lausenette was not making good time. Shortly after dawn he had entered an area of dense undergrowth, and he had to move carefully lest his clothing and his skin be torn by long, stiff thorns. Soon, he thought, it would be safe to cut to the east to the Melbourne track.

He sat down to rest. Suddenly he heard the snap of brush behind him, and his heart raced. He jerked his pistol from his belt and waited until he heard the noise again, closer this time. Turning and moving cautiously back along his trail, Dane hid behind a large tree and, as Tolo came alone, head bent to follow the tracks, he stepped forth.

"Bloody hell, boy, what do you think you're doing?" he demanded.

Tolo made a face, chagrined that he had been discovered, but still playing his game. "My question is, sir, where do you think you're going?"

"None of your business," Dane said, trying to act nonchalant. "But if you must know, I was heading south . . . to find a particular Abo village I've heard about. Seems their customs are a bit different from what we've seen around the station, and I was curious."

"You're headed in the wrong direction, then," Tolo said. "Since two hours before sunset yesterday you've been travelling directly west. And there are no Aboriginal villages that way for a hundred miles. It's too dry out there, even for them."

De Lausenette was fuming at being shown up by the boy. "Why did you follow me?" he demanded.

"To see where you were going. Shall we go back now?"

Both the simple question and Tolo's open look told Dane that the boy knew nothing of Daringa's death. "I think you'd better go back by yourself," he said.

"And if you lose your way again?"

De Lausenette shrugged. He looked up at the sun. True, he'd been stupid, but now that he had regained his senses, he knew he could go east and find the Melbourne Road. But then he realized that if he let Tolo go back, the youth would be able to tell everyone the direction of his tutor's travel. "On second thought, Tolo, I think you'd best stay with me and guide me to the main road. Once we're on the road, we'll meet someone who can give you a ride back home."

"I don't think you're interested in any Abo village," Tolo said. "It's not like you." He paused, scrutinizing the tutor, reading his expression. "You're trying to get away from something, aren't you? Why? What is it?"

Thrown off his balance by the boy's accurate guess, de Lausenette was momentarily speechless. "It's an adult matter," he replied at last.

"Is it because you've been tupping Daringa in the hay shed?" Tolo asked.

Startled, Dane asked, "How did you know that?"

"Don't worry," Tolo said, "we didn't tell anyone."

"*We?*"

"Canby and I," Tolo said.

"A boy about your age?"

Tolo nodded.

"You bloody little bastards," Dane said. "You've been watching!"

Tolo flushed and turned his head. "I'm sorry," he said, "I only watched twice."

"Bloody hell," Dane said.

"Canby said that Bennelong would be angry. Do you flee from Bennelong?"

"No, not at all!" Dane said heatedly. "What do I have to fear from him?"

"He's *kadaitcha*. If he wants to catch you, he can, at any time, and you won't even be able to see him unless he wants you to."

"That's Abo rot," Dane said dismissively. "All right, let's go."

"This way, then," Tolo said.

Tolo, who at first had been confused by his tutor's wanderings, was as surprised as de Lausenette by his own accurate guess that the man was fleeing something. He was not surprised, however, when, before they had travelled a mile to the east, Bennelong seemed to materialize from the bush to stand in de Lausenette's way.

The tutor's hand went for his pistol, but Bennelong moved with the swiftness of a striking tiger snake, knocking the pistol from de Lausenette's hand with the sharp point of his spear, his *nulla nulla*. The tutor jerked his hand to his mouth, for there was a cut and blood was oozing.

Bennelong spoke in a flat voice, a voice that made chills run up and down Tolo's back. "You have killed."

"It was an accident," Dane said. "She fell."

Tolo knew then that it was Daringa who was dead, and he felt a wave of sadness. He also knew that the man who had caused the death had to be punished. The God that his mother talked about said that justice called for an eye for an eye. The spirits of the Abos also taught that blood called for blood.

"The boy, Canby, saw you push her," Bennelong said. He drew back his arm and sent the spear toward Dane's chest, halting it at the last moment with the sharp, iron point resting against the cloth of the tutor's shirt. "I can kill you in this manner. It would be many small pricks, not one final one, and the blood would flow slowly."

"I tell you, Bennelong, it was an accident," de Lausenette said. "I didn't intend to push her."

"Did you force yourself on her, and was she trying to get away?" Bennelong asked.

"He has been tupping her," Tolo said.

Bennelong looked at the boy. "So said Canby. It is true, then?"

"Yes," Dane said, thinking frantically. "I was going to marry her, you know. She was with child."

A look of pain crossed Bennelong's face. "I can kill you with an arrow," he said, in that flat voice. "But that would be too quick. Perhaps I will sting you with the snake, so that you will die slowly, as if from the bite of the tiger snake. Your legs will go numb first. The trouble with that is that you will die in three or four minutes and I want your death to be as lasting and as painful as possible."

De Lausenette was looking around in desperation. His pistol lay ten feet away. He had no other weapon.

"I think it will be the death of ten thousand wounds," Bennelong said, thrusting his spear skillfully to make a small cut on de Lausenette's forearm. The tutor winced at the sharpness and leapt backwards. Then he made an effort to run, but ran into the arms of Colbee, who had just approached.

"Thank God you're here," Dane gasped in mistaken relief. "Colbee, this maniac is trying to kill me."

"With good reason," Colbee said. "However, you will live, for now."

"I claim my right," Bennelong said.

Colbee lifted his right hand. In it was a gleaming white object. Tolo recognized it to be a bone, but he did not know at that time that it was a human femur bone, sharpened and polished.

"Your way, my son," Colbee said to Bennelong, "leaves evidence for the white man's law." He lifted the bone and pointed it at de Lausenette.

Bennelong lowered his weapon. "So be it. I bow to you, Colbee."

"You're not going to let him kill me?" Dane was astonished.

"No," Colbee said. "Your punishment comes from another source, a source that cannot be traced by the white man's knowledge."

As Colbee began to chant, low and soft, shaking the bone at de Lausenette, Tolo saw his tutor's puzzled expression give way to one of relief. The Englishman had been near death at the hands of Bennelong, and now that danger was past. Instead, the older Aboriginal would simply chant at him and shake a human bone in his face.

It went on for perhaps five minutes. Tolo stood quite still, for the sound of Colbee's voice, and the words of the language that he knew, told him that something quite serious was going on, at least in Colbee and Bennelong's minds. Then it was over.

"Take the boy back to the station," Colbee ordered de Lausenette.

"He wouldn't know the way," Tolo explained. "He got lost getting this far."

"Then *you*, boy, take *him*," Colbee replied.

"I can't go back," de Lausenette said. "When word gets to Mr. Mason—"

"He does not need to know," Colbee said. "Do you agree, young master, that this affair is best kept among ourselves?"

"I think so," Tolo allowed. "But hasn't Mr. de Lausenette done an awful thing?"

"Let the spirits decide," Colbee said.

"Well, Colbee, if you say so," Tolo said. "May I tell my mother? She'll be worried, you know, with my having been gone all night."

"We will tell her that you were with me," Colbee reassured him. "Now, if you hurry you will be home before dark by travelling directly, and not in a half circle as this one came."

Tolo found that Misa was, indeed, concerned. She had sent stockmen out to look for her son, and was about to send a messenger to the next station to ask for help when Tolo and the tutor came up the lane from the direction of the woods and Melbourne.

Tolo and Dane's joint explanation that they'd decided to take a nature outing with old Colbee seemed reasonable, but Misa was not really satisfied until Colbee himself appeared and explained that he had sent word to the mistress by that shiftless child, Canby, who on the way had forgotten his mission. Misa, who knew the casual ways of the Abo, could accept that, and she laughed.

"In the future," Misa instructed her son, "you will come to me and tell me of your plans yourself. You can't imagine how worried I was. And you, Colbee, how could you go off into the woods so soon after the death of your daughter?" Then she put her hand to her lips, for Daringa's death had happened while Tolo and the tutor had gone.

"It's all right, Mother," Tolo said, "we know. Colbee told us.

He was in the bush to commune with the spirits because he was so sad."

Dane de Lausenette retired to his quarters. He was more than a little disoriented. It seemed odd that he was going to be let off so easily, but then the Abo was a funny blackfellow, with funny attitudes towards life. The spell, or curse, that Colbee had put on him in the forest did not concern him. He had never been impressed by the Abo's tales of magic. He swiftly undressed and fell into bed, exhausted.

When he awoke to a new day and things seemed normal, Dane sighed with relief. Upon reflection, he realized that he had been foolish to run away from the Mason station. It was his flight that had drawn attention to him, his flight that had aroused suspicion. The more Dane thought about it, the more he came to believe that even with the Abo boy—Canby—as witness, he could have maintained that Daringa's death had been an accident. In fact it had been an accident. To be sure, his trysts with Daringa could not have been denied, since Tolo as well as the Abo boy had seen them. But Daringa's death was quite another matter; no white law officer or jury could have concluded that her death was anything but an accident—or even that he had anything to do with it—not with just the word of an Abo boy to go on.

Still shaken but much relieved, de Lausenette decided that he had been very stupid—and also very lucky. Colbee, whatever his reasons, had decided not to speak to Jon Mason about this matter. That was fortunate indeed; Colbee was a trusted man whose word could be accepted. So Dane's position at the Mason station would be secure, and from now on he would watch his step, to see that it remained that way. His future was too important to him to run any further risks for the sake of casual pleasures.

He spent extra time on Tolo's lessons that morning, determined to carry on as if nothing had happened.

But then on the following morning Dane awoke with a vague but persistent pain in his lower legs. By afternoon the pain had reached his thighs, a numbing torture that felt as if fire were running through every vein, every tiny capillary. He took to his bed at the end of the second day, the awful cramps in his stomach doubling him over. Misa, alarmed, sent an Abo for the travelling doctor, knowing all the while that the doctor would not arrive for several days. Meanwhile she did what she could, dosing the tutor with various patent medicines.

It was all to no avail: de Lausenette died in agony one full torturous week after the onset of the pain in his lower legs, where Colbee's white bone had pointed.

Tolo had promised not to tell of the events in the bush. According to what he had learned from books, from Dane, from listening to other white people, Aboriginal magic was nothing more than ignorance and superstition. And yet de Lausenette had died in agony, just as Colbee had promised. There were, of course, many diseases peculiar to the tropics that were not yet understood by the doctors, and de Lausenette's death could well have been attributed to one of them. But Tolo had seen Colbee dance stiffly around de Lausenette and chant a prophecy of the white man's death. More than once, in the days that followed, Tolo questioned individual Aborigines, including his friend, Canby. He got only vague answers about the power of the spirits.

One evening, shortly before his father was due to return, Tolo questioned his mother. "The Abos are interesting fellows, aren't they?"

"Yes, dear," Misa said.

"In Samoa, before the white man came, did our people believe in spirits?" he asked.

"They worshipped the old gods," Misa said, "until the good missionaries came and told them the truth."

"How do we know what is the truth, Mother?"

"Ah, such big questions for one so young," Misa said fondly. "In the library there are huge books that approach such deep questions, books almost as large as you, son. But if you want to learn, maybe you can pick them up, eh?"

CHAPTER II

The Darb el-Gallaba, Road of the Traders, rose out of the narrow Nile valley and onto the Nubian Desert of the northern Sudan so suddenly that Lieutenant Slone Vincent Shannon was not mentally prepared for the change.

Sitting a bit uneasily on his camel, he observed carefully as he and his party passed from the sweetness of water and green growing things to the sear and blasted limestone bed of the desert, where sand and rock reflected the strong rays of the equatorial sun. He squinted and looked back towards the town they had left, near the second cataract of the Nile. Wadi Halfa was no longer visible.

Another mile farther and Slone had to look closely to see any evidence of the great African river in the cliffs that marked the limits of its narrow fertile zone. The evidence was there, discernible to experienced eyes. Along the old road he began to see hundreds of cairns of small stones, built up stone by stone over the centuries by travellers returning from the desert, in thanks to their gods that they were once again nearing the blessed Nile.

But Slone was not returning; instead he was departing, heading southeast across the endless wastes of the Sudan.

Beside him rode Lieutenant Percy Girouard, the officer in charge of the engineering survey party of which Slone was a member. He was Slone's senior in age as well as rank, having passed his twenty-first birthday while Slone was still not yet nineteen. Both men wore the uniform of the British desert army: knee-high boots polished to a black sheen each night by native servants, tapered khaki trousers fitted inside the boots, a tunic with a choke collar emblazoned with the insignia of rank and service, and the pith helmet, vital protection from the sun for a white man in Africa.

The two officers were loyal servants of the Queen, although they had been born on different continents, oceans apart. Girouard, a French-Canadian, was a graduate of the Royal Military College at Kingston, Ontario. Slone Shannon, fresh from two years of intensive training at the British Royal Military College at Sandhurst, was Australian.

Slone's father, Colonel Adam Shannon, had distinguished himself in the Maori wars in New Zealand and later had helped to bring under control the rampant piracy in the China Sea. A genuine war hero, twice winner of the Victoria Cross, the elder Shannon had retired from the New Zealand militia and settled with his wife, Emily, outside Brisbane, in Queensland.

From his father Slone had inherited the tendency to look younger than his years, and at Sandhurst he had taken a lot of ribbing about his "baby" face. He had endured the jests so long as they were good-natured, but when the taunts had turned nasty, the sons of old England had found that the boyish-looking colonial from down under knew how to handle himself in a fight. Slone's five-foot-ten-inch frame packed a surprising quickness and solidity of muscle.

Though trained as an engineer, Slone's interests were not confined to mathematics. From the moment he had entered Egypt through the port city founded by Alexander the Great, he had been sending back to his parents a continuous stream of letters describing the country, which he found ranged from a lushness reminiscent of *The Arabian Nights* to a barrenness that reminded him of his native Australian bush country.

Leaving Alexandria, Slone had passed through bustling Cairo and then up the Nile past the tombs of ancient Egyptian kings and queens. During the trip he had pored over books purchased in Cairo, and by now he knew a great deal more about the history of both Egypt and the Sudan than anyone else in his party—more than Percy Girouard, who had little interest in history and took things as they came; more than the grizzled sergeant who had been stationed here for years and had organized the camel-mounted group; more even than the native Egyptian soldiers who made up the work force and guard.

North of the city of Khartoum in the Sudan, the Nile's course sweeps through the scorched Nubian Desert in wide bends that on a map look like the letter S drawn by a shaky hand. In six places the flow of the great river is accelerated by granite constrictions—the famed cataracts of the Nile.

Throughout recorded history, men have for one reason or another struggled against the natural obstacles of these cataracts and the desert to journey from Egypt to the south. For some the attraction was natron, a substance necessary in ancient times for the embalming of kings and queens. For others the lure was gold, said to be found in the Land of Punt, the Egyptian name for the lands east of the Sudan. Still others found the Sudan to be a rich source of slaves; as Slone Shannon and his little group moved southwards, they passed thousands of little gravel heaps, the ruins of fireplaces in which the slave caravans had baked their bread.

In the last years of the nineteenth century, the British ruled in Egypt, and the Sirdar—commander-in-chief—of the Egyptian Army was Horatio Herbert Kitchener. A vigorous, ambitious man who was held in contempt by many of his fellow officers, Kitchener was in the process of moving an army to the Sudan—"the Land of Ghosts"—to redress an old wrong: the martyrdom of his hero, General Charles George Gordon on January 26, 1885. Gordon, known as "Chinese" Gordon following his role in suppressing the Taiping Rebellion in the 1860s, was cut down during the conquest and destruction of Khartoum by fanatical Muslim followers of the Mahdi, "the expected one", ruler of the Sudan.

The Mahdi himself had not long survived Gordon, dying in June 1885, but his kingdom had fallen under the heavy hand of his successor, Abdullahi, known as the Khalifa; to Kitchener, this man was now the enemy. For ten years the fire of vengeance had burned bright within Kitchener, and now he felt his goal—liberation of the Sudan—to lie within his grasp.

In October 1896, Kitchener's advance detachments had come by riverboat as far as Merowe, almost exactly halfway between the two bends of the S made by the Nile, between the fourth and fifth cataracts and within striking distance of Abu Hamed, occupied by the Khalifa's forces. To augment these Merowe detachments, Kitchener had decided to depart from the serpentine course of the Nile and move the main body of his army—men, horses, camels, cannon, wagons, food and equipment—straight across the Nubian

Desert, via a railway to be constructed from Wadi Halfa to Abu Hamed, at the head of the second great bend of the Nile.

The mission of Lieutenant Girouard's small party was to lay the groundwork for a more complete survey of the railway route. The railway—on which construction would begin in January of 1897— was intended to put the army within reach of Abu Hamed at the same time as the city was being attacked by the forces moving up the Nile from Merowe.

Once Abu Hamed was conquered, only the fifth and sixth cataracts and some additional miles of burning desert—also to be crossed by rail—would remain before Kitchener's final objective was reached: Omdurman, the new capital city of the Khalifa's dervish empire, across the Nile from the ruins of Khartoum.

To build a railway across a desert, where the temperature rose as high as 126 degrees in the balmy summer days, was an all but impossible task, and Kitchener was relying heavily on his team of handpicked young engineer subalterns, including Slone and Percy. Many of these, like the two lieutenants, had come from distant points of the British Empire, and the engineering group was known as "Kitchener's boys". Already the Sirdar had singled them out for special attention, giving them every opportunity to win distinction in battle by calling them to the front when action was about to commence. Girouard, for example, had won the D.S.O. the previous month, during the occupation of Dongola, downstream from Merowe.

Slone and Percy Girouard were riding side by side along the parallel camel tracks of the ancient trading road. Ahead an Egyptian scout was just visible through the dust raised by his camel and the shimmering heat rising from the sand.

The two young officers had hit it off well ever since Slone had stepped off a British gunboat at Wadi Halfa. Girouard had the darkness of his French ancestors, and his eyes were deep set and shadowy, his lips full and sensuous. He was a bit shorter than Slone, but wider in the chest. He was generally easygoing, and in the desert he did not insist on strict military courtesy, although there was no doubt in the mind of either man as to who was in charge. Slone found him an engaging companion; already Percy had helped him by offering him use of the special cream that the senior lieutenant had acquired in Cairo to protect himself from the sun. For Slone, fairer than Percy, the cream was a lifesaver.

Glancing now at Girouard, Slone found him looking relaxed in spite of the hot and tortuous ride. In a way, riding a camel was like sailing in a small boat in a choppy sea. Some men were sickened by the swaying and jerking, but apart from the feeling that he was perpetually in danger of sliding off, Slone did not object to the motion. He listened attentively as Percy described winters in Ontario, with their lovely snow, crisp air, cheery fires, and hot cider.

The mere mention of a liquid triggered Slone's thirst. He lifted his head and gazed at the horizon to take his mind off water. He was confronted by gaunt, rugged sandstone cliffs rising to the west. Far off to the right a sand devil swirled, trailing its clearly visible stalk into a haze of indistinct cloud at great heights.

Girouard, perhaps sensing that he was losing his audience, changed the subject. "You're a lucky devil, Shannon," he said. "If you don't shirk your duty and you keep your nose clean, you'll find that you're in the best unit in the army—none better as far as chances for fame and fortune are concerned."

Slone laughed. "Sir, to be truthful, I haven't thought too much of the future, not just yet. I've got to get my feet on the ground, get adjusted to real life, so to speak."

"Yes, yes," Girouard said, "but that will come quickly. You'll find that the Sirdar is a fair man, Shannon, a very fair man. When the time comes, when he's cornered the Khalifa at last, you'll not find yourself stuck on the railway. The Sirdar will see to it that all of us are given our chance."

Slone nodded. He had often wondered how he would react in combat. It was one thing to train by fighting mock battles, quite another to look across an open space into the faces of men who wanted, more than anything in the world, to kill you.

They passed a bleached skeleton, half covered by blown sand. "Camel, poor devil," Girouard said, shaking his head. And before the blazing sun sank rapidly below the horizon, they had seen more skeletons. Even camels, the animals best adapted to the desert, had perished of thirst within a day's travel of the Nile. Evidence of past hardships would grow more frequent as the unit travelled southwards. As they climbed one particularly strenuous slope, they found skeletons in piles.

"Good Lord," Slone said, "Where will we get water for the engines, even if we can build a railway through this wasteland?"

"Wells." Girouard said.

"Wells? Here?"

"Never fear. We'll find water," the Canadian said cheerily. "It's Kitchener's luck. The Sirdar says that a general should be scrapped if he has failed to be lucky."

With the trailing edge of the sun just disappearing, the sergeant selected a campsite on a sandy area protected from any increase in wind during the night by an outcropping of rocks—the exposed bones of a blasted and tortured world. Slone dismounted, rubbed his sore backside, turned his camel over to an Egyptian of lower ranks, and with his gear began to look around for a place of his own. He chose a sandy spot under an overhang, put down his kit and bedroll, and sat tiredly on the sand, his back against the rock. He would have loved a bath, even more a plunge into the cool, clear waters of the stream that ran near his father's house in Queensland.

He looked up when the sergeant, a veteran who had been serving the Queen for more years than Slone had lived, came walking towards him. The man nodded amiably and threw a casual salute, then stood looking down at the sand that was protected from the day's sun by the rocky overhang.

"Sir," he said, "was I you, I think I'd move my billet."

"Why is that, Sergeant?" Slone asked.

The sergeant pointed to a mark in the sand quite near Slone's foot. There were other marks of the same pattern, forming a jagged W among the wind-rippled waves in the sand. The sergeant walked slowly, bent at the waist, and examined the ground carefully. "Ah," he said. He pulled his bayonet from its scabbard and pointed. There was another W in the sand, but it was blurred by the presence of something living. The sergeant flipped a short, flat snake out of the sand with his bayonet and quickly decapitated it.

"Nasty little devil," the sergeant said.

Percy Girouard had approached. "Cleopatra's asp," he said. "The horned viper."

The snake was about twenty inches long. Its back was checked brown, the underside white with a bluish tinge. The flat, triangular head had a pair of grey horns, like eyebrows.

Slone, who was no stranger to snakes, Australia being home to some of the more deadly varieties of the world, was not overly impressed; but when the sergeant said that the vipers usually were found in pairs, he moved his kit away from the overhang and spread it out in the open.

After supper, Slone wandered away from the fire and sat by himself, admiring the night sky. He had seen the stars of the southern hemisphere from the mountains of Australia, but never had he seen stars such as he saw this night, stars that looked like coarse grains of fire holding together a great, glowing arch, glittering more brightly than he could have imagined during his past two years in cloudy England. The pellucid air showed him the pale cloth of light behind the stars of highest magnitude, the faint glow visible against the utter darkness of the depths of space. He understood, then, the attention given to the skies by the ancients, for as the temperature dropped—it was cold at night in the desert—the blaze of the Milky Way seemed to lower, to come to him and engulf him in its cold, incredibly distant light. He had a sense of timelessness, for in these very lands, along that river that lay one day's journey behind them, civilization had begun.

He recalled that the stern-faced pharaoh Chephren had sent slaves into the Nubian Desert in search of the green-blue or grey-green gneiss, a stone composed of felspar crystals from which artists carved images of the great king. Chephren's search parties may have blazed the same track that the survey party now followed. Somewhere to the north Moses had walked and talked with God, and Alexander had plotted his empire. The Romans had marked the land with now-crumbling monuments, and the Arab emirs had transformed the cities with their exotic architecture. And now came the British.

Slone knew why he was in the desert, but what in God's name had originally drawn Britishers here, other than the perverse love the English seemed to have for totally unlivable places? What odd drive had led the hero, Gordon, to become the first governor of the undefined area known initially as Equatoria? It would be fascinating, Slone felt, to be able to understand the historical forces and the individual personalities, the intertwining of which had resulted in his being in the desert under an incredibly starred sky with the prospect of battle and possible death facing him.

For a period following the death of General Gordon and his brave men, there had been little interest in the Sudan. After the Mahdi's conquest of Khartoum, Queen Victoria had reprimanded Prime Minister Gladstone for not having sent a relief force to Gordon sooner. But then the government and the English people had almost gratefully put the Sudan out of mind, and for over a decade the Khalifa had been given a free hand with the Mahdist empire, to make of it what he could.

Some close observers were harsh in their appraisal of the Khalifa. On the slow boat trip up the Nile to Wadi Halfa, Slone had read a book written by Rudolf Slatin—called Slatin Pasha—and translated by Kitchener's Director of Intelligence, Reginald Wingate. The Austrian adventurer, who had been a counsellor-prisoner to the Khalifa for ten years, described the Sudan as a tormented land of famine and plague, reeling under the sadistically cruel reign of a despot who practised genocide against those who crossed him.

With the death of Gladstone and the formation of a new government under Lord Salisbury in 1895, imperialism had become fashionable in England once more, and Slatin Pasha's views of conditions in the Sudan attracted wide attention and support. A few weak voices were heard, protesting that the Khalifa could not be blamed for plagues that had moved southwards from Egypt, that he had not really been guilty of genocide, and that the Sudan was not the administrative disaster area described by Slatin Pasha. But the temper of the times was different now. England began to recall with shame how the relief force ordered by Gladstone in 1885—after seeing that it had arrived too late to save Gordon—had merely retreated back down the Nile. The episode seemed to give the lie to the proud boast that the British Empire would always avenge the death, at the hand of heathens, of one of her loyal subjects. There were cries that Gordon must now be avenged.

When another nation of "wogs", the Abyssinians, defeated an army from another European power, Italy, at the battle of Adowa, the disaster poured oil on the fires of vengeance. Now, it was said, the Abyssinians and the Sudanese were about to unite. Egypt herself would be threatened. The evil Khalifa was actively working to divert the mighty Nile and destroy Egypt totally. Moreover, France, that old enemy of Great Britain, had her finger in the stew south of Egypt, in an effort to extend French influence to the upper Nile. For those English whose dreams of empire included a British mandate to rule from the delta of the Nile to the Cape of Good Hope, the situation was frustrating beyond endurance.

However, it was not for a young officer fresh out of Sandhurst to concern himself with these affairs of empire. Slone Shannon's job was to act as second-in-command of a small group of the Egyptian Camel Corps scouting towards Abu Hamed.

After a final glance up at the stars, Slone returned to camp, crawled into his bedroll, and fell asleep.

The next morning the engineering party was up before dawn and well under way by sunrise. Slone was pleased to find himself becoming acclimatized to the desert. On the second day, and during the next few days, he found himself overcoming his constant desire for water. He learned to endure the sun by day and to keep himself warm during the cold desert nights. He concentrated on his job, making notes of the geology of the area and drawing maps of a proposed route for the military railway. As the crow flies, it was three hundred miles from Wadi Halfa to Abu Hamed, but in the desert only vultures flew. The challenge to the engineers was to lay out a route within the required limits of curve—six degrees—and gradient—one in one hundred and twenty.

The scouting party had reached a point less than twenty miles from Abu Hamed when Percy Girouard said that it was time to turn back. If they went any farther, they might be seen by scouts from the Khalifa's forces occupying the city.

On the return trip Slone began to understand the reason for the piles of camel bones along the route. The party had travelled almost all the way to Abu Hamed and then faced the return trip without the advantage of having watered at the Nile. Although Girouard had taken this into account, the once-strong camels were weakening as they reached the little piles of stones accumulated over the centuries by thankful travellers. Slone dismounted, the cliffs along the Nile in sight, and placed a stone on a pile.

"If you feel like placing one for me," Percy said, "please feel free to do so."

Kitchener was in Wadi Halfa when Lieutenant Percy Girouard came out of the desert with his dusty, tired command on a November day in 1896. Girouard decided to take Slone along when he made his report to the Sirdar. Since it was to be Slone's first meeting with the famous man, and since the Sirdar himself was always immaculately neat, Girouard told Slone to have a bath and put on a fresh uniform. The bath helped, and the uniform bolstered Slone's courage; nevertheless, he felt apprehensive about the coming encounter. Kitchener had a formidable reputation.

Herbert Kitchener had been a major serving in Egypt with the Royal Engineers when Gordon died with his men in Khartoum. At first he had been enraged at Gordon's martyrdom; then he had felt humiliation when, instead of bringing justice to the murderers, England did nothing. It was not only the honour of the nation that had been soiled, Kitchener felt, but his own. As a mere major, he was helpless to alter the sad state of affairs, but he could and did write persuasively of the anarchy in central Africa and the loss of a potentially great trade for the empire.

In 1889 Kitchener enjoyed brief hopes that the empire would at last be awakened from its sleep when the Mahdists from the Sudan attempted an invasion of Egypt at Toski, where, as fate would have it, Kitchener—now adjutant general of the Egyptian Army—was in command of the cavalry. His actions helped to repel the invasion with heavy losses.

Though the victory did little to enhance his reputation among his fellow officers in Cairo, who despised him for his ambition and lack of tact, Kitchener's undeniable flair for organization and his firm friendships with influential Englishmen, including Lord Salisbury, earned him fame and rapid advancement. In 1892, when Sir Frances Grenfell retired from his post as Sirdar of the Egyptian Army, Kitchener was chosen as his successor. British officers in Cairo and their Egyptian sycophants were disgusted; according to their view, several other men, by virtue of their seniority and position in the existing hierarchy, should logically have been given the appointment over the upstart Kitchener.

Because the new Sirdar was a large man for an Englishman,

there were those who said that he was brutish. "He may be a general," Winston Churchill wrote to his mother, "but he will never be a gentleman."

Kitchener had an icy, misanthropic manner, which was accentuated by an odd set to his gaze, caused by the paralysis of a muscle in his left eye. He was a man who was difficult to know, and it seemed that only Lord Salisbury and the officers directly under Kitchener's command realized that he was the ideal man for the job at hand. Under constant threat of being relieved as Sirdar in favour of some older, more senior officers, Kitchener set about pursuing his goal of avenging Gordon. Raw ambition drove him, true, but he also had the personal skills and tools to carry out the drive. The desert campaign was not to be a war of lightning thrusts, of fast-moving tactical flair. The task before Kitchener was largely an engineering challenge. He knew that the main reason for Gordon's defeat and death had been the lack of a line of supply and communication. Now patience was needed, as well as perseverance and a grasp of logistical details. Taking the Khalifa's capital at Omdurman would require the capacity to transport not only men but large tonnages of weapons and supplies past the cataracts of the Nile. And it all had to be done on a shoestring in a war of painful frugality.

By the time Lieutenant Slone Shannon had become a part of Kitchener's army, it had made its first attack on a dervish outpost at Firket in June 1896, and in September it had advanced up the Nile as far as Dongola, in the action that had brought Percy Girouard his D.S.O. Because of some errors of judgment on Kitchener's part, some newspapers in the home country were calling for his replacement, but he still enjoyed the confidence of Lord Salisbury, now prime minister, and he was still in command.

When Percy and Slone entered his office, Kitchener returned the lieutenants' salutes smartly and then came forward to take Percy's hand. "You're back early, Percy," he said, ignoring Slone. "Have you found me a route?"

"Yes, sir," Girouard replied.

"We're going to build her to a gauge of three feet, six inches," Kitchener said.

Girouard nodded. A long-running dispute had been settled. For purposes of economy Kitchener had been urged to build to a gauge of three feet, three-and-three-eighths inches, but Cecil Rhodes was building his railways in South Africa to the wider gauge, and Kitchener shared Rhodes's dream of a British railway from the Cape to Cairo. He would build not only to avenge Gordon, but also for the future.

"Sir," Girouard said, "may I present Lieutenant Slone Vincent Shannon."

Slone clicked his heels and saluted.

"Nice to have you with us," Kitchener said, before returning his attention to Girouard. "Percy, I want you to go to England," he declared. "You're to order the rest of the material we need. But hold the reins tight. We are terribly poor."

Girouard smiled, for he had already anticipated Kitchener's need to procure some of the material and rolling stock. "Sir," he said, "I think you'll be pleased to know that I've had an answer from South Africa. Mr. Rhodes has agreed to lend us a number of seventy- and eighty-ton locomotives, which he'd intended for his railways in Natal."

"Excellent!" Kitchener responded.

Knowing that the Sirdar's frugal soul had been gratified, Girouard struck while the iron was hot. "Sir," he hurried on, "since we have material to begin work in January, and since it's been quite some time since I have had any leave, would it be out of order if I spent a few days in Cairo on my way to England?"

Kitchener rolled his eyes. "I suppose not, Percy."

"And since there'll be nothing for Lieutenant Shannon to do here, sir, until construction begins, mayn't he just as well go to Cairo with me?"

Slone at first resented Percy's intrusion into his personal affairs, but when Kitchener, his mind already addressing another problem, merely nodded and dismissed the men, Percy's pleasure was contagious.

"Cairo, my lad!" Percy declared as the two lieutenants left the office. "The city of ten thousand delights. Get your kit packed as quickly as you can, and I'll sort out transport for us. Be sure to pack your dress uniforms. You'll have need of them."

The first stage of the journey was by boat. Kitchener had managed to build up quite a fleet of gunboats, and they figured large in his military plans. After Aswan they took the train, on the Nile's western flank, past cultivated fields and clusters of mud huts under their sheltering clumps of palm trees. To their right, always, were the cliffs that marked the edge of the narrow valley, beyond which lay the desert. Slone asked Girouard about the scores of small, whitewashed cupolas with minarets. "Have they some religious significance?" he asked.

Girouard laughed. "They have significance to the stomach," he said. "They're dovecotes. The peasants—they're called fellaheen in these parts—raise pigeons to use the dung as fertilizer."

Coming into Cairo, they caught a glimpse of the eastern desert that stretched away in the direction of the Suez Canal. The pyramids came into view, looking disappointingly small until Slone realized with an engineer's calculating imagination that they were a full twenty miles away.

The railway station was bedlam. Slone heard English, Greek, and several Arabian dialects spoken among people of olive, bronze, black, yellow, and white skin. Half-naked children scampered through the crowd of people, who were dressed in a variety of styles. Purveyors of bread and water converged on the two English officers, only to be shooed away severely by Girouard. The Arab women had a ghostly look, with their bodies and faces hidden and only their dark, flashing eyes left uncovered to appraise the two soldiers brashly. Jewish merchants hawked their wares from tiny shops. A contingent of Egyptian troops from the army of the Khedive, Egypt's nominal ruler, marched up the platform. Egypt was called an independent nation, Slone knew, but in fact it was a British colony; the Khedive enjoyed little real authority beyond his own palace.

Slone and Percy emerged from the station into a balmy atmosphere, then pushed through streets crowded by short, swarthy fellaheen men, thin-limbed children whose bellies protruded, and lower-class women in blue carrying water jugs on their heads. Black Nubians, wearing only what seemed to be scraps of white around loin and head, rode by on tall camels.

Cairo was a city that existed on two levels: the crowded, poverty-stricken streets of the fellaheen and the comfortable, luxurious world of the British and tourists who came to view the wonders of Egypt's past. Cairo's "season" was just beginning, since the weather from October to April was splendid and brought people from all over the world. Musical cafés featured European bands playing waltzes by Strauss, while from thousands of kiosks and booths merchants shouted for the tourists' attention and money.

The Sirdar kept several rooms on permanent booking at Shepheard's Hotel, and soon Slone was enjoying a bath in a real tub. Then Percy and he went down for dinner in the hotel dining room, where a string orchestra was playing a sprightly air. A bowing waiter showed them to a table, and tall drinks were soon before them.

Slone gave his attention to the menu. Percy, looking around, nodded to friends and acquaintances. He touched Slone on the arm and gestured discreetly to a neighbouring table. "There's the man you'll see when you're ready to go back upriver."

Slone followed Percy's glance and saw a handsome middle-aged man in the dress uniform of a colonel. Slone caught the older man's eye and nodded respectfully. The colonel acknowledged him stiffly.

"Colonel Roland Streeter," Percy said.

The words did not register with Slone, for he had taken his eyes off the autocratic officer. Ignoring one of the colonel's two dinner companions—a middle-aged woman who was most certainly the colonel's wife—Slone had become totally absorbed by the third party. He was unabashedly staring into the smiling green eyes of the most beautiful young woman he had ever seen.

"Slone, I say, Slone," Percy nudged him.

Slone shook his head to clear the image and turned to face Percy.

"It's not considered proper to devour a young lady with one's eyes, you know," Percy admonished.

"Who is she?" Sloned demanded, a bit chagrined at his own breach of decorum, but undaunted.

"Streeter's daughter, of course," Percy replied. "Who d'you think she is?"

"Would it be proper for you to present me to her?" Slone asked. "I mean here, now?"

Percy sighed. "I suppose so. But let's give them a chance to finish their first course."

Slone sipped his drink, his eyes still on the young woman. Her hair was the glorious red of an autumn sunset in Australia, her skin the colour of a pale English rose. She, aware of his scrutiny, cast him a look, a flash of large green eyes from under thick lashes, causing him to take a deep, deep breath. Then she put down her fork, touched her full lips with a pristine napkin, and looked into his eyes once again.

Slone put down his napkin. "Come along, Percy," he said to his friend. "I can't wait a moment longer."

Ignoring the restraining hand that his friend placed on his arm, Slone rose abruptly and started towards the colonel's table. The young woman watched him for the entire time that it took him to cross the floor between tables. Percy, who had risen to follow and was muttering under his breath something about bad form, lagged behind; he caught up just as Slone was standing over the Streeters' table, his eyes on the girl's face.

"Colonel Streeter," said Percy, "it's a pleasure to see you again, sir. May I present Lieutenant Slone Vincent Shannon, the newest of Kitchener's boys."

The colonel clearly had not passed his eye colour to his daughter. His eyes were a cold slate grey. He rose from his chair with a lack of eagerness signalling that he resented the intrusion. He nodded to Slone, then to each of his family in turn. "My wife," he said, "and my daughter." He lowered himself to his chair, in effect telling the two young lieutenants that the conversation was over.

"I'm Kit," the girl said to Slone and then to Percy, "We haven't seen you lately, Percy."

"Now and then the Sirdar insists that I do some work," Percy said with a laugh. He bowed to the colonel. "Please excuse the interruption, sir."

Streeter grunted and lifted his fork.

At that moment the orchestra skipped lightly into the strains of another waltz. Percy was already turning away. In desperation Slone sought a way to keep alive his contact with the girl, the contact that was forming with his eyes locked on hers. Her flushed face was tilted up, exposing the sleek lines of a lovely neck. To walk away was impossible.

"Miss Streeter, with your father's permission, may I invite you to dance?"

Streeter looked up. His fork clanged down onto his empty plate. "Really, Lieutenant," he said, "we *are* in the middle of our dinner."

Kit let a languid, moody smile part her lips. "I'm not at all hungry, Father," she said, rising.

"Of all the dashed rudeness," Streeter was saying as Slone led a vision in white towards the dance floor, where only a half-dozen couples were swirling to the strains of the waltz.

"Don't mind Father," Kit said as she smoothly positioned herself close but not too close to Slone. "He's just hungry and tired."

She was of a perfect height to him. She even smelled like roses. When she turned with a flair and came snugly into the curve of his arm, he felt a jolt of electricity in her touch, and she felt it, too, he was sure of it, for her eyes widened.

"Slone is an odd name," she said. "Is it by chance a family name?"

"No," he said. "Vincent is a family name. Slone, I think, must be a digger name."

"Australian, you mean?" she replied. "I see. That accounts for your accent, then."

He nodded. She was so light in his arms. "And is Kit short for Katherine?"

"Yes."

"I've always loved the name Katherine."

"Not I," she said, wrinkling her nose. It made him want to put his lips there, on the tip of it.

"But you'll have to learn to like it," he said. "I will insist on naming our first little girl after you."

A shocked look on her face was followed by a delicate flush that spread upwards from her long, graceful neck. For a few moments she remained silent, no doubt wondering what to make of this insolent colonial. Slone interpreted silence to mean that she had suppressed any impulse to reprimand him; the worst was over. It *had* been a cheeky thing to say, but it had sounded so right when he said it: "our first little girl".

"Kit," he said, as the waltz was coming to an end, "d'you know Percy Girouard? I mean, is he a family friend?"

"I suppose. No more so than other young officers."

"D'you suppose your father would allow you to join us—Percy and me—for the remainder of the evening?"

She frowned doubtfully, but then her lips curled delightfully. "He'll pout," she said, "but all right!"

The first course of the Streeters' meal was being served as they returned to the table. "Please take my plate to Lieutenant Girouard's table," Kit said to the waiter.

Streeter's cheeks puffed, but before he could speak Kit added, "Father, I'm sure you won't mind. Percy and Lieutenant Shannon have been to the Sudan, and I want to hear all about it." She bent, kissed her father on the forehead, and turned to her mother. "Now, Mama, you'll have this handsome gentleman all to yourself."

Mrs. Streeter smiled.

The rather good cuisine of the Shepheard Hotel's kitchen was wasted on Slone. He had the world at his table, and the world, in the form of slim, petite, sunset-haired Kit Streeter, had green eyes, a voice that seemed to sink through Slone's flesh and vibrate against his heart, and a throaty laugh that was unaffactedly lower than her speaking voice.

It took only a few minutes for Percy Girouard to realize that he was witnessing a skirmish of *amour*, and he was so far out of the action that he might as well not have been there. Now and again, out of sheer perversity, he broke into the dialogue of the two principals—just to remind them that others were present.

Kit Streeter was finding it highly amusing to parry the verbal thrusts of the brash young lieutenant across the dinner table. At eighteen, she was a highly intelligent young woman; she had attended a finishing school for girls, and her mother, a woman of catholic tastes in reading, had rounded out her education. In Egypt now only a few months, her mother and she were nonetheless old hands at army life.

Kit had not once, until that first waltz with Slone, given any serious thought to marriage. Her mother had always warned her in any case against marrying an army officer. Evelyn Streeter, from a fine old family in Kent, had proven a highly suitable wife for the second son of a minor peer, who was following the conventional career path into the army. But having lived it, Evelyn knew that the life of an army wife was not the best choice she could have made, and she had made up her mind that her daughter would not follow her example. It was all right for Kit to carry on minor flirtations with officers and to have friends like the well-bred Percy Girouard, but to marry a career army man? Never.

Until this moment, Kit had had no quarrel with her mother's views. She was in no hurry to wed. She had been leading an interesting life, travelling with her parents, first to India and now Egypt, and in between spending time with her mother's aged parents in Kent, where there were horses for riding, pleasant lakes where graceful swans preened themselves, and grandparents who doted on their only grandchild.

But after the waltz with Slone, things were different. Now, as Kit herself was being devoured by the brown eyes of this handsome young man from far Australia, she was beginning to experience real fright, for she had not been deaf to her mother's warnings. She had no idea, of course, of Slone's personal finances, but it stood to reason that he, like most young officers, was either—like her own father—a second son with no inheritance, or the offspring of a family of small merchants. But her fright also came from another cause—the fact that just to look at Slone made her heart flutter, her willpower dissolve.

After their first course, she accepted his invitation to dance again, and she felt the hard muscles of his thighs brush against her as they waltzed, and the very unladylike tremors that passed through her disturbed her even more.

"What do you want to know about me?" she heard Slone ask.

"Why should I want to know anything about you?" she teased.

"I know all there is to know about you that is important," he said. "You're beautiful. I know that you must be kind, for you have kind eyes. And you're intelligent, I can tell."

"Perhaps there is something I should ask you," she said. "Are all Australians so forward?"

He laughed. "I don't know. They probably are if they are as much in love as I."

"Really," she said, frowning, "you do move much too quickly. Is that the custom in your country?"

"I have so little time," he said. "I'll have to go south again soon."

She laughed again. "Don't give me that old army story," she

said. "Don't tell me you're going off to face death and try to get my sympathy."

There was a lightness in her voice that made him laugh too. "Is that the way your father convinced your mother?"

"No, that was an arranged marriage."

"It seems to have worked well."

"She warns me often against marrying an army man."

"Then I'll resign as soon as we've punished the Khalifa."

"It's been a decade or more since Khartoum," she said. "Will it be ten more years?"

"I think not," he said.

They returned to their table, where Percy sat with only a bottle of wine for company. "The colonel requests your presence, Kit," he said. "It seems he's ready to leave."

"Do you have to go?" Slone asked.

"Yes."

"How can I contact you?"

"It's best that you don't," she said. Then, noticing the black frown that crossed Slone's brow, she quickly added. "But I'm sure you will."

CHAPTER III

"Not too many years ago," Kit Streeter said, as she stood with the two dapper young officers and looked out over the Nile, "a trip to the pyramids was only for the stout of heart. There was no bridge, and one had to spend hours balanced on one of those horrid little donkeys."

Now, as the century was ending, Egypt had opened herself to the world, having realized that her greatest assets were the artifacts of that ancient industry based on death. There was indeed a bridge over the Nile and a comfortable carriage road on the far side. The road was lined with date palms, tamarisks, acacias, sycamores, and figs. As their carriage neared the pyramids and drew to a halt the three travellers were caught in a swarm of half-naked Arabs insistent on being their guides.

Only the magnitude of the ancient monuments could keep Slone's eyes from Kit Streeter.

"I wish that I could have seen them when the limestone was covered with the pure white of the stones from the Tukra quarries," Kit mused, as Slone helped her down from the carriage.

"The large one is the tomb of the Kufu?" Slone asked.

"Also called Cheops," she replied.

Kit walked between Slone and Percy Girouard as they approached the monuments. Then, from part way up the steps on the northern pyramid, they looked out over the desert to the Blunted Pyramid, lonely in a sea of sand.

Percy spoke in a soft voice:

" 'My name is Ozymandias, king of kings:
Look on my works, ye Mighty, and despair!'
Nothing beside remains. Round the decay

Of that colossal wreck, boundless and bare
The lone and level sands stretch far away."

"Shelley wasn't writing about the pyramids," Kit offered, underscoring the fact that she was as bright as she was lovely.

"I know," Percy replied, "but one gets the feeling."

"The Greeks were here," Slone said, "and the Romans. Caesar came to see the pyramids—"

"And Cleopatra," Kit said, not to be outdone.

"The historian Herodotus was here, and Plato," Slone put in.

"What have we here, a pair of classical scholars?" Percy asked.

"My favourite pyramid story concerns François René Chateaubriand," Slone plunged on. "He would not lower himself to be an ordinary tourist, but he sent a servant to the top of the great pyramid to carve his name into the stone."

After a picnic lunch they walked a few hundred yards to the southeast of the Great Pyramid and stood near one of the greatest mysteries in Egypt, the Sphinx. Percy walked around to view the huge face from different angles. He laughed.

"You dare mock the Sphinx?" Kit asked.

"Well, he has lost part of his nose," Percy said.

"It was done in 1496," Kit said, "by a Moslem fanatic who tried to demolish the Sphinx as a heathen idol."

"I suppose he forgot to bring his lunch," Percy said, chuckling.

Kit pulled a little book from her pocket. "I sense a lack of respect in you, sir. For people like you I offer the historian Alexander Kinglake."

"Now I'm in for it, I suppose," Percy sighed. "Well, what's he got to say?"

She read in a level, firm voice: " 'Upon ancient dynasties of Ethiopian and Egyptian kings, upon Greek and Roman, upon Arab and Ottoman conquerors, upon Napoleon dreaming of an Eastern empire, upon battle and pestilence, upon the ceaseless misery of the Egyptian race, upon keen-eyed travellers, Herodotus yesterday, Warburton today, upon all this and more this unworldy Sphinx has watched, and watched like a providence, with the same earnest eyes, and the same sad, tranquil mien. And we, we shall die, and Islam shall wither away; and the Englishman, straining far over to hold his loved India, will plant a firm foot on the banks of the Nile, and sit in the seats of the faithful; and still that shapeless rock will lie watching, and watching the works of a new, busy race, with the same sad, earnest eyes, and the same tranquil mien everlasting.' "

"I recant." Percy said with a slight bow. "I will mock no further."

At the end of a long day they returned to Cairo, tired, their faces reddened by the Egyptian sun. During the entire journey Slone and Kit had not been alone, but each casual look, each touch of the hand as Slone had helped her over obstacles, had been a private and personal sharing.

"Will you have dinner with me?" Slone asked, as the carriage drew up in front of the hotel.

"I can't," she said. "Father is entertaining, and he likes me to be present."

"As a matter of fact," Percy said, "we're invited."

"Thank you for telling me," Slone said with a wry smile.

"Oh, there's plenty of time," Percy said airily. "Dress uniform, old chum."

Colonel Roland Streeter had taken a private ballroom in the hotel. As the Sirdar's Chief of Staff in Cairo, it was his duty to entertain visiting dignitaries—a task he relished—and the guests of honour this evening were a general and his wife, on their way back to England from India via Suez. Other guests included members of the Egyptian government, resident English civilians, one or two token officers of the Egyptian Army, and any of Kitchener's boys who happened to be in Cairo. As a matter of course Streeter had extended an invitation to Kitchener's favourite, Percy Girouard, asking the lieutenant to round up any other of Kitchener's boys who were in the city.

Slone, standing with Percy and sipping champagne, looked up as Kit entered the ballroom. She was dressed in a gown of pastel blue, her sunset hair piled high in an elegant coiffure. She seemed older, more regal tonight. Her green eyes caught Slone's, and she gave him a quick smile as she crossed the ballroom to join her father, who was with the guests of honour.

A small orchestra played softly, and the mutter of polite, muted conversation in the room was like the sound of a summer rain.

Slone continued to exchange pleasantries with Percy and the other officers, each of whom introduced him to some of the ladies present, but as soon as he saw that Kit was free of the guests of honour, he sought her out and swept her onto the dance floor without even asking her permission.

"You seem to have recovered fully from a rather tiring day," he said.

"Who claims that it was tiring?" she asked teasingly.

"I am told that one of the finest drives in Cairo is along the Shoobra Road, past the residence of the Khedive to Heliopolis. I have booked a carriage for tomorrow. Would ten o'clock be convenient?"

She cocked her head at him and frowned, as if she had not quite decided how to deal with this rather assertive Australian. In the end she smiled and nodded, her heart having won the battle over her pride.

"Percy's off to England tomorrow, you know," Slone added hesitantly. He held his breath. For several days Percy had been the chaperone; tomorrow there would be none.

"I'll miss him," Kit mused. "He's really such a pussycat."

Slone laughed. "I would never have thought to describe him in that way." He heard the band going into the ending of the waltz. "Will you still ride with me tomorrow?"

"Yes," she said. "Now I have to go. Mother is not feeling well tonight, and I'm acting as Father's hostess."

He managed to stay away from her for a full fifteen minutes, keeping his eyes on her all the while as she circulated among the guests, smiling and chatting. Finally he could bear it no longer. He headed her off near the dance floor and took her in his arms.

"Slone, *really*," she protested.

"Just this dance."

She shrugged, slipped easily into his arms, and there was no need for further words. The music engulfed them, escorting them on a journey into a world peopled only by two young lovers who, when the music ended, stood stunned, still in the position of the dance. A stern voice caused Kit to jump guiltily.

"Katherine, my dear, we *do* have more than one guest," Colonel Streeter admonished.

"Yes, Father," Kit acknowledged, casting a look at Slone as she hurried away.

"Young man," Streeter said, "I don't know how things are done in the colonies, but in civilized society one does not take a young lady away from her meal in a public restaurant, not does one dominate the young lady's time at a party, particularly when she is the hostess."

"Yes, sir," Slone replied. "I'm sorry, sir."

"I am sorry, too," Streeter said. "You have forced me to speak sharply to a guest, and that does not please me."

Slone was not very pleased, either, but he knew that now was a good time to keep silent. He merely nodded, and Streeter turned away.

Slone took a deep breath and looked for Kit. She was listening to the Indian Army general, her look attentive. Rather than risk further displeasure from the colonel, Slone decided to call it a night. He waited until Kit was standing next to her father, then presented himself to them, made a courteous little speech of thank you and good-night, and hurried out.

Kit was waiting for him when Slone came down to the hotel lobby the next morning. She had a loose cotton coat over her gown and a scarf tied over her hat and under her chin. She was so breathtaking that he was halted in his stride as if he'd been struck with a heavy-calibre bullet. That she, too, was experiencing a similar reaction was evident. Neither spoke as he put her hand on his arm and escorted her out into the brilliant day.

The carriage was waiting. It was an eight-mile drive down a fine road to the ancient city of Heliopolis. The carriage driver sang out information in rather interesting and inventive English. They passed the Shoobra, a residence of the Khedive, with gardens that were among the world's finest, but the sight and the driver's patter were lost on Kit and Slone. Her hand was in his, and the gentle contact was so overwhelming that Slone had no room in his consciousness for anything other than Kit.

The road crossed a flat plain, the sun beating down upon them. Kit, holding a parasol, explained that they were on a historic battlefield: not only had the Sultan Aliem won all of Egypt on this plain in 1517, but the Frenchman Jean Baptiste Kléber had beaten the Turks there in 1800 to make Cairo a French city. Slone wondered at the breadth of her knowledge.

They rested in the jasmine and orange gardens at Mataraeeh, and Kit pointed out the Virgin's Tree, where according to local tradition, Joseph and Mary took shelter as they fled into Egypt with the infant Jesus. Back in the carriage they rode another mile, then descended to stand near a single granite obelisk, thought to be the oldest architectural ruin in the world—the single remaining evidence of Heliopolis, where Joseph took a wife, where Moses studied, where Jeremiah wrote his Lamentations, where Plato formed his doctrine of the immortality of the soul.

Kit, playing the interested tourist, recited some facts memorized from a travel guide. "The obelisk is sixty-two feet high," she said. But Slone held both her hands and looked into her green eyes.

Her voice became a whisper. "It's six feet across the base, and it was quarried from a single piece of stone over five hundred miles from here."

"Amazing," Slone said.

"It is, isn't it? However could they manage to move such a massive thing?"

"What thing?"

"You said it was amazing."

"I was talking about the colour of your eyes."

She pulled her hands from his and walked a few paces, then turned. "Slone, Slone, you're confusing me! Besides, it . . . it just isn't done this way."

He smiled, and his smile made her seem to yield, to forget the glory of ancient Egypt and the proprieties of Victorian society, everything except his enthused if gentle presence. She looked down, remained silent for a moment, then stammered, as he came to take her hand again, "I've known you such a short time."

"Kit, I know that. You must see my side, too. If my time here allowed us a proper romance, I'd like nothing better than to have just that with you. True to form and all. Just like at home. But we have a lifetime to get to know each other better."

"And you're a soldier—"

"You'll like living in Queensland," he said. "You ride, of course."

"Yes," she said, "but—"

"And if you tire of life in the country we can visit Brisbane and Sydney."

"Slone Shannon," she said heatedly, pulling her hand away, "will you please hush. You are taking too much for granted, you know."

He smiled. "Kit, dear, I may seem clumsy, even brash; yet you know I act from deep conviction. I think we're destined for each other. Just as the Muslims believe everything has been pre-ordained, I believe that it was written that I should meet you and that you will be my wife."

"But—but—you don't even ask!" she said, dazed. "You merely state!"

He looked down into her eyes. "All right, Kit," he whispered, taking her hand once more. "Here, before all the old ghosts and gods of Egypt and under the eyes of the one God, I ask you humbly and sincerely, will you be my wife?"

She tried to remove her hand from his, but his grip was firm. She turned her head. The sky was a brilliant blue, the sun like shining daggers. The carriage driver was lounging in the shade, the two bay horses not far away, swishing their tails at flies. "Yes," she whispered and then, louder, "Yes, damn you."

He raised his eyebrows and with a smile said, "Why, Miss Streeter."

"I mean it," she said. "You come plunging into my life like some wild Australian bushranger, and there's no court-ship or romance—just your smugness and your certainty that the foolish girl has fallen head over heels in love with you—"

"I have fallen totally in love with you," he replied.

"And you can't imagine how this is going to affect my mother and my father." She went pale and said, "Oh, God."

"I have given some thought to that," he replied grimly. "Perhaps it would be best not to speak to them about it until after we've taken care of the Khalifa."

"Yes, I agree," she said.

"And as for the lack of romance, Miss Streeter," he said, "when we are white-haired and have our great-grandchildren around us, you will tell them"—he made his voice quaver—" 'Children, your great-grandfather is the most romantic man in the world. Not a day of my life has passed that this bushranger hasn't kissed me breathless.' "

Her face flushed as she laughed. His face drew near hers as he bent and for the first time their lips touched. He could sense her desire, her passion rising to match his. Then, pulling back, he could read in her eyes no doubt—only an apprehension, probably the fear of having to announce to her father and mother that she was going to marry a colonial, a lowly lieutenant, an Australian.

Before leaving for England, Percy Girouard made his personal contribution to the romance. On his own authority he drew up orders for Slone to remain in Cairo to receive the equipment and supplies—including the rather sizable locomotives that were coming by ship from Cecil Rhodes in South Africa—and to get them on their way up the Nile by rail to Aswan, the first stop on the journey to the workshops in Wadi Halfa.

So November passed and December came. For Slone and Kit a conspiracy was at play—a mutual effort to invent reasons to be together for as many hours as possible. Slone did his work in a daze, resenting absences from her and then grumbling when the South African locomotives came, for the rather dangerous job of lifting them from the ship's deck to the dockside tracks required his presence for an entire day.

Late on that same day, a contingent of civilian engineers and railway workers found Slone in the temporary office loaned to him by the military establishment in Cairo. He had been told to expect the newcomers but had been given no date for their arrival. They were all Americans who, he had been told, were under contract to help build the railway into the Sudan.

They were a cheerful, friendly lot, none more so than their principal spokesman, a dapper young man who wore a rather battered beaver top hat. The headgear seemed ridiculously out of place, given the climate.

"Enoch Hook, at your service, Colonel," the young man said, winking to indicate that he was aware of Slone's true rank. "They call me Topper, which is reasonable enough, I guess. My buddies and I are here to build your railway."

"I should hope you'd allow us to give you a bit of help," Slone said, "and not insist on building it all by yourselves."

The group broke into laughter, Topper laughing the loudest. "The general, here, has a sense of humour," he said.

"Gentlemen," Slone said, "I'll see to your overnight quarters. You'll leave by train in the morning for Aswan, where you'll then board a steamer."

"What, leave as soon as that?" Hook protested. "With only one night for sampling the local wares?"

"You did come to build a railway, didn't you?" Slone asked. "You are under contract, I was told."

In due course he had the Americans sorted out and placed in military quarters for the night. Then he went straight to the hotel, where Kit joined him for dinner in the dining room.

There, amid the decorations for the coming holidays, Slone told her that he would be leaving for Wadi Halfa on the day after Christmas. She clung to his hand, and her eyes spoke eloquently of the desperation she was feeling over the realization that shortly he would be gone, doubtless for months.

"I think it's time to tell them, Kit," he said.

"I thought we agreed we should wait till after the defeat of the Khalifa," she replied.

"I know I said that, but I can't wait that long, Kit. I simply can't." Slone gazed at her steadily.

"Oh, dear lord," she whispered.

"I know; I'm dreading it, too," he said. "But it's the best thing to do. What are the colonel's plans for the night?"

"Mother's a bit tired, so Father and she had an early dinner in their suite," she said. She sighed. "They'll be spending the evening in, so I suppose tonight is as good a time as any."

Slone found himself lingering over dessert, anything to delay the moment when he had to face Colonel Streeter. He could not, however, put it off forever. With a grim look on his face and with Kit's hand firmly in his he mounted the stairs, knocked on the door of Streeter's suite, and was standing tall when Streeter opened the door.

"Sir," Slone said, "if it is convenient, I ask your permission to have a word with you."

"Come in, Shannon," Streeter said with a notable lack of enthusiasm.

The Streeters had finished a dinner served to them in their suite.

Evelyn Streeter was seated demurely, her long skirts arranged perfectly, a cup of tea balanced on her knee. Her eyes fell to rest heavily on Kit and Slone's entwined hands, and under the stare Kit tried to disengage her fingers.

"I think we both know what you have on your mind, Shannon," Streeter said. The words seemed to be an effort to make things easier for Slone, but the colonel's tone belied them.

Slone said, "Colonel Streeter, Mrs. Streeter, I believe you both realize that your daughter and I have been seeing quite a bit of each other."

"We do," Streeter said.

"Sir, it is my honour to, ah, state that I love your daughter, ah, very much, sir, and that the greatest honour that can come to me is that she become my wife. I am here to ask your permission, Colonel, Mrs. Streeter, to marry your daughter."

Kit squeezed his hand as if to say, *Well done.*

Streeter was lighting a cigar. Evelyn Streeter, her face unreadable, put her teacup on a tray on the nearby table.

When Streeter spoke, it was not to Slone, but to his daughter. "Katherine, you're eighteen years old. You've always been a sensible girl. Your mother and I have not tried to interfere in this, although, as you know, we both felt that you were spending too much time with Lieutenant Shannon."

"Father—" Kit began.

Streeter held up one hand to silence her. "I expected you, Katherine, to use your common sense, to understand that this war we're fighting is not to be a mere skirmish against a handful of savages." He turned his eyes to Shannon. "You, Lieutenant, do you have any conception of what you're going up against in the Sudan? The Khalifa has had ten years to build his army. He's turned the Sudan into an armed camp. Our army will be facing overwhelming numbers, and many of the enemy will have firearms. And you think only of marriage to my daughter."

"Sir—" Slone said, but was silenced with an imperious wave of Streeter's hand.

"Would you rush into marriage with my daughter before you go south to begin construction of the railway?"

"No, sir," Slone said. "We—"

"Would you marry my daughter and perhaps leave her a widow

within the year?" Streeter asked.

Kit's fingernails dug into Slone's palm. "Don't say such things, Father," she said.

"You will have to admit that it's a possibility," Streeter said. "Now, your mother and I have discussed this, Katherine. We are not against your marriage merely on principle, but under the circumstances we feel that you are being precipitous. We feel that it is unwise for you, Shannon, to ask for a commitment from my daughter until after this war is finished."

"He does not have to ask for a commitment from me," Kit declared. "He has it. I love him, Father."

Streeter puffed on his cigar, a pained look on his face.

"You say, sir," Slone said, sensing a need to be conciliatory, "that you are not against the marriage, just against the timing. I can accept that, sir."

"We will announce our engagement before Slone leaves for Wadi Halfa," Kit said. She spoke firmly, with determination. "The marriage can wait."

"We'll speak of that," Streeter said. "Now, if you don't mind, Mrs. Streeter and I had planned a quiet evening by ourselves."

In the hallway Slone grinned and pretended to wipe perspiration off his brow. Kit clung to his hands, smiling up at him. "That wasn't as bad as I had feared," she said. "I think they took it rather well."

"If that was taking it well, I don't think I would have survived it had they taken it ill," Slone said.

"He's an old bear," Kit said. "You'll come to love him, Slone, just as I do."

Slone laughed. The idea of loving the cold, imperious Streeter had not occurred to him.

Descending, they danced in the ballroom for an hour. Kit said that it would be a good idea if she went up early, and Slone escorted her to her door, then went to his own room.

He was preparing for bed when a knock came on the door. A hotel porter had a message. The Cairo police were holding a man named Enoch Hook, who said he worked for Lieutenant Slone Shannon. Slone frowned, handed the porter a coin, and closed the door. His first impulse was to let the American stew in his own juice, but it was not Hook's lack of social graces that were important now. Hook, a skilled engineer by all accounts, had been contracted by Kitchener himself to help build the military railway, and Percy Girouard had left Slone to see to it that men and supplies coming into Cairo got to Wadi Halfa without delay.

Since Enoch Hook had white skin, the native constabulary had taken him to be an Englishman and had called on the British military police. Obviously Hook had caused a disturbance of some sort, no doubt serious, for when Slone entered the police station, a grim-faced officer of the Egyptian constabulary frowned at him while a British military policeman looked on with some distaste.

"This fellow is one of your men, Lieutenant?" the Egyptian asked.

"Yes and no," Slone said. "He's an American, contracted to the British Army for the railway to the Sudan. He only arrived today, and I had him tucked away for the night, or so I thought. Are there serious charges?"

The military policeman spoke up. "I'm sorry to say, sir, that he got into a fight over an Egyptian girl. He didn't kill anyone, but there'll be some fines to pay."

"I think I can take care of that," Slone said, but he flinched when the Egyptian announced the total amount. "I don't, of course, have that sum with me."

"If you will send it to us tomorrow?" the Egyptian said.

"Yes, of course. Thank you, officer," Slone said.

Enoch Hook, a bit wobbly on his feet, was escorted by two native constables out of the dark bowels of the police station. He waved cheerily to Slone and made a mock bow to the military policeman.

"Had no idea the natives were so touchy about their women," he stammered apologetically to Slone.

"I'll escort you to your quarters, Mr. Hook," Slone said flatly.

"Kind of you, my friend," Hook replied.

Slone decided that the walk would serve to sober the American and leave him less inclined—since it was still rather early, not yet midnight—to venture into the city again. It was quite safe to walk Cairo's streets at night so long as one avoided a few particular areas.

"Kind of you to come to my rescue," Hook said.

"We have a job to do, Mr. Hook."

"Sure, sure," Hook said. "We'll do the job. How about we find a place and have a little drink?"

"I think you've had quite enough," Slone admonished.

"Oh, my, papa's angry," Hook taunted him. "Don't they let boy lieutenants drink in the British Army?"

"Mr. Hook, you've caused quite enough trouble," Slone retorted. "I'm going to escort you to your quarters, and if I can't depend on you to stay there voluntarily, I shall post a guard at your door."

"You're on their side," Hook said. "All I wanted to do was see what was under those veils. Hell, man, how can you tell whether Egyptian women are pretty or ugly as lye soap unless you lift a few veils?"

Slone laughed. The vision of the rather small American taking his life into his hands by trying to remove the veils of Egyptian women was too much. "You're lucky to be alive," he said.

"A couple of rather large Egyptian gentlemen did get pretty excited," Hook said.

They walked in silence, the fall of their boots echoing from the walls of the aged stone houses packed closely on either side of the street. They had passed through the square where the residents of Cairo still milled about in late evening commerce or pleasure, and they were moving towards the warehouse area along the river. For some time now Slone had been viscerally aware that someone was following them.

Hook began to sing. Slone didn't try to silence him. The streets were empty, dark. Some of the fellaheen were known to carry wicked-looking knives, but when Slone looked back, no one was in sight. The military compound where Hook was quartered was only a few hundred yards away.

As Slone and Hook reached an intersection of the street and a dark alley, three large men stepped out of the shadows. They had obviously found a short cut to come out ahead of the pair, and they had arranged themselves so as to block both the narrow street and even narrower alley.

"Hello, there," Hook said, tipping his hat. The three men were dressed in the garments of the fellaheen, and in the dim light Slone saw the glint of metal.

Hook, standing relaxed, hands at his sides, looked at Slone and said, "The two on the right look familiar." He took a step forward, a friendly hand outstretched. "Look, friend, it was an honest mistake. I had no idea you were so touchy about a friendly look at the faces of your women."

"Stand back, Hook," Slone said tensely, wishing he had a weapon, even his ceremonial officer's sword.

"I'm a visitor to your fair city," Hook said, both hands spread, "and I'd hate to have to make a scene, but my friend and I want to go home and go to bed. Understand?"

One of the Egyptians leapt forward, brandishing a curved knife that in the moonlight appeared to be about three feet long. "Give us all your money," he said, in accented English, "and we may let you live."

"I don't think I'll do that," Hook replied with an almost cavalier wave of the hand.

"Hook, you fool!" Slone yelled. "Do as he says."

Action exploded before Slone could move. The Egyptian with the huge, curved knife lunged forward towards the American who, only minutes before, had been so tipsy that he staggered as he walked. Slone plunged between them to try to extricate Hook from the sharp edge of danger, but before he could reach the American, Hook had doffed his top hat and, with one dancing move, much like a matador in a bullfight, crossed in front of the lunging Egyptian. He reached out almost casually to slash the fellaheen across the nose with the stiff brim of his hat. The Egyptian hissed in pain and jerked a hand to his face as blood gushed.

The other two Egyptians, seeing their fellow thus treated, sprang to the attack. Hook became a thing of pure motion, spinning to send one of his heavy boots squarely into the stomach of one of the charging men. He recovered quickly as the Egyptian doubled up and went down, and then he pirouetted gracefully into the air to avoid a wild swing of the third man's weapon. As he came down, Hook seemed to change direction in midair, and his hand lashed out. There was a sound like a rotten limb breaking, and the Egyptian, suddenly limp, melted to the ground.

"Behind you, Hook," Slone yelled as the man with the bleeding nose came at Hook's back. Hook whirled and his hands moved too swiftly to be followed. One blow landed on the Egyptian's neck. A sound like crumpling paper was heard as the man's larynx crushed and he fell to the ground, his chest heaving desperately for breath.

Only the moans of the man who had been kicked in the stomach broke the sudden silence. Hook himself had felt the effects of his deadly blow to the last man's neck, and he rubbed his hand as he bent over the man with the broken neck. Then he rose, satisfied. The entire episode had lasted less than a minute, and two men lay dead.

Slone was speechless. When Hook seized one of the fallen men by his feet and started to drag him into hiding, he managed to say, "My *God*, Hook."

"Sorry," Hook grunted. "If they hadn't been armed I could have been a little easier on them."

"Is that man dead?" Slone asked.

"Him and the other," Hook said. "I'd imagine the third one there has a ruptured spleen. He won't last too long."

Three men dead.

"Help me get the other two into hiding," Hook said.

"You can't do that," Slone said. "You can't just leave that man here to die."

"Look, friend," Hook said harshly. "I saw the inside of that Egyptian jail, and I felt the weight of the constable's stick. I'm not about to face Cairo justice after killing a few of their own people."

"But it was self-defence," Slone said. "They were, after all, attempting to rob us."

"If you want to stay and tell the native police that, then go ahead," Hook said, walking away towards the compound.

Slone, numb with shock, stood where he was.

After a few paces Hook stopped and looked back. He sighed when he saw Slone's determined expression, and he walked back to his side. "All right, partner," he said, "if that's the way it has to be. I just hope you can talk real pretty to those boys."

The explanations took the rest of the night and into the morning. Slone had to use all the authority he could muster to keep the Egyptians from separating them, from taking Hook away for independent questioning. He invoked his commission, his connection with Kitchener's staff, and the name of the Queen, talking firmly and confidently until, just before dawn, Colonel

Roland Streeter walked into the room where Slone and Hook were being interrogated.

Streeter was clearly angry. Turning on the Egyptian policemen, he said scathingly, "This man is a serving British officer! If he says he and his companion were attacked by the men who were killed, then it is true. Do you dare question the word of an officer of Her Majesty's service?"

Some minutes later Slone and Hook followed Streeter out of the police station. The colonel paused just outside, the light of dawn leaving his face in shadow. "Mr. Hook," he said, "I'll have a word with the lieutenant in private."

Hook walked a few paces away and stood with his hands in his pocket, watching the light grow in the east.

"You keep bringing yourself to my attention, Lieutenant," Streeter said. "I pulled you out of that mess because of the uniform you wear, not because of you. Disgrace that uniform again and there will be no help from me or from any other member of the staff. Is that clear?"

"It is clear, Colonel," Slone said, "but I don't think you have a complete understanding of the situation."

"I understand that an officer of the British Army has been detained by native authorities for questioning in the matter of the death of three men," Streeter said. "I do not want to hear the circumstances. I don't give a damn about the circumstances. It is enough that an officer let himself be put into a position where such a thing could happen." .

"We were attacked," Slone insisted.

"Good morning to you, Lieutenant," Streeter said. "If I do not see you again before you return to your post at Wadi Halfa, which I'm going to see that you're ordered to do immediately, I will not be overly disappointed."

"Mr. Hook," Slone said, when Streeter's carriage was clattering down the street, "there's a train leaving for Aswan this morning. I think it would be a good idea if you were on it."

"Sounds as if you might as well join me," Hook said. He grinned. "I have very good ears and the colonel was speaking quite loudly."

Slone tried several times during the day to see Kit, without success. Not daring to knock at the Streeters' suite, he sent messages up, but Kit was out. Finally, towards evening, he sat down in the hotel lobby to wait. A group was carolling, their Christmas airs a jarringly cheerful noise against his lugubrious mood.

Slone had his present for Kit in his pocket. He had intended to give it to her on Christmas Eve, but in view of Colonel Streeter's words he could expect to receive travel orders at any time.

When Kit finally appeared, evidently intending to dine alone, she looked drawn and nervous.

"Slone," she said, coming over to him and sitting beside him. "What happened to you last night? Were you in danger?"

"Not as it turned out," he said, remembering the fury with which the American had demolished three men.

"I know, darling, that you were in the right," she said. "I know that you would do nothing shameful."

He looked at her, wondering what she thought he'd done. But he couldn't blame her. She had her information from her father.

"I did nothing wrong, Kit," he said. He laughed. "In fact, I did nothing. What was done was done by a wild American named Hook."

"Whatever," she said, "we can overcome it together, my sweet." She took his hand. "To soothe Father's ruffled feathers a bit, I had to agree that we would delay the announcement of our engagement until you have returned from the Sudan."

"I see," Slone said. A hint of coldness traced the nape of his neck.

"It's only temporary," she said, "and it doesn't affect the way we feel about each other a whit. I'll be waiting for you."

He took a small box from his pocket. "I was going to give this to you on Christmas Eve, but I think your father may have a train ticket for me before then."

Her face was serious as she took the box, opened it to reveal the ring with its sizable diamond solitaire. "It's beautiful, Slone," she whispered.

She slipped it on the third finger, left hand, and held it up. "It's a perfect fit."

"If you can't wear it there," he said, taking her left hand to kiss it, "wear it on the right."

"I will wear it here, where it belongs," Kit proclaimed. "And if people want to talk, then let them."

"Kit," he said, "have you considered marrying without your parents' permission?"

She shook her head violently. "I couldn't do that to them," she said. "Especially not to mother. When my father was off at his wars, or his post wherever it was, we had only each other, my mother and I." She sighed deeply. "If it came to that in the end—" She paused as a look of pain washed across her face, and then she smiled. "If it came to that, then I expect Mother would recover."

Slone was back in Wadi Halfa in early January, having spent Christmas aboard a British gunboat beating its way up the Nile.

It would be said that the battle of Omdurman was won not in the field but in the workshops at Wadi Halfa, where the Sudan Military Railway was forged. Even in the winter months temperatures soared through the nineties. Dust storms were a regular occurrence. The railhead towards which the construction was pointed, Abu Hamed, was still in enemy hands. The engineers and the Tommies who did the labour moved the rails forward one mile, two miles, sometimes, under good conditions, three miles a day. The Americans, including Enoch Hook and his ridiculous top hat, soon learned to curse the man responsible for putting them into the heart of the Sudanese desert as earnestly as the Tommies.

The officers, Percy Girouard and Slone among them, watched the ridges for any hint of a dervish attack, for the British and Americans were alone in the desert, with the main forces of the army far away, and with each mile of complete track they were coming closer to the enemy stronghold at Abu Hamed. Yet the tracks were extended, and a job was done that would have been difficult even under peacetime conditions, for they were working in one of the most inhospitable places on the face of the earth.

"When Allah made the Sudan," Percy Girouard said wryly one day to Slone, as they sheltered themselves behind a small knoll while a howling sandstorm made every breath agony, "he laughed."

"Yes, I'm sure," replied Slone. "But darkly."

CHAPTER IV

The graceful old house in Sydney—old, at least, by the standards of a country as young as Australia—was still called the Broome House by many, although its master nowadays was a former clipper ship captain, Samuel Gordon. There was still a Broome in the house, Red Broome's widow, Magdalen, and the present mistress of the house was her daughter, Jessica Broome Gordon. When Sam had decided to leave the sea and concentrate on shoreside business, Magdalen had sincerely requested that Sam and Jessica live in the Broome House, not as her guests but as master and mistress.

"You'll be pleasing me so much," Magdalen had said. "You'll get no interference from me in running the house."

In the end Sam had agreed, but only on condition that he be allowed to purchase the house, thus to have it on record that it was his house, so that if he wanted to make any changes he did not have to seek permission from anyone, only agreement from Jessica. Actually, nothing much had changed except the owner's name. Sam had always liked the house as it was. And he was also in favour of continuing the tradition, begun by Red Broome, of making the dining room the setting for a continuing discussion of the events of the empire and of Australia.

So it was that the Gordon table knew the presence of businessmen and military officers, sea captains who brought the latest rumours, members of the government of New South Wales, and visitors from the home country. Always Sam and Jessica sat at opposite ends of the table, Magdalen on Sam's right. The daughter of the house, Rachel—called Java because she had been born there—sat next to whichever guest she had guessed in advance to be the most interesting.

Magdalen had not adjusted to her husband's death so much as

she had become resigned to it. Although she was the senior member of the family, four years older than her brother-in-law, John Lachlan Broome, she was a vibrant woman, attractive and far too vital to become nothing more than a passive grandmother to the lively Java. She felt that the wisest decision she had ever made was to turn the house over to her daughter and son-in-law, for that left her free of any responsibility, with time to do all the things she had been prevented from doing in the past. At first she had dabbled in the cultural affairs of the city, but she had found that she did not always agree with the definition of culture that was put forth by her peers. In the end she had returned to an old interest that she had shared with her husband while he was alive: the ongoing political affairs of her country.

As the nineteenth century used up its last years, change was in the air in Australia. Magdalen, always rather conservative like most older people, was not quite sure she would approve of all the changes that were being made, or discussed, or battled over, but she was firm on one point. She believed, with the most hot-blooded labour agitator, that there would be either unification of the Australian states, or there would be revolution. It was as simple as that. There was something in the Australian atmosphere that made men rebel against the practices of the aristocracy that had been imported from England. It was as if a spirit of freedom exuded from the land itself, and the emanations were strongest in those areas where nature had been the least kind. The spirit that was the soul of a new Australia infected men who scratched a living in the desolate interior, men who had come to Australia for gold that panned out as disappointment, men who had come for land to find that the finest properties were taken. And the infection had spread to the workers of the cities and even to well-bred young ladies like her granddaughter.

Seated at the Gordon table on a cool night in September 1897, Magdalen looked across the table at Java, now a spectacularly beautiful young girl of almost fourteen, poised charmingly between puberty and maturity. The combination of her father's Scots-red hair and her mother's delicate colouring formed a charming picture. She was lithe, slim, and vivacious. The manner of her birth, in primitive conditions in the jungles of Java, had made it impossible for Jessica to have other children, so she was an only child. To the girl's credit, she had recognized early on that both her parents doted on her, and she had confided to her grandmother her resolve not to become totally spoilt. And indeed she managed her young life well, doing her schoolwork effortlessly with top marks, even dabbling in verse—though she was quite reluctant to show the results to anyone.

Tonight Java had adroitly placed herself next to the evening's special guest, Mr. Jon Mason, who had been elected as a delegate from the state of Victoria to a new Federal Convention, this time in Sydney's Parliament House. He had been invited to the Broome-Gordon house by John Lachlan—"Johnny"—Broome, who as one of Australia's leading newspaper publishers agreed with Jon on most issues. In truth, however, Jon was equally good friends with his hosts, the Gordons, for he and Sam had fought side by side during the Zulu War in Africa in 1879.

"Mr. Mason," Java was saying, "while you and the distinguished delegates discuss the methods of distribution of the surplus revenue of an Australian Commonwealth, and the influence of the Upper House on money bills, the people are crying out 'unlock the lands'."

"Jon," said Johnny Broome from across the table, "you mustn't underestimate this young lady. She'll talk your ear off, and if you're not careful, she'll have you joining the Labour Electoral League."

"Not everyone is as conservative as you, Uncle Johnny," Java retorted firmly. The man was in fact her great-uncle, but Uncle Johnny was what she always called him.

Jon and Johnny smiled. Magdalen thought she saw on Jon's face an expression of indulgence that was faintly patronizing. It was not unusual, after all, for young people to be parlour liberals, without thinking through the consequences of their views. But his reply to Java was respectful and well considered.

"Your uncle is not as conservative as you might think, Java," he said. "And if you're looking for my opinion, then consider me a liberal rather than radical. I think there's enough radicalism in the world right now—too much, perhaps, with French socialists saying things like 'Property is robbery'. I know there are landless people in Australia who feel that way, but that sort of thinking will only lead to anarchy. And we don't need to follow English socialists, either. They're off on a tangent, attacking the institution of marriage, saying things like 'The most detestable monopoly is that of the man who takes himself one woman'. Luckily the Australian labour movement—apart from their chant to 'unlock the land'—seems fundamentally sound and sensible, concerned mainly with political issues, like trying to limit the power of an upper legislative house in a unified land." He stopped himself abruptly. "But now I'm making a speech, and I certainly didn't mean to do that. My apologies, Jessica, Sam."

"None needed, Jon," Sam replied cordially. "We're interested in your views—Java in particular, as you can see." He looked at his daughter affectionately.

Magdalen had often heard Sam say that Java was coming of age with Australia itself. He was quite proud of his little Java girl, even if at times she did get a bit overexcited about the alleged mistreatment of the "downtrodden", favouring labour unions as well as the landless, who, she claimed, had still not been given adequate opportunity to share in Australia's future.

It was true enough, Magdalen knew, that most of the good land was in the hands of a relatively few families, called squatters, most of whom had occupied the lands in the early years of settlement. But what to *do* about the problem was not an easy question to resolve.

"You gentlemen in government," Java was boldly addressing Jon Mason, "must start listening to the people. Statements such as that made by Mr. Reid,"—she was talking about the premier of New South Wales—"that he will not allow people to starve, are not enough. More than charity will be needed to prevent an explosion of the people. Would you want to see the masses raise a rebel flag and sing a rebel chorus?"

"I'll confess I'm not surprised to hear you talk that way, my dear. When I was campaigning to be a representative, I spoke with people all over Victoria. People are changing, questioning more. They're reading more, too. Do you know that one country newspaper is printing Ruskin's *Unto This Last* in instalments? Working people are attending lectures on poetry, Darwinism, and the history of land laws. *That's* a good trend, whatever one might think about the land issue."

He continued to speak to Java as if she were an adult male voter, telling her of his beliefs, explaining that he had great hope, great pride in the people of Victoria, that he was sure that Victoria's electorate would support a democratic unification. "I can feel the sap of the future rushing up the stem of the nation," he said eloquently.

"That's just what I tell my son Patrick," Johnny interjected. Patrick, Johnny's youngest child, was a few months older than Java. Neither he nor his siblings nor his mother, Kitty, appeared very often these days at the Gordons' table. Kitty was not well, and she preferred to remain at home in the comfortable house Johnny had recently built outside Sydney. She professed, in addition to her infirmities, a growing indifference to politics, though she never begrudged Johnny his passionate interest in the subject.

When dinner was over, Jessica Gordon caught Jon, Sam, and Johnny before they managed their escape to Sam's study for brandy and cigars. "It's so nice to have you here, Jon," she said, smiling sincerely. "I'm only sorry that your wife and your son couldn't be with you."

At the mention, Java looked quickly at Jon, as did Magdalen. She had been tempted at dinner to bring up the subject of Mason's Samoan wife but had avoided the subject, because race, after all, was a delicate subject.

"I'll tell Misa you asked about her," Jon said.

"Do bring her and the boy for a visit," Jessica said.

"Any time, Jon," Sam put in. "You know you're always welcome."

But when the men had retired, Java looked curiously at her mother and said, "I know Mr. Mason is welcome, but, truly, now, would a brown-skinned woman and a mixed-blood boy be welcome?"

"They would be welcomed by me," Jessica said.

"But not by Sydney society in general?" Java asked.

"I can't speak for Sydney society," Jessica responded. "I think, young lady, that it's your bedtime."

The next morning Java awoke early, and as she dressed for the day she thought of the preceding evening, particularly of her grandmother. Though Magdalen had said little, Java had seen her taking in the entire conversation. She was so frightfully intelligent.

Java and her grandmother had become very close during the years of Java's growing up. They had developed mutual interests, read the same books, and shared their thoughts with an intimacy that belied the difference in their years.

There was one kind of outing they both enjoyed very much: spending an afternoon at the home of a socially active man named William Henry McNamara, who had established a free reading room that was always well stocked with socialist and progressive literature. To some, McNamara's rooms were a disreputable meeting ground for notorious rascals; yet to others they were a respectable gathering place for people of progressive tendencies.

That afternoon Java had a visitor. Sarah Bladen was of Java's age, and her best chum from school. She was a pretty girl who aroused Java's unspoken envy with breasts and hips that were more developed than Java's, but who often worried Java with her preoccupation with the opposite sex. A conversation between the two girls often went off in odd, diametrically opposed directions: Java would hold forth on some social issue, while Sarah, only half listening, would prattle along happily about her latest bout of undying love engendered by a boy who glanced at her in church. Yet they remained fast friends.

"I'm so glad you came," Java told her. "Grandmother and I have planned an outing. You'll enjoy it."

"Shopping?" Sarah asked. "We must stop by that little tea shop where they make those divine cakes."

Sara was quite puzzled when Java and Magdalen escorted her into a crowded little room filled with rather odd-looking people and the smell of tobacco and books. The room was dominated by a well-groomed man in a three-piece suit. He had dark, slick hair, a huge, bushy, black moustache, and piercing dark eyes under heavy eyebrows. He was speaking about the future of Australia. Sarah sighed, realizing that she was in for one of Java's intellectual affairs. She immediately let her mind wander to thoughts of tea cakes and boys with arresting glances.

The man who was speaking was well known to both Java and

Magdalen, both by his reputation and his writings. He was Henry Lawson, newspaperman, writer, and poet. More and more Australians were coming to look upon him as an unofficial spokesman for the people. On that afternoon in McNamara's meeting place on Castlereagh Street, Lawson was in good form, speaking of a new kind of civilization for Australia, a society that would embody ideals of social justice.

"Brotherhood," Lawson said, giving the word an almost mystic meaning. "Consider it, ladies and gentlemen. We will all be brothers, bushmen, stockmen, shearers, the workers of the unions."

Java glanced at her grandmother, whose expression was one of sceptical interest. Magdalen had once admitted that she was not sure she wanted to be sister to bushrangers and shearers, though she recognized in principle the necessity of unlocking the lands, at least to some degree. Her grandmother was, Java reflected, a conservative-liberal, not a person of the people. She had not taken it kindly when Java once called her "mate".

While Lawson talked, Magdalen was wishing that all of the fire-eaters would stick to the main point. Johnny Broome had been writing about it for years in his editorials. Land regulations prevented the poor from becoming land owners at a time when some of the individual Australian states were not self-supporting in food production. Johnny had been pointing out, of late, that the predictions of Alexander Harris, in the mid-1800s, were on the verge of realization, that without land reform the young people of Australia would turn against British rule, bringing closer the real danger of total revolution.

Magdalen's attention was brought back fully to the speaker when Lawson began to point out the flaw in the theory of universal brotherhood. As it happened, Lawson was one of the principal voices for the White Australia Policy.

"The Jap and the American Negro form no problems," Lawson was saying. Java, leaning forward in full attention, glanced at Sarah, whose eyes were glazed over in boredom. Lawson went on. "And the American Indian, the African and the South Sea Savage, and the Aboriginals of Australia will become extinct, and so relieve the preachers of universal brotherhood of all anxiety on their account. The Chinaman will have to be killed or cured, probably the former because two Wongs don't make a white."

There was general laughter. When Java looked to see if Sarah had understood the joke, she saw her friend dozing. "Sarah!" she hissed indignantly, pinching her friend painfully on the arm.

"Ouch!" Sarah yelped, jerking erect and then looking around guiltily as the laughter centred on her.

"How could you embarrass us so," Java later demanded. They had left the meeting and were walking towards the tea shop and its assorted cakes.

"Well, Java Gordon," Sarah retorted, "you may think it's high excitement to hear some bushranger run on about being a brother to a sheep herder and all that, but the next time you plan to do so will you please tell me in advance, so that I can arrange to be somewhere else?"

"I will do just that," Java said angrily.

That evening, when Java and her grandmother were alone, Magdalen said, "You mustn't judge Sarah too harshly. She's a lovely girl, and quite fond of you."

"But she's so unconcerned," Java protested.

"Intellectual snobbery, my darling granddaughter," Magdalen said, "is the worst form of the disease. Your friend, Sarah, has both patience and kindness. I've seen her sit for an hour listening as you talked about politics and the new Australia, although Sarah, it seems, is perfectly satisfied with the Australia she has."

Java considered her grandmother's words carefully. "Yes," she admitted, after a while. "Yes, she is a good friend, and I will do my best, in the future, not to be impatient with her."

They were sitting on the front porch of the house on a balmy evening. In the harbour there was a mixture of tall ships and the smoking, reeking steamers that were taking over the seas.

"Grandmother," Java said, "have you met Mr. Mason's wife, the Samoan?"

"I have. Lovely girl."

"Would my mother and father really welcome her and her son into the house if Mr. Mason should accept their invitation to bring them?"

"Of course," Magdalen said. "Mr. Mason and your father have been friends since they fought together at Isandhlwana during the

Zulu War. Don't forget that your father saved Mr. Mason's life there."

"Yes, I know. Daddy's told me often. But why would a man like Mr. Mason marry a brown-skinned woman? He's English—Australian now. He's very handsome. He's rich."

"Perhaps because he loved her?" Magdalen suggested. She was in her mid-seventies, and she was almost as trim and thin as Java. Her face was only moderately lined, her hair thick and lustrous silver.

"But he must have been aware of the difficulties that it would bring."

"I imagine so," Magdalen said. "Don't let the raving of the Australia-for-whites-only people confuse you, child. Remember that it was the love and kindness of some brown-skinned people that saved your mother's life, and yours in Java."

Java did not, of course, remember anything about the land for which she was named, but she had heard the story many times: how Javanese midwives had assisted at her birth, how her mother had been saved from death by an old Javanese man who had found her in a ditch and taken her to his village. Her mother often spoke lovingly of the women and the old man, but there were no brown-skinned people in the Gordons' circle of friends.

Now, as her grandmother leaned back in her rocking chair and closed her eyes, Java wondered how it would be if she, like Jon Mason's son, was of mixed blood. It was a scaring thought, and she didn't linger on it long. She was not of mixed blood. She was the sole product of a rich and respected man and the daughter of a true Australian hero. For her, the future was bright. Whatever happened to those faceless masses for whom the speakers wept and mourned, she would never be hungry. She would never know social ostracism. Why not, then, forget trying to puzzle out whether men like Henry Lawson were right or wrong and join Sarah in enjoying a new frock, and in speculation about whether or not a certain boy had noticed her?

"Rot," she whispered, sickened at her own thought of becoming an intellectual vegetable. She stood, one hand on the railing of the porch, and looked out over the city and the harbour. One thing she could not do. She could not divorce herself from the vital events of her time. One way or the other she would participate. And, incidentally, if Mr. Jon Mason did bring his wife and his son to visit, she would do her utmost to make them feel welcome, and to be a friend to the boy who, through no choice of his own, had the blood of his brown-skinned mother.

CHAPTER V

Percy Girouard had received a small book of poems by Rudyard Kipling in a package from his family in England. He, of course, had read the poems before, and he chided Slone Shannon as being a semiliterate for being ignorant of Mr. Kipling's poetry. In the desert evenings, with the construction force camped around them quiet and exhausted by the heat and the sandstorms, the two young men would take turns at reading "Danny Deever", "Gunga Din", or "The Widow At Windsor", and would squabble good-naturedly over the right to chant the cockney lines of "Fuzzy-Wuzzy":

> So 'ere's *to* you, Fuzzy-Wuzzy, at your 'ome in the Soudan;
> You're a pore benighted 'eathen but a first-class fightin'
> man;
> An' 'ere's *to* you, Fuzzy-Wuzzy, with your 'ayrick 'ead of
> 'air—
> You big black boundin' beggar—for you broke a British
> square!

The poem had the delightful romping rhythm that had made Kipling the poet of the empire, but in the dark, when Slone remembered the words that ended three stanzas of the poem, they caused a slight shiver. He had not yet seen the enemy, had only heard of him. Fuzzy-Wuzzy. Fuz-Wuz. Dervish. Madhist. Nigger. The enemy had many names, and in the loneliness of a desert night he seemed like a huge figure wielding a gigantic two-handed sword, fading in and out of sight as if by magic, and he had done what no other native force had done: he had broken a British square of fire.

The railway was pouring men and weapons into the Sudan.

Abu Hamed had been taken in August of the previous year with surprisingly small losses, two officers and twenty-five men. As 1898 began, battalions of the Warwickshire Regiment and the Cameron Highlanders were in the Sudan. Berber, upriver from Abu Hamed, had fallen without a fight, the enemy having withdrawn.

The railway builders meanwhile were pushing track across another stretch of terrible desert, along the Nile this time, to that point above the fifth cataract where the mighty Atbara, fresh from the mountains of Abyssinia, joined the Nile. One job remained for the engineers: to bridge the Atbara.

To secure the river, the Cameron Highlanders in April led an attack on a force of twelve thousand infantry and three thousand cavalry under the rulers of the notorious "fuzzy-wuzzies", the Hendendoa tribe. Charging up the Atbara, the British assaulted the enemy in their own entrenched encampment, and the results of the bold manoeuvre were devastating: the dervishes were poorly armed with old brass muzzle-loaders and Remington elephant guns, and within half an hour three thousand dervishes were dead and hundreds more captured, with a loss of less than six hundred on the Sirdar's side.

Back at the railhead, near the river's mouth, Slone was quite proud of the men who worked with and under him. The wild Atbara was bridged in only forty-two days. The Nile had been tamed, with the railway bypassing the cataracts, and the way to Khartoum was open. The river was guarded by a fleet of gunboats with guns so powerful that no Madhist force could stand and fight within their range. At Abadia, just downstream from captured Berber, three super gunboats were being assembled to mount fearsome armament: two twelve-and-one-half pounder cannon, one twelve-pounder, a four-inch howitzer, and four machine guns called Maxims, after their inventor, the Englishman Hiram Stevens Maxim.

Only one thing prevented the army from ending the campaign immediately: the Nile would not be navigable to Khartoum until the end of July, and Kitchener had no intention of marching without water transport and the support of his gunboats.

He came to the Atbara, tall, unsmiling, his jowls darkened by his beard when he arrived, even though he had shaved that morning.

He inspected the bridge and gave it his blessings, his lips curling upward slightly. Few things made him smile, but his "boys" did, his boys and their excellent work.

Slone Shannon, walking beside Lieutenant Girouard during the tour of inspection, kept his mouth tightly closed as Kitchener commented and Girouard answered questions.

"Well, Percy," Kitchener said at last, "you've done well. Very well."

"Thank you, sir," Percy replied; then, not being shy, he added, "Do you think it would be all right now if Lieutenant Shannon and I followed the example of the senior officers and took leave for Cairo?"

"Not to England, Percy," Kitchener cautioned, "if that's your intention."

"No, sir. Thank you, sir," Girouard said, with a hidden wink at Slone.

Slone could not get down the Nile fast enough. He had received only two letters from Kit in all the time that he had been involved in pushing the railway through impossible conditions. Each letter had been warm, and she had expressed her love for him, in clear if not florid terms; but letters were a poor substitute for the feel of her in his arms, the smell of her in his nostrils.

"So we are off," Girouard said, "leaving the other ranks to swelter in the full blast of a Sudanese summer without so much as a thought."

"I can think about them," Slone said.

"But not volunteer to stay with them, eh?"

It was hot in Cairo. A thousand odours assaulted one's senses. The summer heat seemed to make the street merchants even more insistent, to encourage every man, woman, and child to throng the streets. The hotel baked in the sun, with little activity in evidence. There was a room for the two members of Kitchener's engineering staff, something cool to drink and a lovely bath. Then Slone, in a uniform freshened by the hotel's valet service, went to knock on the door of the suite occupied by Colonel Roland Streeter and his family.

It was Kit who opened the door. For a moment her face was

politely blank, but only for a split second before she threw herself into Slone's arms with a little sound of surprise and contentment. Her lips tasted of the orange she had been eating, and it required a supreme effort on Slone's part to loosen his arms and let her step back to look at him admiringly.

"My, my, how tanned you are," she said. "Is this my Lieutenant Shannon or some desert sheikh?"

An Egyptian girl served tea. Both Colonel Streeter and Kit's mother were away from the hotel, and the young people spent delightful hours together, a time for Slone to gaze deeply into Kit's green eyes, listening to each individual syllable of each sweet word as she spoke of how she had missed him.

The unannounced engagement had seemed endless to Slone. It had taken Kitchener twenty-three months to move his army from the Sudanese border to the junction of the Atbara, and it was likely to be more months before the army closed on the Khalifa's capital at Omdurman.

"How's your father's attitude regarding our marriage?" he asked. "Any improvement?"

Kit made a face and bit her lower lip. "In truth, I haven't mentioned it again. I thought it best to wait until you were finished in the south."

"I see," Slone said, but there was just a hint of questioning in his tone. Her father had insisted that they wait to make the engagement announcement until after the campaign, saying something about the dangers to a soldier and the possibility of Slone's death. Was Kit considering that possibility, too?

"How long can you stay in Cairo?" she asked.

"Two weeks, no more."

She mused. "How nice."

"Kit?"

She looked up at him, her eyes wide.

"Let's go downriver to Alexandria. It would take them days, weeks even, to find us. Let's get married and tell them only when we've come back here, when it's time for me to go back on duty."

She shivered and allowed him to draw her close, to kiss her heatedly. When she pulled away she was weeping, large tears forming silently and sliding down her cheeks. "You can't imagine how much I want to say yes."

"Then say it."

"I can't. You know I can't."

There were nights during Slone's next two weeks in Cairo that he was unable to see Kit. Roland Streeter's dislike for the young lieutenant was still very much in evidence, and the quiet woman who was his wife seemed to echo her husband's disapproval. When he did manage to see Kit, most of his time with her was strictly chaperoned by either her parents, Percy Girouard, or the company of many at a dance in the hotel ballroom.

Then it was time to go, and Slone felt that something had died, something had been wasted. Kit clung to him and spoke of her love, and he spoke of his. But he had a painful intuition that something was awry.

Slone went back reluctantly into the furnace of the Sudanese summer. Now and then he helped to drill the men for an hour or two in the early morning, before it became too hot. For the rest of the day he and the men sat in whatever shade they could find, looking at the Nile, willing it to begin its seasonal rise so that the advance of the army would break the tedium. Even battle was preferable to baking in an open-air oven. The summer wore on.

The last wave of reinforcements came steaming up the river: the 2nd British Brigade, a battalion of the Grenadier Guards from Gibraltar, the 1st Battalion of the Northumberland Fusiliers, and, among others, the 21st lancers, fresh from the fleshpots of Cairo to give cavalry support.

The 21st Lancers had been a unit for more than thirty years without once having seen combat—not even a small skirmish. If one wanted to start a fight, one had only to voice in the presence of members of the 21st what wags were saying was the regiment's unofficial motto: "Thou shalt not kill".

Slone was an excellent horseman. He was, after all, a red-blooded colonial boy who had spent most of his youth on a small Queensland station as the son of a military man. He watched the 21st drill in the heat. This was no Cairo parade, with light gear and dress uniforms; the cavalrymen were weighed down with a variety of travel gear in packs and packages. Each man had a broad canvas shade hanging down his neck from the back of his helmet.

The horses had not travelled well from Cairo, but apart from the loss of a few to sunstroke, they soon recovered.

Slone sought out the commander of the unit, a Colonel R. M. Martin, with one purpose in mind. It was, he knew, Kitchener's policy to allow his boys to take part in important engagements, and Slone felt that the best way to fight in the desert would be from the back of a horse. When he expressed this desire to Colonel Martin, Martin looked at him, gave him a brief smile, and said, "All right, Shannon. Glad to have you."

At the time Slone had no idea why the colonel was smiling as he added, "When the time comes, attach yourself to Lieutenant Churchill and go into battle with him."

It was left to the young Winston Churchill to enlighten Slone as to why. "The 21st Lancers are not on the whole a good business," Churchill said, speaking without warmth. "They hate all the number of attached officers, men like you and me, and some of them, you will find, take few pains to conceal their dislike."

"Are you saying that the colonel resents my asking to join the 21st for the battle?" Slone asked.

"He knows that if you had to, you could get an order from Kitchener, and he resents that." Churchill smiled coldly. "Well, that sort of thing annoys me rather than disturbs me."

Churchill was a rather handsome young man, immaculate in his uniform and, Slone was to find out quickly, as welcome in that army as a cuckoo in a thrush's nest.

"Churchill?" exclaimed a 21st Lancers major to Slone. "He makes me sick."

It seemed that Churchill made everyone sick, including Kitchener. He had, in effect, forced himself on the Sirdar with a letter from the prime minister himself, and he was not in the Sudan to fight—so said his fellow officers—but to glorify himself in his writings.

As soon as Slone became aware of Churchill's standing—or lack of it—with the officers of the 21st, he began to distance himself from Winston, who did not protest, not having warmed at all to the colonial. Slone soon found a friendly welcome from a young man of his own age, Lieutenant Robert Grenfell, son of a fine military family and the ideal cavalry officer.

"If you want to fight, Shannon," Grenfell said after they had talked, "then follow me. When there's fighting, my men and I will be in the forefront."

Slone had thought that nothing could be worse than the endless days spent in the camp at the Atbara. Men said that death at the hands of the dervishes would be a relief after camp, with its sand and dust and all the plagues of Egypt. There was one species of spider so large that the natives called it the father of all spiders, and asps whose bite could kill a camel, and *nebek* thorns that dug into the skin like fishhooks. Flies were everywhere, undaunted even by thick clouds of the rankest tobacco smoke. Scorpions seemed to be everywhere. Added to those plagues were boils, sore throats, apoplexy, sunstroke, enteric fever, and venereal disease among those men who dallied with the local women.

When the 21st Lancers left the Atbara camp they could see, as they marched, the barges on the Nile carrying luckier men. The horses, still weak from the trip up the Nile, had difficulty carrying the Lancers with all of their equipment. Stones and thorns attacked the hocks of the horses and the soft feet of the baggage camels. Men died on the march and had to be left in shallow graves, in a sandy wilderness that would, within weeks, swallow up all signs of the passing of an army.

Slone thanked his stars that he had put distance between himself and Lieutenant Churchill. Churchill had caustically remarked to a group of officers that the only dispatches they'd ever be mentioned in were the casualty lists, and as a reward for his charming personality he had been left behind to tend the mess caravan, which consisted of two donkeys and a mule.

The army assembled at Abu Hamed on August 21, sixty miles from Omdurman, twelve hundred miles from Cairo. There were 8,200 British troops, 17,600 Egyptians and Sudanese, 44 field guns and 20 Maxims on land, 36 guns and 24 Maxims on the water, 2,470 horses, 5,250 camels, 230 donkeys, and one young Australian officer whose mind, more often than not, was in Cairo with a certain young lady. From here the grand army continued upriver, marching southwards for hot and arduous days towards Omdurman.

On August 31 the Khalifa ordered a parade of his troops to the west of Omdurman. An army of over fifty thousand men formed up, facing east, to hear the Khalifa summon them to *jihad*, a holy war against the infidels.

The next day Kitchener's army reached a barren plain on the Nile's western bank, just six miles north of Omdurman. The British camped with their backs to the river, the forces arrayed in the form of an arc facing the broad, desolate plain, which was nearly surrounded by higher ground—one nearby hill to the south called the Jebel Surgham, the Kerreri hills to the northwest, and low ridges elsewhere.

Knowing the past history of the dervishes, Kitchener intended to let the Khalifa come to him, forcing the dervishes to attack the entrenched British forces supported by artillery and Maxim machine guns.

From the top of the Jebel Surgham an advance scout signalled by heliograph that the Khalifa's mighty army was moving north from Omdurman, advancing towards them. The long-awaited confrontation seemed imminent; but then, mysteriously, the great mass of dervishes halted and made camp for the night.

Early the next morning, Friday, September 2, a small patrol of the 21st Lancers under Lieutenant Robert Grenfell rode out to the ridge near the Jebel Surgham. Slone Shannon, riding with Grenfell, spurred his horse to keep up as the two galloped together up the long slope of the ridge. It had been reported that the huge army of the Khalifa was on the move again, and the patrol under Grenfell was acting as the eyes of the army to confirm or deny the intelligence.

Topping the dry, dusty ridge, Slone and Grenfell jerked their mounts to a halt and sat side by side. On the plain ahead they saw a five-mile-long monster, a giant living organism composed of individual men and animals, the dervish army creeping towards them.

"My God," Slone said.

The long line had great humps and squares of troop formations at intervals across the empty plain. A sound came to them, a chanted war song. Small puffs of smoke told Slone that they were being fired upon, but the dervishes were far out of range.

"We shall never see such a sight again," Grenfell said in an awed voice. "There must be forty thousand of them."

Grenfell sent a messenger back to Colonel Martin. He and Slone stayed on the top of the ridge, mounted, until a more senior officer arrived and told them in no uncertain terms that they were being damned fools, presenting themselves to the snipers as targets, and moreover drawing fire on others.

Now the enemy army buzzed like a swarm of bees. As the slow minutes passed and the army drew closer, Slone could distinguish the eerie wail of the native war horn—the *ombeya*—as well as the beating of drums and human voices bellowing out their hatred for the white interlopers from Europe.

Oddly enough the vast army of the Khalifa seemed to be ignorant of the position of the British, who were still arrayed in a semicircle with their backs to the river, supported by the cannon and Maxim guns of the boats. Instead of turning for the army's main position, the Khalifa's troops continued to march north towards the distant Kerreri hills. However, the dervishes were within artillery range, and suddenly the British guns, both on land and on the river, began to thunder. A huge segment of the dervish army turned from their line of advance and bore down on the encampment. Shrapnel caused the advancing lines to ripple as men fell, the movement much like waves winding across a field of ripe grain.

The 21st Lancers had been ordered to ride to safety inside the enclosure. Slone saw British and Egyptian troops fighting in the traditional manner, close order line formation, front rank kneeling, rear rank standing. So Englishmen had fought at Waterloo. The directed volleys of the British took a terrible toll, and the return fire of the rampant, charging dervishes was ineffective.

It was the artillery that broke the enemy's attack. As the passions of the dervishes swelled into an angry roar, the British guns scattered shrapnel with deadly effect. Bodies flew into the air on the blast of high-explosive shells, and the rifles of the infantry augmented the carnage.

For veterans of other colonial wars, there was an astounding clarity of observation on that September 2, 1898. Usually a set battle was quickly hidden by the smoke of gunpowder, but on that day the Lee Metford rifles used cordite, which produced less smoke than old-style powder, and there was a wind to carry away what little smoke was created. So it was that the entire battlefield was exposed to view. Anyone with a good point of observation, and that included Slone, saw the dervish attack begin to waver. For more than an hour they had advanced into the muzzles of ten thousand rifles, the terrible machine guns, and the full strength of the British artillery, often stepping over the bodies of their fallen comrades to press forward. Some of the attackers wore chain mail and carried swords captured from Crusaders six hundred years past.

At least two thousand of the enemy lay dead, with twice that many wounded. Hundreds of the wounded crawled towards the Nile, burning for water. Others crawled in vain towards escape into the hills.

The 21st Lancers once again became the eyes of the army, advancing over a ridge to scout and, in the terse words of the Sirdar, "to annoy the enemy as far as possible and head them off if possible from Omdurman".

Needless to say, the 21st Lancers were eager to make a mark for themselves, for they carried a heavy history on their backs; thirty years had passed without the Lancers engaging in so much as a skirmish, and the shame of this fact burned within every man and officer.

Slone, riding with Grenfell as the 21st Lancers pressed forward, saw wounded men and horses and heard their screams of pain. He saw men on all fours scrambling painfully, dragging their own entrails in the bloody dust. A heliographed message from an advance patrol halted movement. The patrol reported about four hundred dervishes on the hill ahead of the 21st. Word came from the Sirdar. "Worry them on their flank and head them off from Omdurman." And, with relief and eagerness, the 21st continued their advance.

As the Lancers topped the ridge, they saw a group of perhaps seven hundred fuzzy-wuzzies draw up to face them. Once again the 21st came to a halt while Colonel Martin considered the situation. His conclusion was foregone. For the first time in thirty years the 21st Lancers had an opportunity. To let this moment pass would be, in the eyes of all the eager officers including Martin, a crime. Seven hundred poorly armed dervishes exposed on good, open ground could not hope to withstand the charge of four hundred well-armed Lancers.

Lieutenant Grenfell jerked his horse's reins. The animal reared. Beside him Slone's own mount seemed to catch the tension. "Let's go!" Grenfell was repeating again and again. "Let's go!"

Slone saw Colonel Martin's arm rise, his sword gleaming in the sun. The heat of the day was forgotten. The shrill cry of the bugle's command to charge came to Slone's ears, and suddenly he was spurring his horse to keep up with Grenfell, the men coming behind, throats opened with wild battle cries. Two hundred and fifty yards away, the enemy waited.

Slone heard the slap-slap of bullets passing close by. His skin was peppered painfully, and he realized, through the red haze of excitement and the contagious bloodlust, that dervish bullets were striking the gound and sending pieces of stones flying like miniature shrapnel. He lowered his head, helmet pointed forward to avert the sting of the flying gravel.

One hundred and fifty yards. Near him a horse gave a high-pitched scream and went down, sending the rider tumbling limply. One hundred yards. Soon the two forces would meet with a clash. Soon—soon.

But, with startling suddenness, a trap as old as desert battle itself was sprung on the rushing Lancers. In a deep, sloping *khor*, or ravine, behind the visible dervishes, awaited another two thousand of the Khalifa's finest horsemen. An old hand at fighting in the desert would have anticipated the trick, but Colonel Martin, in his inexperience, had sent his command into the teeth of it. The ground seemed to open under the very hooves of the Lancers' horses, and there was no choice but to charge down the sloping side of the *khor* into the wall of densely packed men in white robes, men who faced the assault twelve deep. The few dervishes who had been the bait for the trap were stormed backwards into the ravine, some directly on top of their brothers.

The strike of the charging Lancers was a single sound, a tremendous crack of sound. If ever it could be said that a force fell upon its enemies, it could be said of the 21st Lancers as their momentum carried them into the *khor* to shatter the dervish forces like an exploding shell.

Although Slone was engaged in his first cavalry charge, he knew intuitively that his only chance to stay alive was to maintain enough momentum to carry him through the massed enemy in the ravine and up the other side on to clear desert.

Ahead of him he saw that the far bank of the *khor* was steep and studded with boulders. He had retained his seat with difficulty as his horse had pounded into a group of dervishes, but out of the corner of his eye he saw that Grenfell had been knocked from his mount and was trying to get back on. Slone lashed out with his sword to parry a strike by a wicked-looking blade, felt the shock of impact in his arm as a man died from his blow, and then kneed his horse toward Grenfell. He was too late. He saw a dervish strike Grenfell in the back with this sword, and then a long spear buried its tip into Grenfell's body.

The dervishes fought—God, how they fought, attacking man and horse with equal ferocity, firing rifles at point-blank range, driving their heavy spears into the bellies of the animals in an effort to dismount the Lancers.

Slone used his pistol in his left hand, his sword in his right hand. Around him the men of the 21st battled for their lives with the same weapons—pistol, sword, lance—chopping and battering their way forward towards the far side of the ravine. Slone felt hands on his right leg, and he slashed downwards with his sword to mangle the upturned, snarling face of an enemy. Little by little he was moving towards the far bank.

A lance came thrusting towards him, and he parried it with his sword; the fine blade snapped. The lance-wielding dervish came at him again, and Slone threw the broken sword forcefully to strike the man in the mouth. Blood spewed, and with his last bullet Slone finished off the dervish and pushed past him.

A spear flew at him, and he ducked. His horse leapt and whinnied in fear as a bullet cut a bloody flesh wound across its neck. At one side a familiar weapon, a lance, was impaled in the ground. Slone leaned from the saddle, seized it, and pushed onwards, using the lance like a sword as he moved up the slope among boulders, other Lancers riding beside and behind him.

A dervish emir, sitting on a fine black horse, charged down the slope of the ravine directly at Slone. Slone lifted the lance into position, dodging the downswing of the emir's sword as he drove the lance home into the man's chest. The lance broke, and Slone was once again weaponless; but the top of the bank was just ahead, and then he was out of the ravine and other Lancers were gathering around him, effecting a defensive formation. Some of the men still had loaded pistols.

"Dismount, all you who have ammunition," Slone said, "and fire into the ravine."

He himself reloaded his weapon quickly and stood calmly, tall and cool in the desert heat, choosing his targets carefully as the fight in the *khor* continued. One of the men at his side, Grenfell's troop sergeant, had been slashed by dervish swords so badly that his nose and cheeks were torn, the skin hanging in flaps, his eyes dimmed by blood. Still he stood at Slone's side and fired at the white-clad dervishes in the ravine.

"Sergeant," Slone said, "fall out. Find yourself a surgeon."

"No, sir," the sergeant said. "Thank you all the same, sir. Just show me the devils."

Colonel Martin—having, like all soldiers, learned fast in combat—had rallied his men with impressive speed. Having had quite enough of hand-to-hand fighting, he moved his men to flank the dervishes in the ravine and opened up a withering fire. His fire, combined with that coming from the few men who were with Slone, left the enemy no choice but to attempt a charge into the muzzles of the rifles. The concentrated and accurate fire proved too much for them: the remainder of the dervish force fled, leaving the 21st Lancers in possession of the field.

With the blood still pounding in his ears, with his hearing dimmed by the roar of the firing, Slone gave the men around him orders to cease firing. Winston Churchill came galloping up, having survived the wild charge and the precipitous plunge into the enemy-filled ravine.

"Good show," he yelled, his handsome face flushed with excitement. "But, by God, we should have turned right about and charged back through. Another fifty or sixty casualties would have made this a historic performance. Something to make us proud of our race and blood!"

Slone would remember Churchill's words for a long, long time. He wondered what kind of egomaniacal man it took to wish the death of an additional fifty or sixty men so that Englishmen could be proud of their race. Twenty-one Lancers were dead, sixty-five seriously wounded. Well, over a fourth of the Lancers' horses had been killed or maimed to the point of having to be put down. There was carnage everywhere.

CHAPTER VI

In Australia, where men paid homage only to the personal worth that was earned through hard work, where the boast was that Australians "call no biped lord or sir, and touch their hats to no man", King Drought was in the process of humbling or ruining all who made their livelihood from the land. On those far-stretching, sun-drenched plains of the interior, heat waves shimmered over the baked earth. The grass was drying up. Rivers had ceased to flow, leaving only isolated pools of water called billabongs. Even the most prosperous squatters were humbled by the drought, yet they suffered the least, for the best of the billabongs always seemed to lie securely within the holdings of the old settlers.

The cattle- and sheep-droving country in south-central Queensland was hard hit. Crows circled over dying sheep and cattle. Dingos, the reddish-brown wild dogs of Australia, came in from the bush, attracted by the easy hunting of the drought-weakened animals.

Lester Caldwell, so new on the land that his neighbours still called him a "new chum", meaning a recent immigrant, had sold his leather-working shop on London's east side to pay the fare to Australia for his wife and himself and to buy his little piece of land. For two years things had gone well. The rains came. Working together, Lester and his wife, Sabina, had learned subsistence farming, growing most of their own food, and had found that keeping a small drove of sheep alive in Queensland required more hours per day than running a leather shop in England.

Sabina Caldwell was Irish by birth, born in Belfast. As a baby she had been brought to London, where her mother worked as a housemaid while her father talked politics at his favourite pub and occasionally became politically active, writing anti-English slogans on walls. Sabina's mother had married beneath herself, but she had never complained. She worked hard and made the best of it and even managed to pass along to her one daughter some of the niceties of life in the form of piano and singing lessons.

There was, however, no piano in the humble plank house in Queensland, and as the drought lingered and worsened, as Lester's sheep began to die one by one and the lack of food brought hunger to the house, there were few times when Sabina raised her voice in song. In the grim days of drought the only music on the small station was the call of a lyrebird that nested close by. Sabina had grown fond of the male lyrebird, admiring him for his handsome tail, the shape of which gave him his name. She was often entertained and her mind diverted from day-to-day problems by the cock lyrebird's musical calls and his uncanny ability to imitate many sounds, such as Lester's whistle or the bleat of a lamb.

Sabina had inherited not only her mother's penchant for hard work but also her ability to endure privations and accept what came her way. She had met Lester in his leather shop, having brought a pair of shoes to him for mending; she had fallen in love with him and had chosen him as a husband. Therefore she would not complain. She had not been enthusiastic about emigrating to Australia, but her mother was dead and she had no other relatives in England, and Lester painted wonderful word pictures of life in the new land, which would afford greater freedom and the chance to earn a small fortune and be somebody.

A strong girl in spite of being slender and shapely, Sabina had toiled at Lester's side for two years, coarsening her hands, tanning her fair skin under the Queensland sun. Now she was eight months pregnant, and it could not have happened at a worse time, with the sheep dying of starvation and thirst.

She did not bother Lester with complaints of back pain and morning sickness, a nausea that came and went even in the last months of her term. He had enough worries. She was in constant fear that he was going to do something desperate.

"Whatever happens," she told him, "we have each other. We'll muddle through, Lester. We will."

"And if the sheep die, all of them?" he asked.

"We will have the land."

"And nothing to eat, nothing to plant." He was not a large man, but he was wiry and had surprising strength in his thin frame. He had always been a smiling man, but now the worry lines joined sun creases around his eyes and made him look older than his twenty-four years. "We should have stayed in London," he said. "This is God's punishment against me for selling the shop left me by my father."

"We'll make it through, whatever," she said repeatedly, for she knew that he was at the end of his tether, ready to snap.

"And I suppose you're going to tell me that when all the sheep are dead and there's nothing growing and nothing to eat in the house that we can go into a city where I can get a job." He muttered profane words under his breath. "Where I can work for some *gentleman*." He made the word sound profane. "Or I might even drove sheep for Mr. Joseph Van Buren, eh?"

Joseph Van Buren was the Caldwells' nearest neighbour, their only neighbour. Van Buren was a squatter, his holdings well over a thousand acres, a vast range that surrounded Lester Caldwell's little place on three sides and cut him off totally from the best grass, and—more important—from the only remaining water for miles around. The river that ran through Van Buren's land and the Caldwells' property had dried up except for a few holes on Van Buren's land.

Sabina knew that Lester had been thinking seriously about pushing his sheep onto Van Buren land to let them fill their gaunt bellies on the dried grass there, and to water at a billabong. And she knew that if he did there would be serious trouble. Custom and usage in the droving lands allowed a man to move his sheep through a squatter's land, provided that he keep his drove within a certain number of feet on either side of the road. It took only one drove of sheep, of course, to eat all the forage in that area of allowed passage. Therefore, when a man was moving his sheep he sometimes "lifted the panel"—opened a fence to allow his sheep to graze more widely on a squatter's land.

"Lester," Sabina begged, "promise me that you won't do anything dangerous or destructive."

"I've got to do something," Lester said, unable to look at her.

"At least not until the baby is born."

He nodded. Her stomach was huge.

The baby came at least three weeks early on a relentlessly hot day, the temperature over a hundred, not a breath of breeze. She lay on her bed drenched in sweat, willing the contractions to grow, grunting with the pain. There was no one other than Lester, for both of them had too much pride to go to the Van Buren place for help. Sabina had assisted at births in London. She kept Lester calm as the contractions became more and more powerful, had him ready when, with a splitting, aching pain that caused her to scream out, just once, the baby came.

It was a boy, and his first cry was so feeble that it wrenched Sabina's heart. The infant was obviously not strong. He tried weakly to nurse at Sabina's breast, full in spite of a diet that for months had consisted mainly of kangaroo meat. He could take only a few swallows before the effort tired him into fitful, weak complaining and then sleep.

It took the baby a poignantly brief yet painfully full week to die. Each day he grew weaker and nothing Sabina did seemed to help. Since the baby was too feeble to nurse, she milked herself and dripped the rich white liquid into the baby's mouth with a sugar teat. If the baby got more than a pathetic swallow or two into his stomach he immediately burped it back.

Lester was moodily silent as he laboured to dig a grave in the sun-baked earth. Dust swirled around them as they said a prayer and then lowered the small coffin, made from planks torn from an outbuilding, into the bone-dry ground.

"I hate that bloody dirt," Sabina said, as Lester shovelled dry clods onto the coffin.

"It's not the dirt," Lester said. "It's good land."

"It will kill us, as well," she said. "After it breaks our backs, it will kill us."

"Not the land," he said. "The land will not kill us."

"It's time to admit that we're beaten," she said.

"No."

"While we still have each other, we must go," she said. "We can both work in a town. We can save our money and buy a bit of land in a kinder place than this. Listen to me, please?"

He was angry. His face, once handsome, now baked by the sun and lined by worry, made her want to weep for him. "From the time I was this high," he said, holding his hand at the level of his knee, "I wanted to have a place of my own, land that I could call my own. I wanted to walk on my own land and kick a rock and say, well, that's my rock. I did not travel thousands of miles to become a labourer for another man."

He did not come to the house to bid her good-bye. The silence told her that he was gone. The child had been buried early in the morning, and by midday she was alone. She could feel the aloneness. She knew that Lester had gathered the remaining sheep and that he was taking them to Van Buren land. She feared for him, but she could not bring herself to go to try to stop him. He, too, had been hit hard by the death of their first child. He was a man, after all, and a man cannot merely sit down and watch his child die and his wife get thinner and thinner because of lack of food.

To get a breath of air, she went out onto the crude porch of the house and sat in a rickety old rocking chair.

Joseph Van Buren, she knew, was a strong man, possessed of all of the acquisitive instincts of his class. From other neighbours, Lester and she had picked up a little gossip. People said that he had been born wealthy, the son of a half-breed who had risen from nothing to become a wealthy New Zealand shipping magnate. Not much more was known, for Van Buren did not talk freely about his family. But enough had leaked out for folks to know that there had evidently been a disagreement in the family, one that impelled Joseph to come to Queensland to set up a cattle and sheep station on his own. Yet he still maintained his ties with the family, a fact confirmed by the local chap who kept his books, a man given to loose talk when in his cups. Joseph's father, Claus, had died, but letters and money still went to and from Joseph's brother in Wellington. Joseph had a reputation for being ruthless, albeit honest. What his workers were like was anyone's guess.

As she rocked, Sabina heard insects buzzing and humming and from far off came the call of a crow. The midday air was heavy, hot, and dry. She leaned her head back and closed her eyes, trying not to worry. She could not even pray, for she had done a lot of praying over the past months with no positive results.

She dozed and jerked into wakefulness as she heard her baby cry, heard that feeble, pleading sound that had grown fainter and fainter towards the last. She leapt to her feet, started to rush into the house to answer the baby's cry, then stopped herself, hand to her mouth. The sound was not coming from the house.

Yet the cry was repeated, and across the open area around the house she could just see the cock lyrebird, sitting in a bush. He was imitating the cries of her dying baby.

"Hush," she said to him. "Hush now. You're only a bird, and you don't know any better, but please hush."

Somehow, for the moment, the lyrebird obeyed her command.

Lester had lifted the panel and was moving his sheep slowly across parched grass that gave them, at least, something to fill their bellies. When the lead sheep smelled the water, they began to move purposefully, and the drove followed. Lester pushed through the brush along the bank of the billabong and saw his sheep guzzling their fill of water for the first time in days. On his place there was only a muddy spot where the animals could lick a bit of water out of depressions or their own tracks. When the sheep had drunk their fill they spread out along the edge of the water and began to crop clumps of good, green grass, and Lester sat down in the shade and watched them, feeling a bit better. He kept the sheep close to the water that night, sleeping in the open under the stars, and pushed them onto dry grazing the next morning.

Sabina was awakened again by the lyrebird's imitation of her dying child's feeble cries. She knew that Lester might be gone for days if he found good grazing and water for the sheep, but she could not escape a feeling of impending doom. The lyrebird's cries were like knives piercing her heart, bringing back the desperation she'd known when she was unable to get her little son to nurse. Sabina went to the door and cried out, "Shut up, you bloody bird."

It was inevitable that Lester would be discovered. In times of drought it was more vital than ever for a man to guard his good grass, and the dried grass around the billabong where Lester had been watering his sheep was being saved by Joseph Van Buren's chief drover for a time when other pastures had been picked clean. When the chief drover rode into the fields and saw strange sheep there, he went back immediately to the station and rounded up half a dozen stockmen. They came back to the billabong just before sunset. Lester had driven the sheep down to water and was lounging on the bank, whistling. He did not realize that he was not alone until he was surrounded by seven tough-looking stockmen.

"You're on Van Buren land," the chief drover said, his voice nasty.

"Just getting a bit of water," Lester said, spreading his hands and smiling. "Just before moving on, mate. You wouldn't begrudge a man a drink of water for his animals, would you?"

"You're Caldwell."

"Yes, I am. On my way home." He made to move away towards where his few sheep were cropping dry grass. The chief drover seized his arm.

"Just a watering, is it? Then how comes it that the green grass is ruined here, and the dry grass of the pastureland shows signs of heavy grazing?"

"Must have been someone else," Lester said. "I just drove my sheep to water an hour ago."

Although Joseph Van Buren was a man who could be hard, hard enough to carve out a holding in the bush and keep it, he had never ordered his men to attack tresspassers, only to keep them cleared off Van Buren land. Van Buren, however, was not present. The nearest vestige of authority was a constable in the town, two days away from the Van Buren station. Van Buren's chief drover was a man who savoured his capacity for cruelty, and when he punched Lester Caldwell in the stomach he was smiling. Lester bent double for a moment and then came up swinging, managing to land one blow on the drover's chin before heavy fists from the other men knocked him down.

As a boy, Lester had learned to protect himself, for the streets of London's east side had not been Edenic. Lester had learned early on that it was often wiser to resort to bluff than to rely on clenched fists alone. He had started to carry a knife when he was seven years old, and a knife had been with him ever since.

More than one man had joined the chief drover in beating Lester to the ground. He rose slowly, shaking his head, and drew his knife.

"I want no trouble," he said, rising, holding the knife threateningly with his thumb on the handle. He wiped blood from his lips with the back of his left hand and started to sidle away.

"Do you fancy yourself to be a knife-fighter?" the chief drover asked, laughing and drawing his own blade and assuming a fighting stance.

"I don't want to fight you," Lester said. "I'll just take my sheep and go."

"I think not," the drover replied. "You've used up Van Buren water and you've eaten Van Buren grass. I think half of your sheep ought to be enough payment for that."

"You're mad!" Lester exclaimed, moving back as the drover advanced.

"Lads," the drover said, "while I entertain Caldwell, go and separate half of his sheep. And be sure not to pick the weakest ones."

"You can't do that," Lester protested.

"Can't I, now?" The drover leapt, lashed, and Lester had to move fast to keep from being cut. The drover came again, and with a shock Lester realized that the fight was for real, that the knife in the drover's hand represented real danger. A red haze of anger overtook him and he leapt, parried, slashed, and felt his blade cut deep into the drover's arm. The sight of blood sobered him.

"Now that's enough, man," Lester said to the drover. "You're hurt. Let me take my sheep and go and you find a doctor's help."

The chief drover, clutching his arm and, looking down at the blood, roared in anger and pain, pulled a pistol from his belt, and levelled it at Lester's face. Lester tried to throw himself to one side, but instantly the slug entered his cheek, smashed a row of teeth, and left him dazed, lying on his back. He saw the muzzle of the gun pointed directly at his nose and then the world collapsed inward on top of him.

"Bloody hell, Arch," a man said, "you've killed the beggar."

"He cut me," the drover said. "Bury him. Run his sheep in with one of our droves."

For days Sabina watched for Lester and listened to the lyrebird crying plaintively like her dying baby. She cooked and ate the last of the dried meat. Her hunger did not bother her, but the sound of her baby mewling so pitifully was a torture. She sat on the porch in the rocker and hated the land, hated the brassy sky with its absence of clouds and its ever-present burning sun. She went into the house and got Lester's shotgun, the gun he used to pot rabbits and joeys, the baby kangaroos, for the table. There were only two shells left and no money to buy more. She lifted the heavy weapon and, as the lyrebird wailed, fired first one barrel and then the other. The kick of the gun pushed her backwards. When she looked she could not see the lyrebird, but neither did she see any feathers on the ground under the bird's favourite perch.

She endured it for two more days. The bird was relentless. Then Sabina started walking towards the Van Buren station. She had not far to go, for the chief drover had moved sheep to that very spot where Lester had lifted the panel and the owner, Joseph Van Buren, was on hand, seated on a handsome horse. He doffed his hat when he saw Sabina approaching and rode to meet her.

"Mrs. Caldwell, isn't it?" he asked.

"Yes," she said. "I've come to inquire about my husband."

"Why here?" Van Buren asked. He was a tall man, sat his horse well, and was well dressed and well fed.

"I suspect that he was going to lift the panel," she said.

"I see," Van Buren said. "Hold on, I'll inquire." He rode back and asked, in a loud voice, if any of the men had seen Lester Caldwell. The answers were all negative. He rode back. His horse pranced in front of Sabina. "I understand, Mrs. Caldwell, that things are not going well on your place. If you'll remember, I told your husband in the beginning that that plot of land was too small to support a family, that the water supply was not dependable."

"So none of you has seen my husband?" Sabina asked.

"I have offered before to pay a fair price for that piece of land," Van Buren insisted.

For a moment Sabina wished she could say, "Fine, give me the money." But the land was not only hers, it was *Lester's* and hers. She sighed, then looked around. A sheep was standing nearby, gazing at her, and her heart leapt, for although sheep looked very much alike, she recognized this particular ewe. She had raised it from birth after the death of its mother.

"Why are my sheep mixed with yours?" she asked.

"I think you're mistaken," Van Buren replied.

"If you'll look closely at that ewe, you'll find that she has a twisted back leg," Sabina said. "That's where the dingos got hold of her when she was born, while they were killing her mother."

Frowning, Van Buren dismounted and walked to seize the ewe, which did not try to run until the last minute. He examined the leg, then turned the ewe loose. "Can you identify others of your drove?"

She nodded, describing Lester's mark. Van Buren gave orders, and soon several Caldwell sheep had been identified. He stood before Sabina, hat in hand. "Mrs. Caldwell, I don't know how your sheep got onto my land. I don't know anything about your husband. Perhaps he simply felt that he'd had enough, turned his sheep onto this land where he knew there was water, and left. He wouldn't be the first man to do that, you know."

"Lester would not desert me," Sabina said. "I would appreciate it if you would have your men separate my sheep. I'll take them home."

"By rights I could charge you for graze and water," Van Buren said. It was a hard land. It was not a land for London leather workers and their fragile wives. "Instead, why don't you listen to reason. Let me buy the sheep and the freeholding, Mrs. Caldwell."

"Go to hell, Mr. Van Buren," Sabina replied.

"Without a man, you can't possibly make a go of it, not even if it rains," Van Buren said smugly.

"Lester will be back," she countered. "And we'll hold on to our land in spite of the devil and all the squatters in Queensland."

Brave words. As the days passed and sheep died for lack of water, she knew that Van Buren had been right. There was no sign of rain, and it was sheer cruelty to let the poor sheep die of thirst when there was water so near, on Van Buren land.

Sabina drove the sheep back to the billabong and was soon face to face with Van Buren's drovers just as Lester had been. She told them that she wanted to sell. Van Buren's offer was, from his viewpoint, fair. He was buying land that was worthless in drought, sheep that were half dead. From Sabina's viewpoint the amount of money was insultingly small, less than they had paid for the land alone. Yet she had no choice. As a part of the payment she asked for a wagon and a team of horses.

That very day she loaded the few things worth saving and started for the nearest town on the east coast of Queensland. Her only plan was to put the farm, the land, and the lyrebird with his relentlessly cruel cry—all of it—behind her.

With the coming of night she made a dry camp, gave the horses a small measure of water and feed, and sat to watch the darkness come, a darkness broken only by her campfire. Sabina was still and always basically a city girl. She had spent nights alone in the house back on the station, but never alone in the bush. Every sound was a head-jerking, heart-pounding stimulus until, with a sigh, she told herself that, after all, there were no fierce, large animals in the Queensland bush, no lions, no dragons, only the occasional dingo and lizards and, oh God, *snakes*. She slept in the bed of the wagon, slept so fitfully that when the heat of the sun awoke her she was still groggy.

She got under way as quickly as possible, a petite Irishwoman who looked much older than her nineteen years. Her ebony hair, limp with sweat, was tied tightly to her head. Her faded dress was sourly redolent of past days of work and perspiration. She did not take time for self-pity. She could not mourn Lester, not yet. She suspected that he was dead, by what means she did not know. Nor did she regret the loss of the station. She looked ahead only to being in a town again. She had the little bit of money that Van Buren had paid for the freeholding. She would find work, and beyond that she had no plans.

Sabina placed no blame on anyone for her situation. Lester and she had made a choice, and they had been beaten by forces greater than the strength of one man and his wife—by drought, heat, and dust. Nor did she hold any malice towards Joseph Van Buren, at least not yet. She had made no analysis of her position in society, and it would be a long time before she realized that what had happened in her case had happened to many others, giving rise to a political struggle that was steadily engulfing Australia. With no newspapers to read in the bush, she had no way of knowing—would not have understood or cared if she had known—that after another Federal Convention, in Melbourne this time, with delegate Jon Mason not having to travel far to attend, the referendum of 1898 had gone against the federation, making the early unification of the Australian states seem only a distant possibility after all.

CHAPTER VII

When Kitchener's army left the encampment on the Nile to begin the march south towards Omdurman, it was only 9 A.M.. The 21st Lancers, regrouped, many of them still stunned by the hard action in the *khor*, were on the left flank of the army as it advanced towards the two-hundred-and-fifty-foot heights of the hill called the Jebel Surgham, which lay between the British and Omdurman.

The dervish army was divided now into two groups. The main body of fifteen thousand men, near the Jebel Surgham, was under the Khalifa himself and his brother, Yakub. The other group, some ten thousand men, were in the Kerreri hills to the north, where they had engaged Egyptian and British cavalry earlier that morning.

As Kitchener marched his army forward, each British unit was eager to be the first into Omdurman, and this spirited competition led to trouble for one brigade, the 1st Egyptian under Lieutenant-Colonel H. A. Macdonald. While the other brigades, led by Kitchener, were close together advancing in a line up the Jebel's slopes, Macdonald's brigade was off to the right, marching across open country. Macdonald found himself further and further isolated from the other brigade, and ultimately he was exposed, beyond reach of immediate tactical support.

It was at this moment that Macdonald's Egyptians came head on against the main body of the dervishes under the Khalifa and Yakub. Frantically Macdonald sent a runner to Kitchener, who was with the brigades ascending the Jebel.

"Sir," the young lieutenant told the commander, "Colonel Macdonald begs to inform you that he is facing a large force of dervishes and asks if he is to attack." The lieutenant went on to point out that the 1st Egyptians, by themselves, were hardly equal to fifteen thousand of the Khalifa's men.

Kitchener's face contorted in impatience. "Can't Colonel Macdonald see that we are marching on Omdurman? Tell him to follow on."

With help refused him, Macdonald prepared to face the Khalifa and Yakub's hordes on his own. After courageously haranguing his men as to their duty, he and his brigade began to fight the dervishes with all they had.

By now Kitchener's other brigades were nearing the top of the Jebel. The Sirdar, hearing the sound of Macdonald's guns, rode to a vantage point from which he could see Macdonald fighting on the plain below. Realizing his mistake, Kitchener altered his plans to advance to Omdurman. The fight was not going to be in the city; it was going to be right here.

Ordering one brigade to cross the desert to support Macdonald, Kitchener commanded three others to launch an attack on the Khalifa from the heights of the Jebel.

The Khalifa was now opposed to two sides—by Macdonald and another brigade standing firm on his left, and Kitchener and three other brigades harrying his right from the Jebel. Though these dervishes were the Khalifa's best, they were no match for superior British artillery and tactics; soon the Khalifa's devout warriors, who had believed their leader would be invincible with the help of Allah, were fleeing for their lives—and cursing the Khalifa.

At this moment of apparent British victory, however, the other body of dervishes came out of the Kerreri hills to fall upon Macdonald's flank. Macdonald met this new threat coolly: in a series of manoeuvres that later became military textbook examples, he turned one after another of his units ninety degrees to face the newly arriving hordes. Other British and Egyptian units came to fill gaps in Macdonald's line, and within minutes a second rout had been accomplished, with Macdonald's men chasing dervishes back into the Kerreri hills.

Had the two bodies of dervishes—the Khalifa's own force and the warriors from the hills—coordinated their attack and fallen upon Macdonald simultaneously, the course of history might have been far different. As it was, Kitchener, watching from a distance while Macdonald pursued the fleeing dervishes into the hills, commented complacently that the enemy had been given "a thoroughly dusting", and he calmly ordered the march continued towards Omdurman. He never quite realized how much he owed that day to the imperturbable Macdonald.

Meanwhile the 21st Lancers, Slone Shannon among them, were getting on with their own job of advancing towards Khalifa's capital on the left flank, nearer the Nile. Not having participated in Macdonald's fight, they nevertheless knew that the enemy had been shattered on the plain between the Jebel Surgham and the Kerreri hills, and now they encountered fleeing dervishes who, at the Lancers' approach, threw down their weapons and surrendered, pleading for mercy.

The British orders were to prevent the scattered enemy forces from congregating in Omdurman. Slone soon lost his appetite for blood as the Lancers harassed the fleeing dervishes, often dismounting to fire volleys into larger groups in order to drive them into the desert away from Omdurman.

There were areas of the battlefield where one could not see the ground for the dead. Some of the dervishes, knowing that death was coming, had removed their slippers and had placed them under their heads as pillows. One man was still in a kneeling position, his life cut short in the midst of his pleas to Allah. Where artillery had struck there was carnage. The wounded were everywhere, lying in their own gore fighting for breath, clutching shattered arms and legs. The common goal for the wounded was the Nile and its water. A crisscrossing of trails of blood marked their efforts.

The enemy was black and dirty, and he stank; but, God pity him, he was brave. As Slone rode through an area where the efficient artillery of the Sirdar's army had wrought carnage, he began to feel something akin to pride for those slain warriors. Pity for the dying was so strong in him that it was almost a sickness, but, Lord God, he had to admire the way those ragged, filthy beggars had charged into the very muzzles of the British cannon, halting their advance only after crawling over the bodies of their dead comrades to meet their own deaths. Once they had broken a British square, successfully opposing that deadly formation of barrages of rifle with their sheer persistence, by soaking up every bullet that the square of fire could offer, and by continuing to advance. But there was no victory today for the sons of Allah.

Was the day truly only half gone? It seemed that an age had passed since Slone had been awakened by the camp sounds, since the 21st Lancers had ridden gloriously into the dervish trap and into legend. The midday heat oppressed him. Around him he could see that men were relaxing in their saddles, for the danger was over. These pitiable, dying remnants of the dervish would do them no harm. Slone, too, allowed himself to settle in his saddle, feeling the beat of his heart slowing. He sighed deeply and was suddenly very sleepy. His moment of relaxation almost cost him his life.

He was riding on the flank of a small group of Lancers, letting his horse pick its way through and around the dead men on the ground. Something moved almost at his horse's feet, but in his near-stupor of fatigue—when, at last, he had been able to bring himself down from that battle-induced peak of excitement, heart pounding, adrenaline flowing, the reaction was as near to sleep as one can get and still be awake—he was slow to react. A thing, a messenger of death, a dervish who was at least six and a half feet tall, rose up from a pool of his own blood and ran a huge, two-handed sword almost to the hilt into the entrails of Slone's horse.

The horse reared, screaming in agony, then fell back on its haunches. Slone kicked his feet out of the stirrups and jumped to the side of the struggling, dying animal. The huge dervish was leaning backwards, trying to draw his sword from the body of the dying horse. Slone was frozen for a long moment as he watched the drama with dazed interest. The sword came free, and the reeking blade soared high as the dervish leapt towards Slone with a scream of hate.

Slone's heart leapt with fear and a jolt of adrenaline went into his stomach with a force that brought him out of his lethargy to realize that he was a split second away from death. He slapped his hand against the butt of his pistol, felt the reassuring heft of the weapon in his hand, and lifted it to fire into the chest of the charging dervish. He saw the bullet impact and heard the dull thud of it going into flesh; yet still the dervish came on, the huge sword held high. Again Slone fired, aiming for the heart, and as he saw the bullet hit, he heard a despairing scream from the dervish's throat. Still the man was coming, though his legs were beginning to buckle. His sword was beginning to make a deadly downward slash, and Slone fired once more into the man's chest, leaping aside as the blade whistled down, then lifted his pistol and fired directly into the enemy's face. He saw the nose dissolve into blood and mist, and at last the man began to fall, his sword blade hissing past Slone's face to bury itself in the earth.

The group of Lancers with whom he had been riding had started towards him. They reined in, seeing that it was over. Slone, breathing hard, said, "If one of you will find me a horse, please."

"Big ugly beggar," said a Lancer, looking down at the dead dervish.

Two of the men had ridden off to look for a riderless mount. Slone picked up the sword. It was so heavy that he could barely lift it; it had taken a real man to swing that ancient weapon.

A quietness had fallen over the portion of the battlefield immediately around them. Slone put the tip of the sword on the ground and leaned on it. To his front another fallen dervish moved, pushed himself painfully up from the ground, and staggered towards the group. Slone was the first to react, for he had not yet recovered from the fear he had known when he faced death at the hands of the man he had just killed. His pistol seemed to jump into his hand, and he fired the remaining two bullets in swift order into the staggering, wounded man. He had completed the action before he realized that the dervish had held no weapon.

"Damn!" he said. "Shouldn't have done that. I was a bit unnerved by that other big beggar, I suppose."

A Lancer said, "I wouldn't let it bother me, sir. Lots of it going on. You're not the first to have been attacked by one of them fuzzies lying doggo. The chaps have started to shoot without waiting to see if the beggars are going to surrender or fight. The attitude seems to be that when it comes down to a case of you or me, chum, it's not going to be me."

When the battle was over—and for all practical purposes it had been finished there in the shadow of the Jebel with the British artillery and Maxims cutting bloody swaths through the ranks of the dervishes—there would be conflicting versions of Kitchener's conduct of the battle and its aftermath. Some would say that Kitchener had ordered that all dervish wounded be bayoneted. History would show that Kitchener was a reasonable man who made every effort to spare lives when possible, but it was natural for the commander to be blamed for the actions of his troops. When it was discovered that even a wounded dervish could be dangerous, that fanaticism in the dervish's heart still burned hotly even when life was almost gone, it was a natural defence for troops who had seen comrades die to defend themselves, killing the wounded rather than risking the possibility of dying senselessly after the main battle had been decided.

Winston Churchill was critical of Kitchener in this matter, but the main effect of Churchill's writings would be to elevate the foolish and, in the final outcome, the useless charge of the 21st Lancers to a status only slightly less glorified than an earlier charge of a sister regiment, the 17th Lancers, the Light Brigade, at Balaclava in an earlier war. No more could it be said that the 21st had never been blooded. They had taken their spot in the pantheon of military romance because individual heroism overshadowed the innate lunacy of the event.

The army's entry into Omdurman was anticlimactic. The Khalifa had fled. Civil officials met the army and begged mercy. Kitchener spoke to them in fluent Arabic, telling them the population would not be harmed if "you will throw down your arms and not molest us".

Omdurman, unlike fabled Khartoum before its destruction during the siege and defeat of Chinese Gordon, was a sprawling slum, a place of mud and huts barely large enough for a man to crawl inside. The one somewhat impressive feature of the city, the tomb of the Mahdi, was destroyed on Kitchener's orders. The cult of Mahdism was to be erased from the face of the earth. The Mahdi's bones were thrown into the Nile.

Only one relic of the Mahdi's person survived. Slone, again in the company of Percy Girouard, happened to be present when the Mahdi's skull was shown to Kitchener. It was, to Slone, just another skull.

"It's quite well formed, isn't it, sir?" Girouard asked Kitchener.

The commander was holding the skull much like the grave-digger in *Hamlet*. "I think," he said, "that I shall have it silver-plated. Make an excellent memento. Could use it as an inkwell."

Girouard laughed, thinking that the Sirdar was making a joke. Kitchener looked at him quizzically, his odd eye squinted. "You think not?" He sighed. "No, I suppose there'd be a frightful uproar if the word got out among our gentle countrymen. Perhaps we should present it to the College of Surgeons. Don't they have Napoleon's intestines?"

It was difficult to count the enemy dead. Later, historians would estimate that ten thousand dervishes perished on the day of battle and that twenty thousand were wounded, a quarter of those to die within two or three days. Three British officers had died, two Egyptian. In the ranks the figures were twenty-five British dead, eighteen Egyptian or Sudanese. The majority of the British dead were 21st Lancers. Before the army went down the Nile, many more British soldiers would succumb to disease than had been killed at Omdurman.

The dead were buried on a small knoll looking across the river towards the site of Khartoum. There a clump of green trees grew in the gutted ruin in which Gordon had been killed fourteen years previously.

In the chill dawn of September 4, Slone and other selected members of the 21st Lancers were ordered to cross the river to ruined Khartoum. Two gunboats were ferrying representatives of every unit of the Sirdar's army to the crumbling stone quay along the riverfront before the old capital.

As the day progressed and the temperature soared past the hundred-degree mark, the troops were formed up in front of the building where Chinese Gordon had died. The upper story of the palace had fallen in. The staircase where Gordon had come to his last confrontation with his enemies was nothing more than a heap of stone and stucco. In ruins, the palace had become more impressive than it had been when it was whole, for it had now an air of things past, a hint of beauty it had not possessed originally.

Kitchener had ordered flag posts to be positioned on top of the ruins and, as he signalled, the Union Jack spread from one post while a cannon was fired from the gunboat *Melik* and the band struck up a spirited rendition of "God Save the Queen". The Sirdar signalled again, and the Egyptian flag flew beside the Union Jack, although the British flag was four times larger.

Three cheers were shouted for the Queen, then three more for the Khedive of Egypt. The twenty-one-gun salute fired by the *Melik* used live shells, and Slone saw more than one veteran of the battle cringe slightly as the deadly missiles hurtled through the air into the deserted plains outside the city.

The three cheers that were then ordered for Kitchener were delivered with genuine enthusiasm, far louder than those for the Queen and the Egyptian figurehead ruler.

Military pomp had always impressed Slone. There, in the blazing Sudanese sun, with sweat running down his back, he held his back stiff with pride, felt a sting of emotion when the Union Jack spread itself so colourfully from the top of the ruined palace. The Guards' band played the "Dead March" from *Saul*, and then pipers and muffled drums stirred Slone's emotions even more, so that when the band of the 11th Sudanese played Kitchener's favourite hymn, "Abide With Me", he felt tears form and run down his cheeks. He felt no shame, only a sense of accomplishment—he had fought and survived—as well as sorrow for those who had died, and pride in the glory of the British race.

Slone was near enough to Kitchener to see that the Sirdar, too, had been touched by the moving ceremony for the recent dead who had avenged Charles Gordon's death. Kitchener, too, had tears on his cheeks.

Slone Shannon was among those officers delegated to remain in the advance positions of the army. His job was to keep the railway open. For the next weeks and months he fought searing heat, drifting sand, boredom, and rock slides that threatened the railway. He received occasional batches of letters from Kit, chatty letters that spoke animatedly of the social life in Cairo and only lightly of her feeling for him.

Restive, Slone felt left behind by the drift of history. The army was leaving unit by unit, going downstream to Cairo and then to Crete, Gibraltar, or home to the British Isles. Kitchener had been named Governor General of the Sudan. Reginald Wingate caught up with the Khalifa and killed him. Piles of bones on the plains around the Jebel were now memorials to the thousands of dead dervishes.

Then, for three months, there was no word from Kit. Percy Girouard was now gone. The 21st Lancers were gone. Slone was working in heat that often reached 120 degrees, wondering what had happened to Kit, eagerly waiting for each arrival of mail from Cairo. When, at last, new orders came for him, he had been in the Sudan for almost a year. He boarded a gunboat. The trip downriver could not be swift enough for him.

The talk aboard the gunboat was of another affair of the empire, at the polar extreme of the continent, in South Africa. War had broken out in Natal against the Boers. Though a British colony, Natal had a substantial minority population of Boers, hardy descendants of early Dutch settlers.

Slone felt that he had had his war. He wanted only to see Kit, to get her somehow to stand with him before a priest. If she truly objected to army life, then he would do as he had promied her: he would resign his commission. He was sure that he would find opportunity at home in Australia. There was the sheep and cattle station that his father had bought upon retirement. And he had family friends who he was sure would provide employment and opportunity in business.

The officer in charge of the gunboat was a young lieutenant newly arrived from England. He had endless questions to ask about the battle at Omdurman. Slone did not mind talking about it. He was modest in describing his actions during the already famous charge. He omitted mentioning that he had been re-commended for a medal, but even without that knowledge the young lieutenant was impressed.

One question from the young officer came on the day that Slone was to leave the boat. "Shannon," the officer asked, "did the Queen herself reprimand Kitchener in the matter of the Mahdi's skull?"

Slone made a wry face. "Not directly. It is said that she expressed her displeasure. I don't know, actually. I know only that the prime minister sent a telegraph to Lord Cromer and that Cromer contacted the Sirdar." He smiled. "The result was that I was ordered to bury the Mahdi's skull with dignity."

"And did you?"

He nodded. "In the Muslim cemetery at Wadi Halfa."

Cairo seemed to be a quieter place. One could walk for a distance in the streets and not see a British uniform. The hotel still had rooms booked permanently for Kitchener's officers. Slone rushed to his room, bathed hurriedly, put on a fresh uniform and presented himself at the door to Colonel Roland Streeter's suite.

The door was opened by an Egyptian servant. "Will you please tell Miss Streeter that Lieutenant Shannon is calling," he said.

The Egyptian girl smiled politely. "This, sir, is the suite of Colonel Evan Bascomb."

"I beg your pardon?"

"It was once, I am told, the suite of Colonel Streeter. I am sorry, sir."

Slone hurried to the desk. He had not thought, in his eagerness to see Kit, to inquire for messages. The clerk handed him a small packet of letters, and he hurried back to his room. Reading frantically, he found information that left him stunned and angry in the third letter from the top, the third in chronological order. Colonal Roland Streeter had been ordered to proceed to South Africa to join the staff of General Sir Redvers Buller.

South Africa! Thousands of miles, the length of the entire African continent.

Since he had drawn up his own travel orders, Slone had allowed himself a week in Cairo before having to report to British Army headquarters. Nevertheless, he went there early, cajoled a meeting with a white-haired colonel in charge of personnel, and begged for an immediate assignment to British forces in South Africa.

"I say, Shannon," the colonel mused, looking at his record. "You've just had yourself one war." His eyebrows shot up. "Lucky blighter. You were with the 21st Lancers." His bored attitude changed. He looked at Slone with genuine admiration. "Envy you, boy. Probably the last cavalry charge. Can't ride horses into the mouths of machine guns, can we?"

"What are my chances of being sent to South Africa, sir?"

The colonel mused. His words let a small chink of light to the dark mood of desperation that Slone had felt since learning that Kit was thousands of miles away. "I see no problem, my boy. I'll just attach you to an administrative unit that's scheduled to leave Alexandria in three days. Does that suit you?"

"Sir, I'm grateful," Slone said, giving a salute so crisp that he felt a rush of air on his eybrow.

CHAPTER VIII

As Sabina Caldwell travelled through the Queensland bush she came to see that she was not the only one who had suffered from the long drought. More than once she passed deserted huts. Skeletons of dead cattle and sheep made small white heaps in the dry dust. Still there was a stark beauty to it all, and more than ever before she began to get an idea of the enormous size of the land to which Lester had brought her. Five days of travel had not seen any significant change in the countryside, and the distance to the coast had diminished only slightly.

Fear came often to her during the night when a sound would awaken her and the sense of being alone in that wide, thinly populated wilderness overwhelmed her. She had only the sun to guide her along the seldom-travelled tracks. On the sixth day of her journey she encountered a lone drover, a man who looked almost as woe-begone as his starving sheep. Though amazed at finding a woman alone in the bush, he managed to tell her that, yes, she was on the right road for Rockhampton, that the road would indeed get better and that soon she would be encountering scattered settlements. She felt better and urged the horses to pick up their pace just a bit.

Her intentions were to sell the horses and wagon once she reached Rockhampton and then take passage to a larger city, Brisbane perhaps, or Sydney, where she would find work. Her plans extended no further than that.

Ahead of her were the mountains. Day by day they had become more visible. She had passed one isolated outpost and been shown hospitality by the lady of the station. Her horses had been fed and had glutted themselves on water from the station's wells, and she had been warned that travelling through the mountains was not something a woman should do alone.

To such warnings her stoic reply had been, "I expect I'll make it, thank you."

And yet, oh God above, how she hated the thought of it, how she dreaded the dark vastness of the mountains that loomed ever closer and higher. The going now was more difficult, but the effects of the drought hereabouts were not as severe. The occasional watering places and a touch of green provided inspiration to carry on.

Each day was the same, but was a new challenge of will. There were mornings when Sabina wanted just to give up, to pull her blanket over her head and let the days and the endless weeks pass without her. At night she longed for the warmth of her husband next to her and ached for the touch of his hand. With the dawn there was a persistent wrench of emotion as she realized once again that no longer did she have someone who cared, who would look after her, who would nurse her when she was ill, or love and cherish her. It was during that time, during the first two weeks of her lonely journey, that she came to believe without doubt that Lester was dead, that Joseph Van Buren had been insultingly wrong in guessing that her husband had merely deserted her.

There was no one to see her weep, only the odd, mangy, hungry dingo, a passing crow. Nor was there anyone to hear her voice as she lifted it defiantly in a gay song. There was only the creak of the unyielding springs of the wagon, the rumble of the wheels on hard baked ground.

But somehow, near the end of a day that was glorious for its clean, blue sky and in spite of the heat, Sabina basked in a feeling of well-being. She was driving the wagon through scattered copses of trees, looking for a good place to camp. The sun was low. she had covered many miles that day, or so she estimated. She dreamed of a place with comforting trees and a little stream into which she could wade, clothes and all, to soak and soak until the dust—half of Australia it seemed—was washed off her skin and out of her pores.

The road climbed a low ridge and started down into a shallow valley, where a line of trees indicated the possibility of a stream; she was heartened. Then, as the wagon rattled down the road, she heard the sound of singing. Out in the wild bush the presence of any other people almost certainly indicated drovers—men—and she was a woman alone many miles from the nearest civil authorities. More than murder could happen in the bush and never be known.

She pulled the wagon to a halt and listened. She could not trust her ears at first, for in the blended voices she heard more female than male. She clucked the horses into motion. Soon Sabina saw the smoke of a campfire, and then she was clearing the last rise and saw, on the banks of a pretty little stream, a wagon, two tents, two tethered mules, and four people seated around the fire. One man, three women. The man, holding a rifle in his hand, had risen. Sabina waved and called out a greeting. The man watched her suspiciously as she drew the wagon to a stop just a bit upstream from the camp and dismounted.

"Where's the rest of your party?" the man asked.

"You see it," she said, beginning to unharness the horses, who were snorting and pawing in their eagerness to get to the water. "I do hope you don't mind company."

"Not at all," said a voice full of the Irish, a voice that came from a bosomy, rather blowsy woman with pale red-Irish hair. "I've got a delicious stew going here, luv, and you'll be welcome to eat with us."

The conversation to that point had been carried on at the tops of their voices. Sabina unharnessed the horses, led them to the stream, and waited while they drank, snorted, blew through their nostrils, and drank more. The Irish woman came walking up the bank of the stream, hands thrust into pockets on her full skirts.

"I was so pleased to see other women," Sabina said.

"Yes, the bush is a man's world," the woman said. "I'm Ellie. I think I hear a bit of the Irish in you, as well."

"You do," Sabina said. She told Ellie her name.

"I'd guess you'll be wanting to bathe," Ellie said. "There's a fine place just downstream, beyond that little bend. It's sheltered so that our Stevie-boy won't be able to see. Nice and private, and the water so cool it's quite lovely."

"Yes, thank you."

"And then by that time the stew will be ready."

"You're very kind," Sabina said.

The water *was* lovely. She waded in, her simple dress still on; then, seeing that the place was quite secluded, she stripped, rinsed her garments thoroughly, hung them on bushes, and luxuriated in the fresh coolness of the water, splashing and blowing contentedly like a water buffalo. She had brought fresh clothing with her from the wagon, and after letting the warm evening air dry her, she donned the clean underthings and slipped on a dark-blue work dress, feeling wonderful. Good smells were wafting her way from the pot being stirred by the woman named Ellie.

"Tucker's ready," Ellie called out as Sabina walked past to hang her wet clothing on the sides of her wagon. Her horses, their legs hobbled to prevent wandering, were cropping grass along the bank of the stream. Darkness had come, and the stars were beginning to glow overhead. She joined the others and was introduced.

The other two women were Dolly, a slight girl, not older than sixteen, with huge, deerlike eyes and a quizzical expression; and Nancy, a stolid girl, thick in the waist but with attractive dark hair and a round, smiling face that made Sabina feel welcome. Steve Wells, the man, was a curly-haired, bushy-eyebrowed Welshman, who evidently had been drinking. When a Welshman drinks, he sings, and so while Ellie was dishing up joey stew, Steve conducted a concert with wildly waving hands, and Dolly and Nancy sang along with him. Sabina knew the songs well, and when she joined in, her voice clear and fine, the Welshman raised an eyebrow and gave her a beaming smile.

The stew was excellent. As they ate, Ellie, who seemed to be the guiding spirit for the group, asked polite questions, and soon Sabina found herself, for the first time, telling her distressful tale.

"Crying shame," Steve Wells said. His voice was quite slurred. "What we ought to do is shoot all the rich bastards."

"Let's not do that, Stevie-boy," Ellie said with a laugh, "for I intend to be a rich bastard myself, once we've set up shop in Cloncurry."

"I was married once," the stolid Nancy said. "A lovely boy he was, too." Nancy spoke with that newly accented English that marked the Australian-born. "A little beauty, he was; I was his sheila and he had no other."

"Yeah, yeah," Steve said. "We've heard all that before, Nancy."

"It's true," Nancy said, looking at Sabina pleadingly. "In spite of what anyone says, it's true."

"Leave Nancy alone," little Dolly said.

"Sure," Steve said. "Be glad to. But you, girl, go to the dunny and then get yourself into bed. It's your turn tonight."

Dolly stood, slim and childlike. "You are a right bastard, aren't you, Stevie." And then she was gone, walking off into the trees.

Sabina, made a bit uncomfortable by the undercurrents that she did not understand, stood up and said, "Ellie, the stew was wonderful."

"We were pleased to have your company," Ellie replied. She, too, stood. "I'll walk with you."

They walked to Sabina's wagon in silence and stood beside it—each of them with an arm leaning on the sideboard—looking up at the stars.

"It's a long way from Ireland, isn't it, luv," Ellie said.

"And London. That's where I lived mostly."

"This is a harsh country for a woman alone," Ellie volunteered.

"I'll find work."

"As a housemaid?"

"Whatever there is," Sabina said. "I won't go back to London."

After a silence, Ellie said, "I suppose I should apologize for our Stevie-boy, but if I did, I'd be taking on a full-time job, so what's the use?"

"No worries," Sabina assured her.

"I could tell by the look on your face that our little family has you curious," Ellie said. "But I guess you tumbled to it when Stevie-boy said it was Dolly's turn tonight."

"Actually . . ." Sabina started, and then she paused, not willing to voice her thoughts, embarrassed by it all.

"He's not much of a man," Ellie commented. "But it's neccesary for us to have a man, even one like him. He's handy with a gun, and so his mere presence makes it less inviting for a drover or a shearer to try to hustle one of us."

"Ellie," Sabina said, "you don't have to try to explain. It doesn't matter, really. You've been friendly and helpful to me. I'll always remember that once, out here, in the middle of the bush, I met a woman like you."

Ellie laughed. "Maybe I'm just making excuses to myself."

"Yes, well," Sabina said.

"We started from Sydney. As you've no doubt noticed, none of the three of us is a real queen. Oh, we're all right, I suppose. I have the big bosom. Dolly appeals to them that dreams about girl-children, and Nancy—well, she's so down-to-earth that men like her automatically. But we weren't making it in Sydney, luv. I mean there were times when the tucker on the table wouldn't have attracted a cockroach. So we've started out on Stevie-boy's brilliant idea. We're like a travelling show, you know? We hit the small bush villages. The cattle stations, too, where sometimes the men haven't seen a woman in months."

Sabina's face was feeling hot. She had known about prostitutes back in London, she had even met one or two, but it had been a long, long time since she'd been in the presence of a working girl.

"We're heading for Cloncurry. It's a boom town. The mines. Men coming in from all over and not enough women, you know? We're going to set up a house there."

"I wish you the best of luck," Sabina said.

"If we are lucky, we'll have it to ourselves for a time, before the lookers move in," Ellie said. "Me, I'm going to put my money in a sock and save it until I have enough to set myself up in a little dress shop in Sydney."

"You'll do it, I know," Sabina said, encouraging her.

"Well, we'll see," Ellie said. She sighed. "I guess it's time to call it a day, eh?"

"Being with you people has made me forget that I'm tired," Sabina said. She was curious. As Ellie started to turn away she asked, "Ellie, how much is a man willing to pay for—for—"

"For a few minutes of the old slap and tickle?" Ellie laughed. "Darlin', in the bush he'll come up with half a month's pay for thirty minutes." She laughed again, and in the light of a rising moon her eyes sparkled as she looked closely at Sabina. "With your looks, luv, you could demand *all* of a month's wages."

Sabina giggled nervously, caught on the cusp of titillation and shame. She could not, of course, even entertain such a thought seriously.

Ellie's company was travelling northeast towards a small bush village on the western side of the Great Dividing Range. Because their routes coincided, Sabina found herself travelling with the three women and their shared man for several days. Sometimes Ellie rode on the wagon seat with Sabina, sometimes Dolly or

Nancy. Generally the conversation was about nice things of the past and not about the dubious profession of the three women, but now and again Sabina found herself asking questions.

"But what if the man is fat and ugly?" she asked Dolly one day as they were bouncing along over the road.

"I just close my eyes and pretend he's bloody Prince Charming," Dolly said. "Tell me, if you were bounced by Prince Edward himself, would you feel honoured?"

"I don't think so," Sabina said.

"I'd think I was being bounced by just another fat man," Dolly said. "So what's the difference?"

When they arrived at the tiny bush village that centred around the local pub, Sabina found a woman, a widow, who took in boarders. She took a room, having decided to rest a day or two before continuing her journey, for now the foothills of the mountains were around her, and from that point on the route would climb and wind its way upwards.

After enjoying a real bath and eating a fine meal cooked by the widow, Sabina was drawn by her curiosity to visit the pub. Arriving shortly after nightfall, she saw her three friends there, arrayed in costumes that made them stand out from the few colourless local women. They were never without a man and often disappeared for a length of time. The local women didn't seem to notice.

Steve Wells sat at a table by himself, drinking steadily. Now and then one of the women would come and sit down with him for a minute; after two or three such occurrences, Sabina saw that they were passing money to Steve under the table.

Sabina, who herself had attracted the notice of no less than three local swains, was seated alone when Ellie came to join her. "I think I've earned a few minutes' rest," Ellie said.

"You have been, ah, quite active," Sabina said.

Ellie laughed.

"Why do you all give your money to Steve?" Sabina asked.

"Safer with him," she answered. "It would be all too easy for some bushranger to take everything any one of us had."

"You give it to him, and then what?"

"He saves it for us."

"Do you mean that you're trusting him with the money you

intend to use to set up your dress shop?" Sabina asked.

"Oh, he's all right," Ellie said. "Drink's cheap. He doesn't gamble. We just consider him to be a necessary overhead for the business."

Sabina was sceptical. The system used by Ellie and her friends seemed to her to have too many flaws. First of all, she had never trusted a man who, like Steve Wells, had a weakness for hard liquor. Second, she had lost all respect for Steve on the first night they had camped together, when he had so callously ordered Dolly to take her turn in his bed.

Nevertheless, the matter was none of her affair. Ellie was older than Sabina and seemed to know what she was doing; and it was not Sabina's place to worry about the morals or fortunes of three whores. She returned to her room and busied herself using the facilities at the boardinghouse to wash and iron all her clothes. She told herself that after just one more night she would start up the mountain trail by herself.

It was little Dolly who changed her mind. The three women and Steve had rented a vacant house on the outskirts of the village. Late in the afternoon Sabina walked there, thinking that by that time the girls would have recovered from a hard night's work and would not yet have left to start another night's merry-go-round at the bar.

Ellie opened the door for her and smiled a greeting but she was obviously troubled.

"If I've come at a bad time . . ." Sabina began.

"No, luv," Ellie said, "come on in."

Nancy was bending over Dolly, who was seated and wearing only her underthings. Sabina gasped as she saw livid bruises on the young woman's thin arms. Dolly's face made her want to weep, and she wanted to hit whoever had beaten her friend. One of Dolly's eyes was swollen closed, and she peered up at Sabina through a nasty-looking bruise that nearly shut the other eye.

"It's not as bad as it looks," Dolly said. "What I hate about it is that the bastard has done me out of at least one night's work."

"Who did this?" Sabina demanded.

"Don't get excited," Dolly replied. "He was just drunk. I shouldn't have provoked him." She giggled. "Told him the village dog had bigger ballocks than he had, I did."

"Did Steve do this?" Sabina gasped. Ellie nodded.

"He doesn't do it too often," Nancy said.

"He's hit one of you before?" Sabina was incredulous.

"Not too often," Nancy said.

"I don't believe this," Sabina said. "And you stay with him, after he's wreaked havoc with this little girl?"

"He's better than most," Dolly said.

Once again that night Sabina sat in the pub. The widow who ran the boardinghouse had come with her, and now and then one of the locals would sit at the table with them. Sabina kept a close watch on Ellie and Nancy. Their services were not in as great demand as they had been the first night. It was a small town. What men there were with money to spend had spent it the previous evening. Soon the girls would be moving on, towards another dusty settlement to the northwest. Sabina would be heading northeast.

Towards what? Skivvying? Cleaning someone else's house? Picking up someone else's dirty linen? Although she made friends easily, she was a stranger in a huge, strange land. She had no family, nothing to induce her to want to go back to England. She had been taught by her mother to be a good girl, and heaven only knew the temptations that had come to her in London when she was young. She had always lived by the traditional values, and— she counted up on her fingers, keeping score—those values had lost her a baby, a husband, a home. She faced a future alone, with the necessity of earning her own living.

One of the biggest reasons for her next big decision was the fact that she liked Ellie, felt motherly towards the abused Dolly, and felt comfortable around stolid Nancy. At least she would not be alone. She would have friends who had already opened their hearts to her.

With your looks, luv, Ellie had said, *you could demand all of a man's wages.*

Next morning she waited until Steve had taken himself off to drink at the pub, then went to the house and found Ellie awake, cooking lunch. Nancy, stark naked, was bending over a washtub for a bath. Dolly was still in bed, her face looking a fright, beginning to turn multicoloured now. Ellie set an extra plate.

Dolly got out of bed slowly, moaning with soreness.

"I don't want that ever to happen again," Sabina told Ellie, nodding towards Dolly as she struggled towards the table.

Ellie shrugged.

"How much money have you all saved?" Sabina asked.

Nancy looked blank. Dolly shrugged and grunted with pain. "I'd have to have Steve tote it up," Ellie said.

"Will it be enough to rent a house, a nice house in this town where you're going?"

"Cloncurry," Nancy said.

"Because with a nice house, clean beds and linen, and you three in pretty clothes, you could ask for more money," Sabina said.

"Steve will find us something," Ellie said.

"We all know where he keeps the money," Nancy said. "It's right there, in his little trunk."

Ellie was looking thoughtful. "Are you sure you should poke around in there?"

"Yes," Nancy said. "It's ours, anyway. Besides, I saw him take some cash from a little box inside the trunk just before he went out."

Ellie opened the trunk. Nancy pointed out the box, and Ellie opened it. "This can't be all of it," Ellie said, fingering a very few pound notes. She rummaged through the trunk without finding any other bills.

"What could he have done with it?" Nancy asked.

"Here, what's this?" Ellie asked, looking closely at a piece of paper that she had unfolded. "The bastard!" She handed the paper to Sabina.

"It's a receipt from the Longreach Post Office for a money order. It's drawn to a bank in Sydney for deposit into the account of Steven R. Wells," Sabina said.

"Well, at least he's keeping it safe in a bank," Dolly said.

Steve Wells chose that moment to open the front door and walk into the one-room house. He halted, his face dark. "Why are you prowling around in my case?" he asked.

"No worries, Steve," Ellie said, "we just wondered how much money we have . . . for opening a house in Cloncurry, you know."

"Why didn't you ask me?" he said.

"We're asking you now," Dolly said. "Here's a deposit slip.

How many more? Have you sent money back to your bank in Sydney more than once?"

Steve leapt forward and seized the receipt from Dolly's hand. "Are you saying now that you don't trust me to watch after the money?"

"Just asking, Stevie-boy," Dolly replied. "I think we've got a right to know how much money we have, since we worked on our backs to earn it."

"I'll have to tote it up," Steve said. "Give me a while."

"I'm interested right now," Dolly said. "I'm also interested in knowing just how long it will take, once we reach Cloncurry, to draw our money from the Sydney bank so that we can open a house."

"You just leave that to me," Steve said.

Nancy spoke. "We have, Stevie-boy, we have. Now we want to know."

Wells turned and stalked towards the box. "I don't like your attitude. Who's put this nonsense into your head, this trouble-maker here?" He pointed to Sabina. "She's been trying to turn you against me ever since she joined us. Well, if you think more of her advice that you do mine, so be it. I'm leaving."

"Not until you give us our money," Dolly said, running to seize Steve's arm. He brushed her off with a strong push. She fell heavily. Nancy moved to block the door.

"We haven't done anything to you," she said. "You're still our"—she smiled insultingly as she said it—"business manager. You're not going anywhere until you've given us our money."

His fist shot forward over a short distance. When it hit Nancy's chin, there was a sharp sound. She crumpled. Steve Wells looked at Ellie, snarling, then at Sabina. "You pitiful whores," he said, "did you really think that I was going to pimp for you the rest of my life? Did you really expect me to stay with you, rent you a house, have men look at me as if I'm some kind of animal?"

Ellie was calm. "I was afraid of that," she said, speaking to Sabina. "The bastard was stashing the money for himself all along."

Sabina, who had never been intimately exposed to a whore's mentality before, began to understand what made women like Ellie live as they did. Ellie's worth had been established in Sabina's eyes. She was valued at so many pounds for so much time in a man's bed, and that was all. Her worth as a human being was measured only in money, and so in her mind, when men misused her, it was only her just desserts. Ellie did not seem to be at all upset to discover that Steve had been planning all along to betray them.

"Get out of here," Sabina said. "Get out of here before I kill you!"

Wells laughed in her face, then turned to go, slamming the door behind him. Sabina ran to bend over Nancy, who was beginning to moan in pain. Dolly had pulled herself to a bed and was sitting on the edge, tears squeezing from her swollen eyes.

"What can we do now?" Dolly asked between sobs. "We can't possibly rent a house in Cloncurry. I'm so tired of sleeping on the ground, Sabina."

"You won't have to do it much longer," Sabina said. "All of you, pack your things. I'm going to get the wagons ready."

"Where are we going?" Ellie asked, astonished.

"Cloncurry," Sabina said cheerfully. "There are men there who haven't been with a woman in months, men with money burning a hole in their pockets. We're going to find us a fine house, with real beds and clean, starched linen, and we're going to dress like models of fashion and charge an arm and a leg for a night of pleasure in our fine house."

"But we have no money to get started," Ellie said.

"I have money," Sabina said. "I'll handle all of the financial details. You will turn all your money over to me, just as you've been doing with Steve. Only there will be a difference. After I take out a percentage for the house and for my business management, the rest will go into bank accounts in your own names. Ellie, in a few short years you'll be able to open that dress shop in Sydney."

"Ellie," Dolly asked, hope in her voice. "will it work? Can we do it?"

"We can, if we also find us a man to protect us," Ellie said.

"No men," Sabina insisted. "We will protect ourselves."

Ellie looked doubtful. Dolly turned to Nancy, who was still dazed, and took her into her arms.

Later, with the two wagons loaded and underway, Dolly was beside Sabina on the driver's seat of Sabina's wagon. She looked frightened, uncertain, and Sabina could guess what she was thinking: Sabina was a wilful woman, but in times of trouble, it took a man to look after a girl.

"Sabina," the girl said after a long silence, "what if Steve changes his mind and comes after us? We've made a lot of money for him, after all."

"And you let him take all of it," Sabina said.

"I guess we were just kidding ourselves," Dolly said. "Actually, that's the way it is with most whores." Sabina had not heard her use the word before; she knew enough about the prostitutes now to realise they used it when they felt low. Dolly went on. "The fancy men always keep most of the money, doling out a little to the girls now and then for a new dress or something. That's just the way it is."

"No more," Sabina said. "You ask what will happen if Steve comes after you?" She nodded grimly. "Well, he had just better not."

Three nights later, as Ellie was beginning to dish out the stew for supper, Wells appeared. The women had travelled until almost dark and then found a campsite beside a little stream. It was Sabina who first heard the sound of an approaching horse. She made no comment as she moved casually to the side of her wagon and stood there as Steve Wells rode into camp and dismounted to stand in the light of the fire.

"Hello, ladies," he said. "I want to apologize. For everything. I'm sorry I hit you, Dolly. And you, too, Nancy. Look, I didn't intend to steal your money. It just made me angry to find out that you didn't trust me, that you thought I'd steal from you."

Dolly and Nancy looked towards Ellie, who looked at Sabina.

"And you, Sabina," Wells said, "I want to apologize to you, too. Look, we can make a lot of money together, now that you've decided to join us."

For a moment Sabina feared that Steve's smile and his soft words would win over the three women who had depended on him. It was little Dolly who, hands on hips, stood facing him and declared, "Steve, you said your piece back in town."

"Now, be sensible, Dolly," Steve argued. "Do you think Sabina is going to be able to take care of you? What's she going to do with a shearer who's had one too many and decides he doesn't want to pay?"

"We'll manage," Dolly said. "At least she won't try to close my eyes for me every month or so."

"Ellie?" Steve said.

"We've decided," Ellie said. "Go on back, Steve. You've got money, what else do you want?"

"I want to be with you," he said.

Nancy laughed. "Isn't that touching? He wants to be with us."

"All right," Steve said, his voice changing and his face going nasty. "I've tried to be nice. Now I guess I'm going to have to beat some sense into all of you."

Before Sabina could react, he had seized Dolly and was striking her in her already-bruised face with the flat of his hand. Nancy screamed and leapt on to his back, clawing and scratching.

Sabina had Lester's shotgun in the wagon, within easy reach. She had purchased shells for it at the first town she had come to. She took the gun in hand and moved to stand in front of the battling trio.

"Steve," she shouted in a hot, fierce voice.

"You're the one," Wells said, pushing Dolly aside and, with a shrug, tossing Nancy off his back. "You're the one who caused all this trouble between us."

"If you try to touch me, I'll kill you," Sabina said.

It was done without thinking. He leapt for her, hands outstretched. There was a quick blast, followed by another. She had been holding the shotgun loosely, at waist level, and the recoil of both barrels knocked her to the ground, where she landed solidly on her rump. The impact of two heavy loads of shot bent Steve Wells double and forced him backwards. He lay motionless, his midriff a raw and mutilated area of blood.

Sabina stood up and carefully placed the shotgun on the wagon seat and walked over to look at Wells.

"Is he dead?" Dolly asked in a whisper.

"Yes," Sabina said.

"Good," Dolly said fiercely. "I'm glad."

"What are we going to do?" Ellie asked, her eyes wide, one hand at her ample bosom.

"That's up to you," Sabina said. "I killed him. The three of you had nothing to do with it. I'll turn myself in to the authorities in the next town or—"

"No," Dolly said heatedly. "You will not do that."

"Or what?" Nancy asked.

"Or we can bury him, turn his horse loose, and go on about our business," Sabina said.

"We can't just—" Ellie said.

"Can't just what?" Sabina asked. "Can't just kill a man, bury him, and forget him? Someone did that to my husband. Why can't I do it to a man who beats my friends and steals their money and threatens me?"

"I'll get the shovel," Dolly said, persuaded.

Sabina shooed the horse away, still saddled. Sooner or later he'd either be found or would find his own way back to the stable where Wells had rented him. They dug the grave four feet deep, deep enough so that the dingoes and scavengers couldn't dig up the body, dumped Wells into the hole, covered him, and then Sabina tried to erase all signs of digging by scattering the excess dirt and smoothing it over with brush. To her great surprise she slept quite soundly that night.

The town of Cloncurry in northwestern Queensland was a booming, thriving, bustling town in the heart of rich copper fields. It was, Sabina thought after seeing it, all that had been promised and more. It was raw. The population was mostly male. Work was plentiful, so that all of the men had money in their pockets.

They drove into the town through arid plains broken by rocky hills. It was hot, but not as hot as it had been—this they learned later—in January of 1889 when the temperature set an Australian record by reaching 127.8 degrees Fahrenheit in the shade. To add to the heat, the air was poisoned by the fumes from copper smelters so that often one had to gasp deeply to clear the lungs. However, there was a charming house available near the centre of the town. The house cost so much that Sabina decided to raise the fees she would charge for the girls—her first business decision.

The place had once been used as a boardinghouse so that partitions had been added to cut huge rooms into smaller rooms. This was exactly what Sabina needed, for she intended to expand the business as quickly as possible. It wouldn't be possible for Ellie, Dolly, and Nancy to meet the demand, in spite of their willingness.

There were many expenses; money spent for furniture, for food, for beds and beddings, for attractive clothing—especially lingerie—for the girls. Sabina had her friends complaining bitterly before she considered the house clean enough, before the little rooms had been painted and wallpapered in warm, comforting colours.

After the sun went down and the day's heat abated, the house cooled off nicely, so the girls could work in relative comfort. The word spread quickly. The miners came first, and then the drovers and the bushmen. To keep the men from being impatient as they waited their turn, Sabina purchased an old piano and entertained them with songs. She had expected to have a more difficult time convincing the clients that she herself was not available, but surprisingly the miners, bushmen, and drovers took her at her word, and it was soon common knowledge that Miss Bina was merely the hostess.

On the advice of Ellie, Sabina had become just "Bina". For a surname she chose the name of the priest of her church back in London, and she laughed, wondering if the good man would have been honoured or shocked to know that the madam of the finest whorehouse in Queensland's bush had taken his name, Tyrell. Bina Tyrell.

She enjoyed the entertaining, the singing, and the piano-playing. She liked watching the men as they watched her, their eyes soft, a smile on their lips when she sang of what was for most of them home—old England—of family, loved ones, and sweethearts. She hired a young man to act as bartender, but let him know from the beginning that there would be no free samples for him, either at the bar or in the rooms. As the money came in, she redecorated the house until it was a showplace, with gardens outside that had to be watered daily by one of the new household servants, an Abo man. She took an interest in the men who came to the house, chatted with them between songs, knew them by their first names, joked with them as if she were another man. And quite often she turned down offers for her body that astounded her in their generosity.

"Bloody hell, Bina," Ellie said, when she heard Bina turned down a mine owner who had named a sum that, to Ellie, seemed princely.

"Don't worry," Bina told Ellie. "We're getting along all right, aren't we? Have you looked at the balance in your bankbook lately?"

"Bina," Ellie said, "it's not as if you're a virgin. You've been married, after all, and you've even had a child. You've got the name, just by living in this house. And there's not one of us, even Nancy, who isn't making more money than you, and you having put up the cash to get us started. The next time one of them rich ones offers a fortune—"

"Perhaps," Bina Tyrell said wistfully, as she walked back towards her piano. There, at the keyboard, she was happiest. There, as she sang a gay song, followed by a love song and then a naughty song, she could forget how the lyrebird had imitated the sound of her dead baby, could forget that she would never know what had happened to the man she had loved.

She, too, was saving her money, although she had less purpose than Ellie, who continued to talk about how wonderful it was going to be when she had enough to open that little dress shop in Sydney.

She recruited two new girls who had wandered into town to test their skills at making a profit out of love, and now with five rooms working steadily the money came in with surprising rapidity. It was inevitable that someone would want to share in the wealth.

CHAPTER IX

Dirk De Hartog looked up at the hint of light in the eastern sky. Around him, men were making their last preparations, checking their weapons, perhaps saying a silent prayer. He heard the sound of a horseman coming up the rocky slope. That would be the scout. He heard the exchange of a recognition code in Afrikaans, and then the scout was a darker shape moving through the dimness.

"It is all clear, Colonel," the scout said. He was not much more than a boy, the scout, but a good man who knew the country around the little Natal town of Frere.

"We will move out," Dirk said.

His second-in-command rode back along the forming line, passing along the order in a soft voice. The commando unit consisted of only thirty men, but they were armed with good, German-made rifles, and a special squad of men was responsible for transporting and for putting into action two of the recently invented English automatic guns, Maxims.

Dirk had never seen the Maxim gun used against men. He had seen it demonstrated, and had fired it himself; after that firing, with his ears ringing and a queasy feeling in the pit of his stomach, he had felt revulsion. The Maxim spat out heavy, deadly, .450-calibre rounds at an incredible speed. Dirk, who had known war, could not see how any man could survive such a barrage.

He took his place at the head of the column, directly behind the scout. The sky was getting lighter. He saw the outline of railway embankment, spurred his horse, and drew the animal to a halt with shod hooves clattering on the cross ties. The scout had picked the spot well. There was cover for his men near the track, cover which offered a splended field of fire. He began to dispose his men. Sappers, specialists in field fortifications, placed the charges on the tracks.

Dawn. The sun was not far behind. It would be hot, as usual. Dirk left his horse under cover and walked along the men, who were positioned well.

"It is quite possible," he told them, "that we shall strike the first blow. If so, we have an honour and an obligation to make that blow a swift one, a hard one. May God be with all of you."

These were farm boys, mostly, but then most Boers were farmers. "Farmer" was what their name meant in their native Dutch, and they were proud to bear the title. South Africa had attracted European explorers and empire builders from many countries over a long stretch of time, and the Boers had found it convenient to keep the Dutch name as a way of distinguishing their own clan from the smatterings of other Europeans who had settled across the southern tip of the continent. Some French Huguenots were called Boers as well, but what they all had in common was a staunchly conservative—some would have said a reactionary—moralistic faith. They saw themselves as other exiled pilgrims had in the past, as God's elect, carrying the good word into the wilderness.

Dirk's boys were sturdy and dependable, like most Boers, and now they were caught up in what their leaders thought of as a war of liberation from the thrall of British domination. Dirk wondered how many of them realized what was at stake, what they were fighting for. We knew that before this fight was over, many of them would be dead. He found a seat on a rock and watched as the sappers finished placing their charges and began to dust away their tracks with besoms of brush.

Dirk had mobilized his commandos at the request of General "Slim-Piet" Joubert, a man who had some experience in fighting the English, having beaten them at Majuba Hill during the first Boer War in 1881. Joubert now was moving south with an army of fourteen thousand good men from the two Boer republics, the Transvaal and the Orange Free State. Joubert's objective was to advance through British Natal and take the port city of Durban as quickly as possible. It was possible, for the British forces in Natal were weak.

Boer mobilization had been accomplished smoothly, for the Boer states had been on a war footing for some time. Every man between the ages of sixteen and sixty did unpaid military service, considering it a privilege as well as a duty. When it had become evident that the English wanted war, that they were intent on reinforcing their garrisons in South Africa, Boer citizen soldiers had reported for duty riding a good horse and carrying ten days' food and a rifle with thirty rounds of ammunition. If a man did not have a good, modern rifle, he received a new Mauser.

The commando units were formed quickly and openly in the Transvaal and the Orange Free State, and more covertly among Boers living in Natal, and in the British Cape Colony to the south. The plan of battle had been drawn up by the young state attorney of the Transvaal, Jan Smuts, and it was simplicity itself: the Boers, taking advantage of their ability to instantly mobilize, would drive at once for the coastal cities—as Joubert's forces headed towards Durban, other units would move through the Cape Colony to seize Cape Town. With the coastal ports secure, the British would not be able to land reinforcements.

Dirk De Hartog's part in the initial plan was to interrupt the British use of the railway running northwest from Durban through the junction town of Ladysmith and onwards to Johannesburg in the Transvaal. If, while putting that railway out of order, the commandos could capture arms, ammunition, and other supplies, so much the better.

The sun was an hour high when Dirk first heard the sounds of the approaching train. He made a last-minute check for preparedness, saw that his men were ready, and watched the macabre muzzles of the Maxim guns swivel as the gunners tested their mobility of aim. The British train came around a distant bend, and it was the one Dirk was expecting, an armoured train carrying men and matériel north to the garrison at Ladysmith. The train was moving at normal speed, smoke billowing from the engine, leaving a dark, curving trail in the sky.

The charges were set off when the engine was a quarter of a mile down the straight stretch of track. Almost immediately Dirk heard the high squeal of iron on iron as the engineer put on his brakes.

The strike had been timed perfectly. The engine came to a stop only a few feet from the break in the tracks. Instantly the engineer began to reverse thrust. The big drive wheels spun. A hidden charge was detonated directly under the engine, not powerful enough to overturn the heavy locomotive, but enough to knock the rails and ties from under it and leave the smoking iron giant helpless, like a powerful horse caught in a sling, its legs now limp and ineffective.

"Hold your fire," Dirk was calling out, for the armoured cars behind the locomotive were silent. They were not silent long, however. Guns were thrust out of firing ports, and the din of rifle fire came to be answered with a storm of bullets from the Boer rifles. The two Maxims began to chatter demonically. It took fire and smoke to force the British Tommies out of the armoured train cars. The Tommies came out in a rush, well organized, only to wither instantly in the storm of bullets from the overpowering Maxims.

In the hushed silence that followed, Dirk stood still, in shock. Looking around at his troops, he saw that the results of the raid had had the same numbing effect on his men. Only one man of the commando force was dead, two others were but wounded slightly; yet the railway embankment was littered with the British dead.

"May God have mercy," Dirk said, under his breath. As he had told his men, it was quite possible that his action was the first of the war, the first time that Boer had met Brit over the muzzles of weapons since the president of the Transvaal, "Oom Paul"— Uncle Paul—Kruger, had rejected the latest of the British ultimatums. In future actions more men would be involved, thousands, and more than two Maxims would be pouring out their metallic stream of death against frail flesh.

He shook his head to clear away his astonishment and then bellowed an order. The men swarmed down onto the train and began to search. The engineer and fireman were alive, standing, dazed, in the locomotive with their hands raised. They were not molested. Dirk wanted living witnesses to the efficiency of the raid. He wanted the British to know that this war would not be fought in set-piece battles, battles in which the British would have the advantage because of superior artillery and more disciplined troops. This war would be fought not just on one battle line but throughout South Africa. Wherever the British were they were in danger of being hit by a swift-moving guerrilla unit that could form overnight and disappear almost instantly. Perhaps the sheer brutality of using automatic guns against men, the grisly evidence that would be left lying beside the wrecked train, would make the

British rethink their political positions.

Dirk De Hartog had not wanted this war. He prayed silently, as his men salvaged all the weapons and materials of battle on the train, that the Boers could persuade the British with just a few swift strikes that they were indeed a force to be reckoned with, fully committed to defending their independence of British rule.

Dirk was in his mid-forties, a strong and hardheaded Boer who looked and acted younger than his age. He had not fought in the short and limited engagements of the first Boer war, but he had done his share earlier, in 1879, against the Zulu hordes, fighting beside the British, not against them. Since the Zulu War, he had devoted his life to tending the De Hartog holdings near Pietermaritzburg, in the Natal Colony, where his neighbours and many of his friends were British.

It was Paul Kruger himself who had sent word through Joubert that he wanted Dirk at the head of a small, mobile commando unit, for it was well-known that Dirk De Hartog knew the land as well as any man living. He knew Natal like the back of his hand, and there the initial battles would be fought. In addition, he knew all that vast area north of the Orange River that was the Orange Free State, and he had also hunted and travelled the lands north of the Vaal River—the Transvaal. When he was called, he answered. He was not entirely sure that Oom Paul was right in taking the Boer republics to war against the British but, in spite of the fact that he lived in a British colony, his first loyalty was to his people. It would be the same for Boers who lived in the Cape Colony. Not all of them would understand the reasons for the war, but many of them would fight.

Indeed, not many people understood why, in October of 1899, Boer units were on the march. Dirk's sister, Anna, who was somewhat of an iconoclast, said that the root of Boer hatred of the British lay not so much in their desire for freedom as in the Boers' grim, almost fanatical religion. The Boers believed, along with Paul Kruger, that God had purposefully sent this select group of Dutch people to the lands of South Africa.

"You Boer men," Anna had said, "constitute a secret society. Your mysticism makes you so different from anyone else that an Englishman can no more understand your mind than he can that of a Chinaman. You are narrow, bigoted, and far too passionately nationalistic."

Only occasionally did Dirk rise to his sister's provocations. Ordinarily he merely let her talk. She was an odd woman, this Anna, warm and loving, and still a young woman. Yet she had, in effect, removed herself from participation in life outside their home near Pietermaritzburg when the young British officer whom she had nursed and loved had gone back to Australia at the end of the Zulu war. Then too, Dirk had to admit that Anna had analysed the situation with some accuracy.

"The trouble is, too, that if gold had *not* been discovered in the Transvaal," she contended, "making a very decent but poor nation suddenly very rich, the Boers of the Transvaal would still be loyal British subjects, with their hands out begging for the comfort of British largesse."

Dirk did not wholly agree with Anna's cynical political assessments, but he acknowledged that gold had much to do with the war, for gold had brought in new people, the Uitlanders— foreigners. The Boers did not mine their own gold but let out concessions to foreigners who were mainly British or British colonial. The Uitlanders paid nearly all of the Transvaal's taxes, were liable to military duty along with the Boers, and yet were not allowed to vote. Since by 1899 the Uitlanders had come to outnumber the Boers in the Transvaal, the situation had grown quite awkward and unmanageable. It was exacerbated by the efforts of Cecil Rhodes to unite all of the various South African colonies and republics into one nation under British domination, a consummation devoutly opposed by the more established and entrenched Boer burghers.

Dirk De Hartog was persuaded that the war was the direct result of the unrealistic belief that one Boer was a match for any number of British. The first Boer War had fuelled this legend, because then Joubert had badly mauled an unprepared army of ill-trained redcoats on the Transvaal-Natal border. But things were different now: the British would not be as poorly prepared this time. To be sure, they were outmatched for the moment, with fewer than ten thousand men split between Natal and the Cape Colony. But already British officers were at work raising white units in Rhodesia, and well-trained troops of the British regular army were en route to Natal from India.

Preparations for war had bred further preparations for war. Boer mobilization had encouraged British mobilization. When the British declared their intention to reinforce their garrisons in South Africa, Jan Smuts issued an ultimatum on behalf of the Boers, demanding that British troops on the borders of the Transvaal be withdrawn and that all British troops who had arrived in South Africa after the first of July be removed. The ultimatum expired in October, and thereafter a state of war existed between Great Britain and the Republics of the Transvaal and the Orange Free State.

The results of Dirk De Hartog's first attack on a British troop train made his stomach queasy. Soldiers lay everywhere in the agonized frozen postures of death—good men, British soldiers. The day was advancing, and he felt the onset of the usual overbearing heat. Before another train could be brought up to attend to the bodies, they would be bloated and the scavengers would have been at them, but he could not risk taking the time to bury them lest by some accident his commando unit should be caught in the open. Using packhorses and mules laden with captured weapons and matériel, the commandos travelled to an appointed place, stashed the weapons, and then dissolved without a trace back into the Natal countryside.

CHAPTER X

At forty, Anna De Hartog was a pale-haired, shapely woman whose attractiveness was still intact. Her body had softened into that of a mature woman, with rounded hips and breasts, but her waist was still slim and well-defined. Even without makeup she was pink-cheeked, and her way of moving spoke of perfect health. In the absence of Dirk she was consistent master of the De Hartog household and all of its fields and pastureland, if not always master of a younger version of herself, Sianna De Hartog, who, at nineteen, very definitely had a mind of her own.

"If my mother were alive," Sianna was saying, "she would most certainly allow me to do my part for my country."

Sianna was small in stature, but shapely. Her face was not quite a reflection of Anna's, but it had a definite De Hartog shape, oval, well formed, and she had the De Hartog blue eyes. All three of the De Hartogs, Anna, Dirk, and Sianna, carried the family resemblance. Sianna's hair was not quite as pale as Anna's, but it was as thick and luxuriant.

"Your country is Natal," Anna said.

The girl whirled away, frustration lowering her brow. "Aunt Anna," she said, trying to keep the anger out of her voice, "we are Boer. Boer! And my father is already out there somewhere, fighting to make Natal a Boer republic, like the Transvaal and the Free State. Or to make one glorious Boer Republic of all of South Africa. Doesn't that concept thrill you?"

"The De Hartogs have done quite well in a British colony," Anna said.

"I do hope that you don't speak like that when other Boers are present," Sianna said. "They'd call you traitor."

Anna sighed and put down her sewing. "My dear child," she said, "the war has barely begun. Before you go running off to do your share, let's at least wait to see where you'll be needed. If Jan Smuts is right, the commandos will be in Durban within days, and the war will be over. If not, then perhaps it will come to you, since we sit not ten miles from the Johannesburg-Durban railway."

"Oh, you can be so—so—" She could not find a word, for she loved her aunt, and in spite of the fact that Anna had been a stern disciplinarian all of her life—her mother had died shortly after she was born—she would not want to hurt Anna. "Dear Anna, you yourself were in the field in the Zulu war. You were allowed to do your share. How can you ask me to sit here idly while our very way of life is being threatened by the Uitlanders?"

"If you are so idle," Anna said, with a smile, "I'm sure there's work that needs doing."

"Ooff," Sianna said, spreading her arms in dramatic disgust.

"Patience," Anna said. "Where would you go? You can't just strike out for the north and hope to meet the commandos moving down towards the coast."

"I could find my father."

"Your father would not want you running about the countryside alone, nor would he want you with his commandos. A fast-moving unit such as his has no facilities to care for the wounded. You must know that."

"But there will be hospital units," Sianna said. "I can find one."

"Perhaps you could," anna said. "But I think it is best that you wait."

"I can't wait," Sianna said. "I won't wait. All of my friends have gone now."

"Ah, so you have only male friends?" Anna asked, with a raised eyebrow.

"You know what I mean," Sianna said. "Yes, all of the boys I know are gone, many of them with my father." She sat down directly across the table from Anna and looked straight into the older woman's eyes. "Oh, Aunt Anna, I ache to be a part of it. Can't you remember how it felt to be young and to have a chance to do something significant?"

Anna smiled and put her hand on Sianna's shining, dark-blonde hair. "Yes," she said. "I can remember." She could also remember the sea of blood, and the severed limbs outside the surgical tent. She could remember how, during the Zulu War, Dirk had brought home two wounded British soldiers, one of whom had carved his image directly onto her heart. "You will only have to be patient a while longer."

"What do you mean?"

"I have not told you," Anna said, after a sigh of resignation, "since I didn't think I'd be able to hold your feet to the ground, but Dr. Hans Van Reenen is at this very moment organizing a mobile hospital unit, drawing personnel from both Pietermaritzburg and Durban. He approached me two weeks past about joining as a nurse."

"You, Auntie?" Sianna asked, a look of dismay and disbelief crossing her face. "At your age, going off on an adventure, leaving me here to do nothing but tend the house and keep the servants occupied?"

Anna smiled at Sianna's conception of her: in the young woman's eyes, Anna was already old. "Don't worry," she said gently, "I told the doctor that I had had my war. I also said that there was another De Hartog who was a very fine nurse."

Sianna leapt to her feet. "Oh, Aunt Anna! Then I must start to get ready!"

"There's time."

"Please, will you help me decide what to take?"

"Only two uniforms, underwear, an extra pair of shoes, a warm coat, your toilet articles. You will be travelling light."

Sianna had her gear ready within an hour, and then she fretted for five days before Dr. Hans Van Reenen finally called at the De Hartog house. He was a grey man, small, wrinkled, and his eyes, having seen the dead and wounded of two past wars, were sad. He smiled indulgently at Sianna's eagerness and told her that she would be called for secretly in the night.

"Do you know, Doctor, where you will be going?" Anna asked.

"Northeast," Van Reenen said. "We're to meet up with the main army as it moves down the railway towards Durban."

For a long moment, in the dark of night outside the house, Anna held the girl in her arms as they watched Dr. Van Reenen ride away.

"Don't worry," Sianna said.

"No."

"I'll write when I have the chance."

"Please do."

"Tell my father when you see him that—" She could not speak, for her throat was suddenly constricted as tears formed.

"I know," Anna said. "He will be very proud of you."

Two nights later, Sianna was riding away, mounted astride like a man. It was so dark that Anna didn't know whether or not she looked back. And then she was alone in the night, the house sleeping behind her. She made her way to the kitchen and lit a lamp. She knew that she would not be able to sleep, so she brewed a pot of tea and sat down for a few moments of sympathetic concern about her niece's new adventure.

So Sianna had her wish. She was off to war. Anna worried less about Sianna's being wounded than about disease and exposure. Southern Africa could be harsh. In the field Sianna would face torrid days and cold nights. If the war lasted through the summer and into the South African winter—June, July, and August—rains would turn everything to mud. An unhealthy dampness would permeate everything, and it would be impossible to maintain sanitary conditions and fight a war at the same time.

"Lord God," she prayed aloud, "bring her back to me safe."

Midnight. She poured another cup of tea, smiling to think that surely she would be up and down three or four times after drinking all that liquid so late at night. Still she could not face her empty bed. Empty bed? She was startled, for *that* thought had not come to her in years. Her bed had always been empty. Anna the spinster. Anna, who had turned down not one but several attractive suitors.

She pulled off her shoes and propped her stockinged feet on a chair, heedless of the hang of her skirt. There was no one to see, no one to know that Anna was reminiscing, going back in time, doing what she had sworn never to do; remembering a young Australian soldier.

Dirk had plucked him from under the spears of the Zulu, on the Buffalo River near Isandhlwana, and had brought him home, almost dead, to be nursed by his sister. For a short, glorious, guilt-ridden time, her bed had not been empty. Ah, no. Not empty but full of warmth. Love. To remember how once she was loved, yes.

But God punishes sin, and her punishment had been to watch

the young soldier ride away, to know that she would never see him again, and then to have to face her brother—thank God both her parents had been dead—and tell him that she was carrying Jon Fisher's child. That she, good Boer girl that she had been, was pregnant by a British soldier. This, then, was a part of the punishment, for Dirk was a product of that stern, Calvinistic Boer society. He had always been a loving brother, and he was profoundly shocked. His shock, however, turned quickly to concern. He could almost understand. It had been an emotional time, when the Zulu hordes threatened, and men died; he said he understood that perhaps she felt a bit proprietary about the Australian, for she had nursed him back from the brink of death. But, understand or not, he could not allow his sister to suffer the disapproval that would fall upon her in their strict society.

As Anna sat in her kitchen and recollected, she wished for the power to do it all over again, this time to change things. Not everything, for, heaven help her, she would take Jon Fisher into her bed again if she could relive that moment. But, given another chance, she would protest Dirk's actions to protect her. For in his brotherly love for her, Dirk had injured the lives of innocent people. She wished she could have said, "*No*, Dirk the guilt is mine, and I will live with it. The child is mine, and she will know it, and I will hold her and love her, and I will make up to my child with my love the fact that she is fatherless."

Now the mood was on her, the old guilt heavy; but her guilt had nothing to do with the fact that she had loved Jon Fisher. Those moments that she had spent with Jon so long ago glowed within her heart still, and they would be hers forever, hers to cherish, to take out and count as if they were hoarded gold coins. No, her regrets were not for having loved Jon, only for what might have been had God been in a kinder mood. For the others she mourned. She mourned for the frail Boer girl who had been Dirk's fiancée, the girl whom Dirk had rushed into marriage immediately after he had learned that his sister was to have a child. Only a Boer woman could understand why that shy, frail girl had understood the dilemma and had been willing to do the difficult things that Dirk asked. She was a dutiful Boer woman, and she had married Dirk to love, honour, and *obey*. She made no protest when Dirk took her, and Anna, away from the De Hartog house near Pietermaritzburg, far away to the north where, on an isolated ranch owned by one of Dirk and Anna's uncles, a ranch run by a dependable Matebele foreman and peopled only by other blacks, Sianna was born to Anna and yet presented to the world as the first fruit of Dirk's marriage.

It was indicative of the events, and of the time, that Anna did not think of Dirk's dead wife by name, only as Dirk's wife, for she, more than anyone else, had been the victim of Anna's one true time of happiness, her time with Jon Fisher. The load had been too much for that vulnerable, retiring girl, and when it became evident that she was not to bear fruit of her own, the sadness was too much for her, the load of deceit too heavy. She died only two years after Sianna's birth. Guilt prevented Dirk from seeking another wife. Love of Jon Fisher made Anna totally incapable of going into another man's arms. And the punishment went on and on, for Sianna talked lovingly of the "mother" she had never known, while calling her true mother "Aunt Anna".

"Bring her back to me, Lord God," Anna prayed. "Preserve my daughter in safety and guard her from the disabling shock of this war."

CHAPTER XI

Drought was still king in Queensland. Matthew Van Buren, nineteen years old and heir apparent to a portion of the business empire that had been assembled by his grandfather, Claus Van Buren, and his father, Joseph, rode through swirling dust past several dried-up water holes before he found one that still held muddy, tepid water. Drovers were at work, shuttling groups of animals to and away from the billabong. He was recognized and hailed but the men continued their work, leaving him to ride on towards the station after his horse had had his fill of the murky water.

At the house he was greeted warmly by a domestic who reported that Matthew's mother and father were in the parlour. He dusted himself off a bit, left his hat in the kitchen, and stood in the door unobserved for a moment, looking at his parents. Mathilda Van Buren, heavy, dressed in dark skirts, was with her Bible. His father, Joseph, was at his desk, head bent to the account books.

"Is this the greeting your son gets after a long absence?" Matt said softly.

His mother started, looked up, and let the Bible fall to the floor. Joseph's face became creased in a smile as he leapt to his feet and strode across the room to take Matt into his arms. They were of a height, but the older man was thicker of body. Mathilda's first thought was to greet her son, but there was, after all, a Bible on the floor and that had to be treated with the proper reverence—picked up and placed carefully on the table. Only then did she move towards father and son and take her due as Matt left off shaking his father's hand to embrace his mother.

"Look how dusty you are," Mathilda said, holding her son at arm's length. Tears of pleasure formed in her eyes and ran down to intersect the laugh lines of her smile "And why might I ask are you not at college?"

Matt didn't want to have to face *that* immediately. "What kind of greeting is this? Mothers are supposed to say, 'My boy, you look splended, and you must be hungry.' "

His mother laughed. "If you're hungry, I imagine you still remember where the kitchen is."

"What about college?" Joseph asked.

"Well . . ." Matt began. He was strongly built, as were most of the Van Burens, with a thick torso, sturdy legs, and a face that was broad, open, and handsome. It was said that he had taken his good looks from his American grandmother, Mercy Van Buren. Now that face betrayed him, telling his father everything.

Joseph turned away, his head down, obviously fighting anger. When news had come of the war in South Africa, he had written to his son, warning him not to be infected by the patriotic fervour that was sweeping all of British Australia. Now it had happened.

Matt stood, his arms hanging limply, waiting for the explosion. Joseph was not known for his even temper, and he knew full well that his father expected him soon to take over some of the responsibilities of the Van Buren financial empire, which included not only his father's Queensland station but also the shipping enterprises inherited from Grandfather Claus, in both New Zealand and Australia.

Joseph finally turned back to his son. "So," he said grimly.

"I . . . take it you've guessed," Matt said evenly.

"What are you talking about?" Mathilda asked, her bewildered eyes nervously searching Joseph's and Matt's faces. She hated to see Joseph get upset, for it gave him indigestion.

"Now listen, Father—" Matt said, lifting one hand as if in defence.

Joseph looked upwards, as if towards heaven. "It isn't enough that the Van Burens seem to have lost the knack of bearing sons. It isn't enough that my brother and I are getting on in years. It doesn't matter if, after all, we now let the work done by my father and my mother in building these things that we have go to waste, to let what they built dissolve and disappear."

Matt loved his father, but he had a strong streak of the Van Buren spirit of independence himself, and it had been his father's idea, after all, for him to go away to college, to study economics and business in order to take over the Van Buren shipping and trading enterprises. He had never fought against the idea, for he did feel an obligation to his family. But once in a while, not too often—perhaps once in every man's lifetime—events occurred that were of more importance than a family business.

"I'm sorry to upset you, Father," Matt said. "However, the decision has been made. I am enlisted in the mounted infantry. We'll be leaving for South Africa in less than two weeks."

A gasp of anguish came from his mother. She sought the support of her chair and looked up at him, her kind, loving face now contorted by tears.

In spite of himself, Joseph felt a surge of pride. Of course he had plans for his son. Of course he wanted his son to begin to assume more responsibilities in managing the family businesses. Nathan Van Buren, Joseph's brother, was not in the best of health. The husbands of the two Van Buren girls were good men and held responsible positions in the company; still, they were not Van Burens. But now all his plans would have to be shelved. An affair of empire took precedence. Any red-blooded British subject would now rise to the defence of the mother country. Loyalty to the Queen was as much a part of Joseph as was his conviction that unification of Australia would prove impossible, at least for the present.

In many ways Matt had always been the ideal son, dutiful, proud of his heritage and of his father, the right man to take over when the time came. But there was in him that same streak of stubborn pride, of individuality that had caused Joseph to strike out on his own when he was quite young, to become one of that elite class of prosperous Australians who were paradoxically still called squatters and who stood astride thousands of acres of the finest land in Australia like proprietary colossi. Matt's enlisting in the mounted infantry came as no surprise, nor was it the first time that father and son disagreed. Matt had a tendency to follow populist thinking, and he had started more than one heated argument at the Van Buren table by stating that there had to be some method of making land available to all those who wanted it, including newcomers.

But now there could be no argument. In fact, pride welled up in Joseph and he moved once more to embrace his son, then both went to Mathilda to comfort her.

"Enough tears, my dear," Joseph said. "It's fitting for Matt to go to join our British brothers in defence of the empire."

"But couldn't he go in some administrative capacity?" Mathilda asked, still sniffling. "Joseph, you know people. You're an influential man. Surely you can get him a staff appointment or some such."

"Mother," Matt said gently. "No."

"But—"

Joseph looked at her sternly, and this, along with the look of disapproval on her son's face, made her quiet.

Later, father and son rode together through the parched land. There was both a grandeur and a sadness about the condition of the bush. In the drought was evidence of the power of the elements, of nature and her sway over mere man. And there was a feeling of pity for the animals, cattle with ribs protruding, sheep made lazy by hunger.

"No worries," Joseph said. "It will pass. The rains will come. Inevitably they will come and then we'll have flood. It's one thing or the other in the bush, my boy, as you know."

"I love this place," Matt said. "One day, if I can ever find a better way with words, I'll be able to tell you, Father, how much I admire you for building our businesses and how grateful I am that I'm to have a part in their future."

Joseph cleared his throat, suddenly tightened with emotion. "I think you handled the words quite well," he said. To cover his proud, fatherly tears, he spurred the horse and led his son at gallop past the one billabong that still had water. "Since you've been here last, I've acquired that bit of land," he said, pointing ahead. Matt saw a decaying shack and scorched land. "Belonged to a new man named Caldwell," Joseph said. "Couldn't make it, of course. I paid his wife a fair price for it after he'd chucked it in and left her."

"Did you offer to share the water with him?"

Joseph expected a scornful reply, for it was a touchy subject, but he withheld comment.

"Sorry," Matt said. "Now is not the time to get into *that* discussion, is it?"

"I don't know of any proper time to consider giving what a man has worked all his life to build," Joseph said, and that foreclosed their debate.

Two weeks later Matt Van Buren, lieutenant, was aboard ship. On the dock a brass band played "Soldiers of the Queen". With a great hooting of horns and much smoke the troopship got under way. Matt stayed on deck for the festivities. The ship picked up speed as it left the harbour. He leaned on the rail, listening to a soldier nearby who had a banjo and was playing and singing:

> "Good-bye, Dolly, I must leave you
> Though it breaks my heart to go,
> Something tells me I am needed,
> At the front to fight the foe."

A serious-faced man in civilian clothing came to lean on the rail next to Matt. He had dark, slicked-back hair, piercing eyes under heavy black eyebrows, and a wide and generous mouth. "How goes it, mate?" he asked.

Matt, with much on his mind, merely shrugged. Already he was having to deal with complaints from his men. The recruiting sergeants had promised beer, biscuits, and tobacco, and now, with none of that in hand, they were packed aboard a small, stinking ship like sardines. Already the stench coming up from the horse stalls below decks was beyond endurance.

"Should have made provision for disposing of the manure," said the civilian.

"Indeed," Matt agreed. He looked more closely at the man, saw a wide, friendly bushman's smile.

"Patterson's the name," the civilian said.

Matt was immediately impressed. He had heard that A. B. Patterson was going to the Boer War, but he had had no idea that the famous newsman and poet would be on his ship.

"My pleasure, Mr. Patterson," he said, shaking his hand.

"Banjo," Patterson said. "If I'm going to follow your stinking horses all over the south of Africa I at least want to be called by the name my friends use."

Like most young Australians, Matt could recite Banjo Patterson's "The Man From Snowy River" by heart. "We're honoured, sir, that you have decided to attach yourself to our unit," he said.

"The British Tommy Atkins will have Kipling," Patterson said. "I think our diggers deserve someone, even if they have to settle for an old bushman like me."

Matt checked his watch. "If you'll excuse me, sir," he said. "I have to see about my men."

"Of course, but if you don't mind, I'll come along," Patterson said.

They walked towards a group of ambulances lashed securely in position on the deck. A smart-looking orderly saluted Matt and said, "Well, we're under way at last, sir."

"That we are," Matt said.

Patterson stopped, smiled broadly. "Aren't you a bit old for this duty?" he asked the ambulance orderly.

"Not at all, sir," the orderly said. "They wouldn't give me my old rank."

"Which was?"

"Sergeant major, infantry, sir," the orderly said.

Matt was impressed. The orderly probably had more experience, more knowledge of war than all of the men in the mounted infantry, and yet now he was an ambulance orderly.

"Well," Patterson said. "I don't think the Boers will fire on ambulances."

The old sergeant laughed. "Way I hear it, sir, the Boer has no respect for helplessness. He might even fire on mounted infantry."

That was not the last time that Patterson walked with Matt on his regular tours of the ship as it yawed, rolled, and bounced across the Indian Ocean. When the ship at last reached Cape Town and the troops disembarked from a ship that stank so badly of manure that half the city was offended, Matt happened to be with Patterson when the newspapermen interviewed a Boer woman. Matt was interested, since the woman was the first of the "enemy" that he'd encountered. She was short, but broad and strong looking. Her complexion was olive, her eyes sharp and lively.

"Why have you come, you Australians?" the woman asked. "I cannot understand it at all, why you Australians and New Zealanders and Canadians come here to lightheartedly shoot down other colonists of whom you know nothing. It's terrible. And you're such fine men, too, such fine fellows."

The Queensland Mounted Infantry was ordered into the field immediately. They provided much-needed reinforcement, for up to that time the Boers had been decidedly outfighting the British soldiers who had been in place when the war began.

The Australians found the African veldt to be much like their own outback, and since most of the men in the unit were bushmen, stock riders, or shearers, they felt at home. The officers who, like Matt, were mostly squatters or sons of squatters, had confidence in their men, and chafed when they found that the Australian units were to be attached to larger British commands.

The Queenslanders quickly took the measure of their enemy's tactics. The highly mobile Boer commandos were, as in Dirk De Hartog's raid against the armoured train, stalking the British as a hunter would stalk game. The British, often victims of their own high regard for tactical traditions, had been trained to fight in compact formations, facing the enemy squarely. The Boers, skilled in their own ways of fighting, chose not to indulge in such face-to-face folly or other suicidal Napoleonic charges, but sniped away with their good German Mauser rifles from behind rocks, systematically slaughtering the unsuspecting British who often could not see their enemy.

At Sunnyside, with a hundred Canadians and two hundred of the Duke of Cornwall's Light Infantry in support, the Queenslanders were ordered to attack a Boer laager, or camp. Matt was pleased to see that the Australian officers were left to decide on methods and were not under the direct orders of a British officer. He was told his objective, and he was left to get his men there in any way he chose.

"There's good cover this way," he said, pointing to the landscape and the corresponding map, giving orders to his sergeants. "We'll take every advantage of it."

"Just like stalking a kanga-bloody-roo, eh, sir?" asked his sergeant major.

"That's the idea, Sergeant," Matt said. "Now, the other units will be closing in from the north and west. We'll go in from here. We want all three units to reach the laager at the same time, so that the Boers are under fire from all of our forces at once."

"Goodonyer, sir," said the sergeant major. "You just stand back, sir, and we'll bugger them Boers un-bloody-believable."

In the months to come, Matt would recall wistfully the ease with which the Queenslanders completed their first assignment. Taking advantage of every scrap of cover, like a hunter stalking a deer, the mounted infantry closed on the Boer laager. When the firing began, the Boers were caught totally by surprise. Forty men surrendered quickly. In times to come it would not be so bloodless, so quickly over, so gloriously simple.

CHAPTER XII

Clive Taylor was a big man. He stood an even six feet tall, and his well-developed arms were as big as some men's thighs. As chief constable of Cloncurry, he got little back talk from troublemakers unless they were so far gone in drink as to be completely without caution. Clive was thirty years old, and he alone knew that he had left a wife behind in Brighton when he sailed for Australia in 1895. He had come for gold, had found none, had worked for a few terrible months in the copper mines, and then he had found his natural element, law enforcement. His size and his agreeable personality had led to rapid advancement, so that by the time Bina Tyrell and her girls arrived in booming Cloncurry and opened a house that immediately became the most popular place in town, he had become the kingpin of all law enforcement in the city.

Taylor was a good constable, fair, courteous to all, always willing to share a pint with a mate, and totally unsympathetic to those who broke the law. In Clive Taylor's town, you toed the line, mate, or you felt the point of Clive's big boot as he booted you into jail. He was, in short, the right person needed for a demanding job, the right man for Cloncurry in an age of boom and growth, a town with little regard for the moral scruples observed in the more settled parts of Queen Victoria's vast empire.

Clive was only as honest as he was prepared to be. A little money under the table from the operators of various gambling houses was, he felt, no more than his due. Thus, when Bina Tyrell opened a "sitting parlour", a "home away from home for the lonely man", it was only right that Clive should have a few quid from her as payment for his benign protection—for keeping an eye on the house so that drink and desire did not lead to violence among the clientele, and for refraining from arresting the occupants of the house, along with their clients, all of whom were in clear violation of the law.

"Don't trouble yourself about it, luv," Ellie told Bina when Clive first made it clear that he expected to be a regular participant in her profit-sharing. "Just accept it, because it comes with the territory. You set up a house, you pay off the law." She looked at Bina slyly. "Sometimes free samples keep 'em happy, too."

Bina frowned. "He hasn't been asking for *that*, has he?"

"Him?" Ellie laughed. "No, I don't think the likes of Clive Taylor would have to pay for his fun."

"Please, Ellie," Bina said, "you know I don't like you to use such language. We project a homely atmosphere here. We are, at least outside the rooms, always ladylike."

"Bet your arse we are," Ellie said, giggling perversely.

The money was pouring in. In addition to the full partners, Ellie, Dolly and Nancy, there were now five associates, one of them French, not especially pretty, but genuinely French and not ashamed to specialize in those odd stimulating practices that took their name from her nationality.

To Bina's surprise, Taylor's monetary demand was reasonable.

"It wouldn't make sense to be greedy, Miss Tyrell," he told her when they were discussing the business. "That would be like killing the goose that lays the golden egg, wouldn't it?"

"You're a wise man, Mr. Taylor," Bina had replied.

Now and again Clive would drop in at the house, usually very late, when the girls were entertaining their last customers and the cleaning women were working in the kitchen and the parlour. Sometimes Bina would still be awake, sometimes not. He would accept one free drink from the bar, sit in one particularly comfortable chair, and read the daily paper; then he would leave. If Bina happened to be up and around, he might pass a little time talking with her; otherwise he showed no interest in her. So it surprised her one night when he put down his paper and said, "I want you to ride out with me tomorrow. I'll pick you up at ten in the morning."

He had not asked. She did not question. She knew that Clive Taylor could cause her much trouble, could even put her out of business if he cared to. Everyone in Cloncurry knew that the Tyrell House was a brothel, and no one really minded so long as no one seemed to notice, or called attention to that departure from morality in devout, Christian Queensland. Not even the local priests mentioned Bina's house by name when preaching against the sins of the flesh, perhaps because they secretly knew that Bina's girls, by their presence, siphoned off the viler passions of the womanless men in town, thus making the streets safer for "decent" women, of which there were a growing number in Cloncurry.

Nevertheless, the situation was a delicate one. To put Bina out of business, all Clive Taylor would have to do would be to arrest a couple of her girls, or raid the house when it was full of men and almost assuredly catch one or more prominent male citizen in the net. If he made his arrests openly enough, the Cloncurry newspaper would be forced to print the story, and sin thus exposed would have to be eradicated.

From this came Bina's acquiescence when Clive told her that he wanted her to ride out with him. She went with him, though it was a scorcher of a day. There had been a few showers here and there, a tantalizing hint that the long drought gripping all of Queensland might be ending soon, but on that particular day the sky was brazen and the sun a fireball of baking heat. Even though Clive's surrey had a canvas top with neat little fringes hanging down to dance with the rocking movement, Bina felt perspiration begin to run down her back and dampen her underclothing before Clive pulled the surrey to a halt.

He had driven some distance to the north of Cloncurry and up a sloping gradient, slowing as the road worsened. He pulled the surrey into the shade of a lone and tired-looking tree, wrapped the reins once around the brake handle, and turned to look at Bina.

His head was large and well shaped, and he kept his sandy-brown hair cut neatly. He had warm, friendly brown eyes that could go hard suddenly, a soft mouth that smiled nicely.

"So here we are," he said.

"Yes," she said. She returned his smile. They had talked little during the drive, and she had gathered that the hard, efficient, fearless lawman was shy when alone with a woman. She was not pleased with developments, for she feared that Clive had romantic ideas about her. It was well-known that she did not participate in the profession practised by her girls, and yet it was not unreasonable that a man who was alone might harbour romantic dreams about her. She would have to be very, very careful, for a man's pride was a touchy thing, and she could not afford to alienate Clive Taylor by putting him down too severely.

"I thought you might like to see this place," Clive said. "You haven't been here before?"

"No," she said. "I've not been outside the city since we came to Cloncurry."

"It's quite a famous spot. Here in 1884 there was a battle. It was just about the only fight that could really be called a battle between whites and the Abos. The Abos have never been great fighters, and usually they have got the worst of everything. But the Kalkadoon tribe that lived in these hills finally got fed up with being pushed around by the whites, what with them taking Abo lands without so much as a thank-you. They fought and fought well, for stone-age men with stone-age weapons. They fought so hard and wouldn't surrender, so they were exterminated almost to the last man. They call this place Battle Mountain."

"How interesting," Bina said, wondering when he was going to get to the point. She wanted nothing more than to be back in the house where, at least, she could cool herself with a bath.

"I brought you here in case you wanted to battle over what I'm going to say," Taylor said, and his eyes were hard now, his voice strong. Bina revised her opinion of him: he was not at all shy. "I've been watching you. You don't entertain clients. You have no men friends."

He paused, but she made no response.

"But the girls tell me you had a husband down there in the bush. Is that true?"

"It's true," she said.

"Is that why you don't have much to do with men?"

"I loved my husband," she said.

"Past tense," he noted. "You think he's dead?"

She looked up at the sky and used her handkerchief to wipe perspiration from her forehead. "I think he must be. I could never believe that he just deserted me."

"I don't think any man would," Talor said. He put his hand on her leg, squeezing her thigh. She jumped and tried to push his hand away, but he would not move it. "Bina, maybe I should court you and bring you flowers."

"Please remove your hand," she said.

"No, 'fraid not," he said. "And there's going to be more than that."

She felt faint. The heat was oppressive. She stopped trying to remove his hand from her thigh, and she shivered.

"But I'm not going to court you. For reasons of your own, you don't seem to need a man. For bloody good reasons I don't need a woman in my life full-time, but I do need a woman occasionally. I've decided it should be you."

"You have no right," she said heatedly.

"No, not in an ideal world," he said. "But this isn't an ideal world, Bina. It happens that as chief constable I have certain powers. I think you understand what I'm saying. And I'm not a gentleman. I do my job pretty well. I keep violence off the streets, and there's very little crime in Cloncurry. But I suppose you can say, Bina that the old adage that power corrupts is as true here as anywhere."

"You're telling me that unless I do as you want, you'll bring the law against me and my girls?" she asked. She was having difficulty breathing. His hand was by now deep in the material of her skirt, pressing against her stomach, trying to force her legs apart.

"That's it, mate."

She pushed him, hard, and he almost fell from the surrey. Leaping down, she ran a few feet to the other side of the tree and halted. She looked down a rocky slope towards Cloncurry, where the fumes of the copper smelters added interesting colours above the houses. As she heard him come up behind her, she stood motionless, then suddenly whirled. "Do you intend taking me right here," she asked, "in the dirt like an animal?"

"No," he said, with a smile. "Nor did I bring a blanket. When it happens, I want it to be in a bed, after a pint or two, and you fresh from a bath, maybe with me having given you some pleasure in the tub."

She felt relief. At least it was not going to happen now. She would have time to think about it, to decide whether or not she wanted to give in to his blackmail. She did, after all, have a choice. Her percentage of the house's income had been considerable. Her initial investment had been paid back, above her earnings. She had, in short, enough money to leave Cloncurry.

But to do what? she asked herself, as he took her arm and led her back to the surrey. She had enough to do what Ellie used to dream of, open a little shop, but she did not have enough to live on for long.

Besides, she had grown accustomed to Cloncurry. As the surrey jingled and bounced down the high street towards her house, men waved and tipped their hats, addressing her courteously as Miss Bina. When they reached the house, the girls were having their midday meal. They were dressed in their finest, and even Ellie, one of the oldest of them, looked happy and healthy. What would they do without her? Probably they would find another man like Steve Wells, who would bleed them of all their money and perhaps beat them as well.

Moreover, Bina knew, she would miss them. Ellie, especially, had become like part of her family. Little Dolly—although Bina was not that old—was almost like a daughter. And good, steady Nancy was as reliable a friend as one could ask for.

With Clive gone, Bina joined the girls at the meal, eating well in spite of her concern. After the lean times on the station, when she had eaten 'roo meat until her stomach swelled, it seemed that she could not get enough of good food. As a result, she had developed a more womanly figure, plush, like the French cabaret star, Anna Held, whose pictures were displayed in the new girl's room. Bina's waist was not as spectacularly slim as Anna Held's, nor were her hips so wide and inviting, but the effect was the same: a beautiful hourglass figure, a real woman. Of course, if she continued to eat as she had been eating since arriving in Cloncurry, she'd soon be entirely too much woman. She would, she decided, start on a diet. Tomorrow. That much admitted, Bina realized that she had already yielded to the fact that she would be in Cloncurry with the morrow, and that meant she would be entertaining Clive Taylor that night.

There was still time to change her mind. She did not have to stay. By putting herself on the wrong side of the law, operating an illegal business, she had made herself vulnerable to blackmail by men such as Clive Taylor. But that still did not mean that she had to give in.

In her room she opened drawers, started to take out under-clothing, and got down a carpetbag in which to pack. Then she sat on the bed and was very, very angry. She had been forced off the station. She had had no choice: it was either sell to Van Buren or stay there and starve. Was she going to allow a man to force her off another station, out of the house she had bought, remodelled, and made into a home for herself and her girls?

"No, you blackguard," she hissed aloud. "You'll not make me run again."

He came just before midnight. She had long since had her bath and wearing a modest blue peignoir. She remained in her chair as he entered. He looked at her and smiled. He smelled of lilac water and soap. He, too, had bathed.

"Has milady's bath been run?" he asked.

"I've had my bath," she said, standing.

"I want to—"

"I will bow to your wishes to a certain extent," she said. "I will not engage in heathen orgies."

"Lord," he said, "I didn't think you'd be so straitlaced, seeing the business you're in."

She walked to the bed and with a shrug denuded herself. She had to resist the impulse to cover intimate points with her hands as she lay on the bed and looked at him coldly. "I do want to get *some* sleep tonight," she said.

As he toyed with her, she lay limply, eyes closed. When he took her, she felt only hatred until, from some store of remembered passion deep inside her—that aspect of her marriage to Lester Caldwell had been quite successful—she felt things happening and, in spite of herself, began to answer his need so that in the end they were together.

She lay in his arms. He was breathing hard and grinning at her. Her eyes were wide, almost frightened, for her pleasure had been both violent and vocal.

"Good Lord, Bina," he whispered, "what are your girls going to think?"

"You bloody bastard," she said, but she was smiling smugly. She giggled. "They'll think you were abusing me, that's all. I expect any moment for one of them to burst in here with a very large knife in her hand."

"I think I'll have something similar again soon," he said, grinning as he kissed her lightly.

She was silent. Resentment was coming back. True, her body had responded, and it was true that the thought of "something similar" was no longer repugnant. But, dammit, the choice should have been hers.

CHAPTER XIII

Johnny Broome, who had become the patriarch of the Broome family of Sydney upon the death of his brother, Red, was an old hand at judging the progress and the effects of those "affairs of the empire" that periodically saw the blood of young British and colonial men fertilizing the soils of far and odd places. As editor-owner of one of the most influential newspapers in Australia he voiced his opinions freely in the editorial columns. When conflict had first threatened to break out in South Africa he had written, "This is a war that does not need to happen. We are not facing fanatic natives, as the army of Herbert Kitchener faced in the Sudan. The Boers are solid, God-fearing men who, this editor suspects, would listen to reason were it phrased without the jingoistic utterances that are currently coming from Windsor Castle and 10 Downing Street."

While Johnny Broome wrote against war, the other Broome who worked at the newspaper didn't exactly pray for conflict, but all his sympathies were with Great Britain. There was no doubt in his mind that the stubbornness of Paul Kruger and the Boers and the dictatorial stand taken by Kruger against giving Englishmen the vote in the Transvaal were the roots of the dispute. Kelvin Broome saw no possibility of avoiding war unless the hardheaded Boers could be brought to reason, which was quite unlikely.

Kelvin Broome was a product of the bush. He called his boss Uncle Johnny, although, in fact, he was a cousin of the older man. The Broome family had been established in Australia by Kelvin's great-grandparents, Jenny Taggart and the first Johnny Broome, and it was now quite widespread.

In his late thirties, Kelvin had a look of rugged confidence, a sun-lined face, strong nose, and finely textured hair that was thinning just a bit at the crown. If he had been the kind to tolerate a nickname, he would probably have been called Sandy, but there was a seriousness about him that precluded such familiarity.

During the decade of the 1890s, beginning when Kelvin was a cub reporter learning his trade the hard way, without favouritism from his "uncle", he had proved his worth as a journalist, particularly as an investigator, by covering the labour strife that quite often produced violence in the streets of Australia's major cities.

Kelvin was, of course, a regular at the Gordon table, where, about one evening each week, what Johnny called the "Broome Debating Society" solved all of Australia's problems, and often tackled the larger problems of the world as a whole. In the wake of ultimatums flying between the Boer Republics and the British, Kelvin was trying to get his boss to send him to South Africa. He was planning to have another go at him at a dinner attended by a few old family friends, among them Joseph Van Buren from Queensland, who had stayed on in Sydney after seeing his son off to South Africa. Also present was the always-welcome Jon Mason, in Sydney on one of his frequent business trips.

Java, dressed in a new gown purchased especially for the occasion, was full of herself, because tonight's dinner party was her affair. She had bagged the guest of honour, none other than the famous Henry Lawson himself. She had so wanted to have Mr. Lawson read aloud some of his poems, or perhaps one of his short stories, but both her mother and Magdalen said that it would be rude to ask Mr. Lawson to sing for his supper. Still, he was there, and Java had placed herself immediately on his right, and everyone was thoroughly impressed.

For some time the conversation was about federation. New referendums had been held. In New South Wales 107,420 voters had said yes to federation, 82,741 no. In Victoria, South Australia, and Tasmania the federalists had scored clear victories. The Queensland results had been close, with the yeas running only a few thousand ahead.

"You have to remember," Joseph Van Buren said, "that less than fifty percent of qualified voters even bothered to voice an opinion. If you ask me, the country is against federation."

"Isn't it odd, Joseph," Johnny Broome teased, "that you find yourself in agreement with the radicals, who see unification as a conspiracy against the labouring man?"

Joseph snorted. "The idea of federation just has not caught on with the people as a whole," he said. "A few idealists are pushing it, and what I'm afraid of is that the bleeding-heart brigade will win. And if they do, and socialism gets a foothold, it isn't just landowners like my family who will have to be concerned. First thing you know, Sam, they'll be dividing this nice house of yours up into little rooms and installing poor families in them."

Henry Lawson spoke, smiling easily. "Perhaps some land reform will be inevitable, Mr. Van Buren," he said. "When five families control an entire colony, as they do in Western Australia, things are unbalanced. But I don't think we need concern ourselves with the threat of socialism as much as we have to watch for the liberal tendency to forget a problem that plagues Australia and will cripple her in the future unless we start to work on it now. Since federation seems to be inevitable, let's make sure we address the problem by writing policies into the constitution to exclude totally the cheap nigger, the cheap European pauper, and the cheap Chinaman."

Java's face flushed, and she glanced quickly at Jon Mason. He was sipping his tea, his eyes on Lawson. His expression didn't change. Java wondered how he felt when he heard such statements of racial bigotry, how he could let them slide.

"Because, after all," Lawson went on, "two Wongs don't make a white."

Joseph Van Buren roared in laughter. Others laughed less enthusiastically.

"Henry," Johnny Broome said, "I understand you've changed your stance about sending men to South Africa."

Lawson shook his head. "I'll admit that I've let myself be caught up in the madness," he said. "I still don't think it's dinkum to send our boys out to Africa to shoot at strangers, to give some fat Brit general a title and to put more profit into the pockets of Mr. Money Bags the munitions maker. England is not fighting for survival, nor even for England. She's fighting for the gold and diamond syndicates, and Australians are going not to fight for freedom but to have a little knock-round, a spree. And going to war just for the hell of it, to have a bit of fun, isn't a good reason, if you ask me."

"But you wrote a poem," Johnny said, spreading his hands in question.

"Yep," Lawson said. "Part of it goes like this:

> But since our boys are going, though the
>   cause seems cronk to me,
> I'll say it's in accordance with the things
>   that have to be,
> And trust they'll manage with the best
>   the work they're set to do,
> For the honour of old New South Wales from a
>   worldly point of view!"

"Hear, hear," Joseph Van Buren said.

Kelvin Broome chose that time to remind his boss once more that the newspaper was still not represented in South Africa. "Uncle Johnny," he said, "with things hotting up over there, it doesn't seem right to have me here in Sydney."

"You could buy Banjo Patterson's stuff and print it," Lawson suggested.

"No," Johnny replied, "I think the newspaper will need a man of its own there. Perhaps, Kelvin, you'd better go. Make your preparations and take the first fast boat you can find."

"Oh, splendid," Java said. "I'm so glad, Kelvin. You will write to me, won't you, and give me the real information, things that you can't print in a family newspaper?"

"If it can't be printed in a family newspaper," Jessica Gordon remonstrated, "you'd have no business reading it in a letter from Kelvin, young lady."

"Oh, Mother," Java said.

"So you're going off to Sambo land," Lawson said to Kelvin. "I think you'll have to worry more about the nigger than about the Boers. Sleep easy with niggers around, or some big greasy buck nigger might crawl in without knowing through a slit in your tent and rip out your innards with a nasty knife without so much as an explanation.''

Jon Mason rose, looked at Lawson, his face calm and composed. "Sam, Jessica," he said, "you know that I number you among my dearest friends, and the hospitality of your house is precious to me. However, I find that I don't wish to remain in Mr. Lawson's company any longer. So if you'll excuse me, I will take my leave.''

He was going out of the arched doorway before the shocked silence was broken by Henry Lawson. "Well, dog me," he said. "If you had warned me, Mr. Gordon, that we had a nigger lover present, I would have been a bit less factual in my comments.''

"Excuse me," Java said. She ignored the look of disapproval from her mother and ran out of the room. She caught up with Jon Mason on the front stoop. "Mr. Mason," she said, "will you—can you—please forgive us?''

He smiled and took her hand. "My darling girl, there is nothing to forgive, either you or your parents.''

"I'm so sorry," she said. "He's such a nice man, mostly.''

"And he writes well," Jon said. "Look, Java, we all know that there's bigotry in Australia, and perhaps it will get worse before it gets better. That doesn't mean that we have to condone it or listen to it. But it's my place to apologize, for my voicing my opinion as I did of Mr. Lawson's views, I embarrassed you and your parents and put a damper on the spirit of the occasion.''

"You did no such thing," she said. "I'll bet everyone except maybe Mr. Van Buren was glad that you did what you did.''

"Nevertheless, I shall call in the morning and apologize properly.'' He bade her good night and walked down the street.

Java sat in her grandmother's rocking chair on the porch for a long time after Jon had left. It was such a complicated world, and the thing that complicated it was people and their opinions. One of her uncle Johnny's little sayings came to her and she smiled to herself.

"Opinions," Johnny had said, "are like belly buttons. Everyone has one.''

The slightly risqué adage expressed her feelings well. It was just too bad that some people's "belly buttons" were more prominently displayed than others. Henry Lawson's views on race got wide distribution simply because of his writings and were, as a result, magnified beyond their true worth. But there was little that a young girl could do about it.

CHAPTER XIV

When you've shouted "Rule Britannia", when
    you've sung "God Save The Queen",
When you've finished killing Kruger
    with your mouth,
Will you kindly drop a shilling in my
    little tambourine
For a gentleman in khaki ordered South?

Kipling wasted no time in praising the men who went south—
"Fifty thousand horse and foot going to Table Bay!"—and the
men who were celebrated by the unofficial poet-laureate of the
British Empire entered the war with Kipling's spirit of patriotism,
fearing only that the Boers would be beaten before their units
could get into action.

To begin a new century with high adventure was a lure that
would attract many men of note, and the war would create fame
for others. A forty-two-year-old lieutenant colonel of Dragoons,
Robert Stephenson Smyth Baden-Powell, had been ordered to
raise two regiments in Bechuanaland and Rhodesia. With these
militiamen he was to harass the enemy rear along the western
borders of the Transvaal and the Free State.

Baden-Powell was a man of character. When he was about to
leave his public school, his headmaster had begged him to stay on
because of his "healty moral influence". But Baden-Powell moved
onwards to university. Understandably, the lad who was such a
favourite with adults had been called "Old Bathing Towel" by his
classmates at Charterhouse. During the Boer war he was to leave
that condescending nickname behind forever and would become
known to the world as "B.P", hero of the siege of Mafeking.

B.P. had prepared himself for his moment with service in India and in the Matabeleland of Rhodesia, where he had learned not only to be a superb rider but also a successful leader and military teacher. He had a passion for scouting, and he loved nothing better than trekking through enemy lands and outdoing Sherlock Holmes in interpreting vague tracks and signs. When the war in South Africa began, B.P. was working on the proofs of his soon-to-be-published *Aids to Scouting*, a work that would convince the British public that this one man was God's gift to the British, their answer to the Boers' almost supernatural ability in field craft. To prove his mastery of the art of scouting, to show that he could fit into a war that was to be the first truly mobile war, with Boer commandos roving the vast African plains, Baden-Powell chose a dusty little Bechuanaland town called Mafeking, eight miles from the Transvaal border. It was a tiny place of about a thousand souls, where the only two-storey building was the Catholic convent near the hospital and most of the other buildings were corrugated iron-roofed huts. Here Baden-Powell went to ground—and did not move.

Dirk De Hartog's Natal commando unit had been sent west and was now under the overall command of General Piet Cronje, with his immediate superior being General Koos De La Rey.

Dirk knew De La Rey and respected him highly. The general was over fifty, a dark man with shaggy eyebrows, an aquiline nose, a lined face, and a great, bushy beard that was turning grey. He greeted Dirk's arrival with a smile that was almost hidden by his beard, returned Dirk's salute, and then gave him a hearty clap on the back.

"At last I have a troop commander who can *move*," the general said. "Now we will take this war to the enemy in his own land, eh?" As an afterthought he inquired, "How's your family?"

"They're well, General," Dirk replied.

"Good. Now then, to business. You will be my eyes, Colonel. There is word of British irregulars moving from Rhodesia. Your first task will be to locate them and then to repeat your feat in Natal by blocking reinforcements or supplies from the south. But first, give your men a rest. You've ridden hard to get here, and you can move out in the morning."

"If it's all right with you, General, we'll get under way right now," Dirk said. "My men can rest in the saddle."

It was not hard to locate the Rhodesian-Bechuanaland ir-regulars. Baden-Powell had built a complicated system of trenches, redoubts, and forts, al linked by telephone. He had laid minefields around Mafeking. The town was in that transition zone between grassland and desert. Two things made it important. First, it was the largest station on the railway between Kimberley and Bulawayo. Second, there were huge stocks of provisions in the town's stores. The food and supplies were of importance to Koos De La Rey, whose men lived off the land, borrowing and expropriating as need be to remain mobile.

Baden-Powell had made his defence line eight miles long to include the native *stad*, or town, with its seven thousand blacks. He had drawn cattle guards and watchmen from the native force. He had mounted half a dozen seven-pound muzzle-loading cannon and seven Maxims, and he was expecting more artillery on an armoured train coming up from the Cape Colony.

Dirk De Hartog scouted the town and reported back to De La Rey. De La Rey listened with interest, and then gave Dirk new orders. Since there were ten thousand men available to take Mafeking, Dirk was to move his own men south, to straddle the railway and wait for whatever came.

Dirk kept his men busy tearing up the railway line. Soon they heard it coming up from the south, announcing itself by a plume of smoke and the sound of steam. This train would not be so easy to stop as the one in Natal, for it was better armoured, and it carried more British troops, seasoned men who had come prepared to fight at a moment's notice.

The train could not move forward, for the Boers had torn up the line; it was trapped as Dirk's men blew up the line behind it. The British quickly organized their units and put up a brisk fight before they surrendered. In the painful aftermath, there was work for the surgeons on both sides, and Dirk shook his head over the casualties he had suffered.

Dirk ordered his remaining men to tear up more of the track, then led his force to rejoin De La Rey. He found the bearded, glowering general standing on a rise, looking down at Mafeking.

"General," Dirk said, "I expected to find you and your men in the marketplace down there when I got back."

De La Rey snorted. "I would have given orders to attack the town days ago, but, well . . ." He fell silent. Even in that army—an army of willing volunteers where discipline was more a matter of cooperation than obligation—one did not openly criticize one's superiors.

Dirk, however, understood. He knew the commanding officer, Cronje, to be a cautious man. While it was true that Piet Cronje had beaten a superior British force in the war of 1881, and had ended an abortive raid on Johannesburg by Uitlander forces in 1896, there were those who suspected that he was past his prime, too old, and, as a consequence, too timid.

"Yes," De La Rey said, "the commander has congratulated me for shutting up the meercat in his hole."

"But how many men will it take to keep him there?" Dirk asked.

De La Rey sighed. "Too many, I'm afraid." He shrugged. "In any event, my friend, I will be moving south, and I have asked Cronje to attach your commando unit to my command."

"Thank you, sir," Dirk replied. He had no desire to take part in a siege. *Siege!* "General, by the love of God, don't they know that our best chance to beat the British is to push to the sea quickly, to seize the ports and block the influx of British reinforcements, so that we'll have to fight only those troops that are in South Africa now?"

De La Rey growled but did not answer. He would have preferred to be in Natal, moving as fast as his horses could carry him towards Durban or, barring that, to have the authority to dash through the Cape Colony, gathering Boer fighters as he went, to close the port at Cape Town.

De La Rey, with Dirk's commando unit scouting ahead, marched south. Behind them Cronje arrayed his army around the dusty little rail town and called on Baden-Powell to surrender. When B.P. politely declined his invitation, the Boers formed their laagers around the town and began a halfhearted bombardment with their good German cannon.

The first message sent out to England by the besieged Baden-Powell made him a famous man and roused the nation and the empire into spasms of glee and dewy-eyed admiration for British pluck and wit.

"All well," Baden-Powell sent. "Four hours' bombardment. One dog killed."

Travelling by fast steamer, Kelvin Broome arrived in Cape Town in time to read the headlines that reported B.P.'s next communiqué. The Boers had brought up against Mafeking one of their huge Creusot cannon called "Long Toms". Cronje had, in a gentlemanly way, informed B.P. that he was quite reluctant to use such a weapon of terror against the town. When the gun was eventually fired, with much noise and the death of one chicken, B.P. reported to the world: "One or two small field guns shelling the town. Nobody cares."

Kelvin decided that he had to meet this laconic, brave man himself, that he would portray the heroic stand at Mafeking for the readers back in Australia. He began to inquire about how to get to Mafeking and discovered that in spite of B.P.'s blithe messages and overall British confidence, the war was going rather badly for the empire. Koos De La Rey was speeding south, taking town after town. The towns along the borders all the way to the Orange River were surrendering without so much as a shot being fired, for most of the inhabitants were Boers by blood.

There was simply no way of getting to Mafeking. There was not even a way to get into the important town of Kimberley, where Cecil Rhodes himself was besieged. Kimberley, only a few miles from the high wire fence at the Free State border, was one of the richest prizes of all, with its great metal workshops. But it was of course the diamonds underground that had made it famous.

Kelvin found it rather surprising that the early stage of the war featured deliberate sieges and not more vigorous battle and movement. Since he could not go to Mafeking, he sought out the location of several Australian units and made his way north with reinforcements to join with the Queensland Mounted Infantry. He was billeted with a company commanded by a Lieutenant Matt Van Buren, who looked vaguely familiar. After a bit of talk, in which the two Australians discussed their respective voyages across the Indian Ocean—Kelvins's swift and relatively comfortable journey had brought him to Cape Town faster than Matt's rough and unpleasant crossing aboard the troopship—the two men asked each other about acquaintances they might have in common back home. Finally, Kelvin exclaimed, "Now I have it! I met your father at Sam Gordon's house, and you look very much like him." It was almost as if they had known each other for years. Kelvin decided that since he liked this young man, who seemed to understand the Boer mentality and way of fighting, he would throw in his fortunes with the Queenslanders and see what happened.

CHAPTER XV

Slone Shannon found shipboard life to be luxurious in comparison with the past year in the Sudan. The tea was hot and strong, the food tolerable, and the bed linen clean. He changed ships at Gibraltar. Some of the men who had fought in the Sudan were homeward bound. Others, including Slone, boarded a shining new troop carrier and sailed south along the African coastal routes first covered by the intrepid Portuguese explorers, and then ever farther south to the bay that lay under the distinctive flat-topped outline of Table Mountain.

Slone's thoughts were not totally of the war and what orders he would be handed when he reported to army headquarters in Cape Town. He had travelled unattached to any unit, his individual orders in his pocket, and thus, once he arrived in the South African port, he was able to assign his own priorities to his activities. After a bit of difficulty in finding a room in a second-rate hotel, he made his way to army headquarters, but not to report in. He inquired of a grizzled sergeant major behind the desk about Colonel Roland Streeter. Streeter was indeed attached to headquarters. Slone breathed a sigh of relief and thanked his lucky stars that the colonel was apparently one of those officers who simply did not do field duty. The sergeant even volunteered the colonel's home address.

The Streeter residence was a low, comfortable bungalow in a setting that gave a view of both the bay and the mountain. A spacious garden sported glaringly brilliant flowers, and among them knelt Kit Streeter, her sunset hair hidden by a bonnet, her hands plunged into the rich soil. Slone, seeing her from the front fence, started to speak, but then he saw that she was engrossed in her work. Opening the picket gate quietly, he walked towards her along the cobblestone path.

She heard the sound of his footsteps and tilted her head, her green eyes squinting against the tall figure in khaki approaching her. She lifted one hand to further shade her eyes. He paused three paces away, his throat constricted by her beauty.

"Slone," she whispered.

As she leapt to her feet, she scattered the bulbs she had been planting and dropped her trowel.

"Slone," she repeated, and he met her with open arms.

She smelled of roses and fresh air. At first her face was pressed against the fabric of his tunic as he clung to her fiercely, still unable to speak, and then she leaned back against his strong arms, trusting the strength of them as she drew her face back to look into his eyes. Tears were running down Slone's cheeks. Her own eyes were full to overflowing. She reached out and brushed away a tear and said, ever so softly, her voice full of her concern, her love, "Oh."

He laughed, feeling giddy. Her low-pitched laugh joined his, and then both were silenced as his lips sought and found hers.

"I knew you'd come," she said.

She took his hand and led him to a shaded veranda. A flowering vine made for privacy, and the scent of the bloom was heavy and sensuous. Both were breathless when they separated once more.

"Did you get my letters?" she asked.

"No." Slone thought it better to let her believe that his passions for her, and not her information about her father's new assignment in South Africa, had led him to find her in Cape Town.

"Oh, blast," she said. "And still you came to find me?"

"I had to know why."

"You should have known."

"I guessed that your parents had something to do with it," he said.

"My letters—"

"I've been in the Sudan, moving around a lot, and then en route. They'll probably catch up with me after I've been here in South Africa for six months."

"Oh, what you must have thought," she said.

"I knew that I loved you, that was all that mattered."

"Oh, Slone, I do love you."

"And now there's another war," he said. "I suppose your father will use this one as an excuse, as well."

"We won't let him," she said. "We simply will not let him keep us apart."

"Goodonyer," Slone said, and when she looked at him questioningly he said, "An Australianism. High praise. Good on you."

Her lips were a bit puffy. He leaned, placed his fingertip there. "Forgive me. I've bruised your lips."

"A sweet pain," she whispered. "If you kiss it lightly, perhaps it will go away."

He was administering first aid when Evelyn Streeter's voice caused Kit to jump guiltily.

"Well, really, Katherine," Mrs. Streeter said as she approached along the veranda.

"Good afternoon, Mrs. Streeter," Slone replied, bowing.

"You?" Evelyn said. "Good Lord."

Slone was holding Kit's right hand; feeling a ring, he looked down and saw his gift there on the third finger. She had promised that regardless of what people thought she would wear the ring on her left hand; its presence on the right proved that she still did not consider herself formally engaged.

"You have a habit, young man, of imposing yourself upon this family when you're not wanted," Evelyn Streeter said. "Please go."

"No!" Kit said strongly, stepping forward. "Slone is my guest, mother. More than that. You have no right."

The older woman drew herself up. "Very well," she said. "The colonel will be home shortly. We'll see what he has to say about this shameless exhibition, Katherine."

"I'm still quite unpopular here," Slone said, when Kit's mother had stalked away.

"Not with me," she said. But she was looking grim, her forehead furrowed. "Slone, I think I'd best face Father alone the first time."

"Are you sure?" he asked.

"Yes. Oh, God, I hate to ask you to go."

"I'll be back."

"Are you posted here in Cape Town?"

"I haven't reported in yet," he said. "I'll postpone it for a day or so."

"Tonight. Come tonight, after eight. That will give me time to talk with my father."

He kissed her just once more, then she walked with him to the fence, opened the gate, and squeezed his hand in farewell. As he retreated down the street he turned back. She still was standing there, and she remained there until he turned a corner and was out of sight.

Left alone, Kit stood in thought for a long time. She had difficulty understand her mother's rudeness. Evelyn Streeter had always been such a lady, loving and considerate. The change in her had started, Kit felt, in Cairo. Almost unnoticeably she had begun to develop a certain waspish sharpness. Her temper was easily frayed now, and she spent a great deal of time in bed. Various doctors had been consulted. Currently, an army surgeon, an old friend of Kit's father, called on Evelyn with regularity, and on the table beside Evelyn's bed there were assorted medicines.

Leaving the front garden, Kit went into the house and found her mother lying across her bed, her eyes closed. "Are you feeling bad, mother?"

"How do you expect me to feel, discovering my daughter carrying on shamelessly with a common soldier?"

Kit's face flushed. "First, he's not a common soldier. He's an officer. Secondly, I don't consider a kiss to be shameless carrying on."

"You have distressed me terribly," Evelyn said. "Please leave me to bear this alone."

This infamous technique, too, was relatively new with Evelyn, a stratagem so often used by mothers to make their children feel guilt. It worked with Kit. She sat on the side of the bed, took her mother's hand and massaged it, asking if she could get her anything, anything at all.

Roland Streeter was usually home in time for high tea. Today was no exception. Kit had everything laid out, a steaming pot, fresh biscuits on plates. Her father brushed her cheek in passing, said he would be out as soon as he had changed, and inquired about her mother as he entered the bedroom to see Evelyn lying on the bed. Kit had walked to the door after him, and her heart swelled as she saw her father, tall, straight, distinguished, seem to melt as he moved swiftly to kneel on the floor and touch his wife's face.

"Evelyn," Streeter said softly. "My dear?"

Evelyn raised her head. "Oh, my poor, poor darling," she said, reaching out to cup Streeter's face with her hands.

"Mother, couldn't we save that discussion until after tea?" Kit asked.

"You'd like that, wouldn't you?" Evelyn asked, pulling herself up to sit on the edge of the bed. "This is what she has done now, Roland."

So it began. Kit stood, her face pale, as her mother described a scene of pure abandonment on the veranda. Too stunned at first to protest, she waited until her mother had finished, and then, in command of herself, she said, "May we please go in to tea now?"

To her surprise her father was calm, his face sad, but placid. "Yes," he said. "Come, Evelyn."

"Now that you know," Evelyn said, smiling sweetly, "I would like a bit of tea, thank you."

No further mention of Slone was made during tea. When Evelyn had finished, she rose and said, "If you'll excuse me. I'm rather tired."

When she was gone, Streeter turned to Kit. "So your young man has been assigned to South Africa," he said.

"He arrived today."

"Wasted little time in finding you."

"We are in love, Father," she said simply.

"Yes, well," he said, looking a bit uncomfortable.

"It wasn't as mother described it."

"I know," he said, not unkindly. "What is his assignment, Kit?"

"He hasn't reported in yet."

"And I take it your intentions have not changed since Cairo?"

"That's right, Father. I want to marry him." She sat down next to him and took his hand. "You do understand, don't you?"

"I had hoped that you would choose a more suitable husband."

"How can you judge whether or not he's suitable?" she objected. "You hardly know him."

"He'll take you away from me—from us. He'll take you to Australia, won't he?"

"We've talked about living on a cattle ranch—they call them

cattle stations—in Queensland. We've come to no absolute conclusions." She took a deep breath and said, "I'd like to announce our engagement. I'm sure that if Slone is ordered into the fighting, he will not want to get married until the war is over."

"It would upset your mother greatly."

"I don't understand Mother lately," she said. "I thought she'd be happy for me, knowing that I'd found the man I love."

"Your mother has changed in many ways," Streeter said. He looked up towards the ceiling for a long time, and his face made Kit keep her silence. "We wanted to spare you, Kit, as long as possible," he said. "At first we said nothing because the doctors couldn't be sure. It began in Cairo. I think you noticed."

She looked at him, fear growing in her. "If you mean did I notice a change in Mother, yes."

"They say that it's a *thing*, a growth, near her brain."

"Oh, God," Kit whispered.

"It grows slowly, so slowly. And it's gradually changing her, making her a different person."

"What do you they say—how long—"

He shrugged. "Months, years. They don't know. She will be blind, they think. Have you noticed that she seems to be having difficulty with her sight?"

"Now that you mention it, yes."

"So now you know, Katherine. What you do now will be up to you. I've thought long and hard about my attitude towards young Shannon since we've come south. Perhaps I was wrong. If I had not objected so strongly to him in Cairo, if you'd gone ahead and announced your engagement, perhaps she wouldn't be so strongly against it. But that's past. Now it's up to you. I won't stand in your way any longer."

Her first reaction was one of total bitterness. He would not stand in her way any longer, but he'd just thrown an obstacle across the path of her love that was impassable. She would have no choice but to make Slone wait. She could not desert her mother under such circumstances. She remembered how he'd said, "He'll take you to Australia, away from me." Only after using the singular pronoun had he changed it to "us". Had that been unintentional, or had he been trying to tell her he knew that soon enough he would be alone in that world except for his daughter?

"I will stay with her, of course," she said.

Streeter kissed her on the cheek. "I had no doubt of it. You're made of good stuff, Kit."

"Excellent stuff," she said, being sardonic in order to keep back the tears.

"There is one thing," he said. "Neither your mother nor I want to be the object of pity and curiosity. Do you understand?"

"I do," she said. "I'll tell no one but Slone."

He went stiff. "Above all," he said, "I wish to avoid looking the pitiable figure in front of junior officers. I ask you to keep this a family confidence."

"But—"

"Is that too much to ask, really?" He rose, looked down at her. "Your mother is losing her sight, losing her very personality, losing everything that makes her who she is. Can you not set aside your own affairs for a matter of a few months?"

She had begun to weep silently. She nodded.

"I'm sorry," he said.

"I will do as you ask," she whispered.

When Slone came to the front door of the cottage just after eight o'clock, she was dressed in blue, her hair piled in autumn glory, her slim, regal neck cupped at its base by lace.

"Good Lord, you're beautiful," Slone said. He forced his eyes past her and, seeing that the parlour was empty, breathed a sigh of relief. She gave him her lips for a quick kiss, then pulled out of his arms and led the way into the room, sitting opposite him, hands cupped in her lap.

"The colonel?" Slone asked.

"Slone—"

He waited, chilled by the tentative sound of her voice.

"Father and I had a long talk this afternoon," she said. "He has no objection to our marriage."

Slone's face melted into a big smile, and he started to rise, but she stopped him by raising one hand. There was a look on her face that made him dread her next words.

"He asks only that we wait until the war is over."

He sank back. That could be a long while. He had been speaking with fellow officers, and had learned from them that the war was going badly. The first pitched engagements had been fought in Natal. At Talana Hill, just outside the Natal town of Dundee, a British counter-attack up steep hills out of a position that was described by one officer as a "chamber pot" had produced a "victory" of sorts. The Boers had withdrawn, but British losses were around five hundred, while the Boers suffered only one hundred fifty casualties. The Talana Hill engagement seemed to set the tone of the early going in the war; and after a larger battle at Lombard's Kop, one thousand British prisoners were marched through the Boer capital at Pretoria. Meanwhile, the twenty-four thousand men of the combined Transvaal and Orange Free State armies had linked up near the important rail junction at Ladysmith, south of Dundee, and only heroic efforts by the greatly outnumbered British defenders had prevented the fall of the town. Now the Boers were laying siege to the city, just as they were at Mafeking and Kimberley.

To ask Slone to wait until yet another war was over was, he felt, too much. He opened his mouth to say so, to tell her that this conflict had the makings of a long war, to beg her to give him her promise not only with her kisses but with a formal announcement of their engagement.

"Slone," she said, "do this for me, please."

He heard something in her voice, desperation, fear, something that he could not identify. It touched him.

"No engagement announcement?" he asked.

"Please?" There were tears in her eyes.

He rose confidently to his feet, lifted her from her chair, and enfolded her. "It will be as you say."

She gave him her lips, and for one wild moment pressed the softness of her belly against the hard return of his embrace. Then she pushed him away.

"We can be together until I have my orders," he said.

She shook her head. The tears were dampening her cheeks. "Please, no," she said. "Write to me when you've received your assignment. I will write to you every day."

"I don't understand," he grumbled. "Do they hate me so much?"

"Slone," she said, "please come back to me?"

"Of course," he replied. "But will it do any good? If they hate me so much—"

"Just come back."

Watching him leave was the hardest thing Kit Streeter had ever done. She had a feeling of loss so deep that nothing seemed worthwhile. She lifted a curtain at the window and saw him disappear into the darkness, becoming just a shadow, and then suddenly he was visible again as he walked under a gaslight. Her heart twisted in such pain that she cried out and moved to throw open the door to go after him. She halted on the porch, literally feeling the presence of her father and mother inside the house, drawing her back.

"Come back to me, Slone," she whispered. "Come back, and regardless of what else is happening, I will not ask you to wait again."

Slone reported formally the next morning and was greeted with interest by an engineer colonel. "You've come just in time, Lieutenant," the colonel said. "We have just the spot for you, lucky devil. Report as quickly as you can."

He was assigned to an engineer unit already loaded on a small ship in the harbour. Before the sun set he was looking back at Table Mountain from the sea, headed for Durban. From that Natal port the unit would advance by rail towards Ladysmith, repairing track torn up by the Boers on the way. They would have the help of civilian contractors with whom they would make contact in Pietermaritzburg. The voyage around the eastern flank of South Africa was a quick and easy one, and they spent mere hours in Durban before boarding a work train.

Slone, his mind hundreds of miles away in a garden in Cape Town with a sunset-haired girl, was looking idly out of the window as the train pulled into the Pietermaritzburg station. He saw a familiar figure, short, strong, topped by a tall hat. He wasn't sure, though, until he had left the train and approached the commanding officer of the engineer unit who was talking with the man in the hat. As he neared them, the two finished their conversation and Enoch Hook turned to look directly at Slone.

"Well I'll be damned!" Hook laughed. "How the hell are you, General?"

The American civilian engineers were directing repair efforts being made by Tommies and native labour in the vicinity of Frere, south of besieged Ladysmith. Slone rode in the locomotive cab with Hook and the engine crew as the armoured work train cautiously inched its way northward.

"Not too many miles ahead," Hook said, "I think there are some people we don't want to see, like maybe a few thousand Boer sharpshooters."

The railway bed had been stripped for a full mile, the iron rails twisted and bent. As the crew began work, unloading new rails from the work train, Slone heard a young Tommy say, " 'urry up, lads, and put it back together so that the Boers can rip 'er up again."

Enoch Hook, standing next to Slone, was looking around at the rocky, dry ridges on either side of the track. "They could be watching us right now," he said. "There's nothing they like better than blowing up a train."

A company of thirty foot soldiers had set up a series of watching posts around the stationary work train. Two Maxim guns were mounted on an armoured car of the train.

"Our boys would have something to say about them blowing up this train," Slone said.

"Thirty rifles and two Maxims," Topper said. "Not bad. But the average Boer commando has three hundred men, and you never know what weapons they might have. Mausers could finish us off in short order."

CHAPTER XVI

At the Frere headquarters of the engineering unit whose job it was to keep the line open to Durban, Slone Shannon studied the faces of the odd gentlemen pictured on two of the five playing cards he held and looked across the poker table into the eyes of Topper Hook. Hook smiled broadly.

"Name your poison, General," Hook said.

Slone put down three cards. Hook snapped three replacements off the deck. There was a third gentleman, making a total of three kings. The other two cards were low-ranking number cards.

"I believe I understand this infernal game well enough to risk five shillings," Slone said.

Three of the Americans at the table folded their hands. Hook mused and puffed on a cigar and then tossed five shillings onto the table, said, "And five more," and leaned back to regard Slone with his poker face which seemed to indicate total hostility.

"Perhaps I don't understand the game at all," Slone conceded.

"Don't knock it," Hook said. "It's good enough for Queen Victoria. Should be good enough for her officers in the field."

"Five more it is," Slone said.

Hook said, "Two aces—"

Slone, grinning broadly, put down his three kings and started to reach for the pot.

"—topped by three treys," Hook said, laying down his full house.

Slone leaned back and sighed. "Are many men killed while playing this game?"

"It's slightly more dangerous than being under siege by the Boers," Hook said, raking in the money.

"Well, since you have told me that it is the American national game, I think I shall leave it to you Americans," Slone said, rising.

"And I was told that the British Army never gave up," Hook grinned.

"This particular unit of Her Majesty's Army thinks that it is highly desirable to have some money left for food until we are paid next, and only God knows when that will be." He walked out of the frame building, looked up at the African night sky, saw the stars ablaze and remembered the look of the sky from the Sudan, remembered how Kit Streeter had looked when first he saw her. He was standing thus, head raised, when a runner found him. He brushed dust off his khakis and walked with long, quick strides to the headquarters shack near the tracks.

The officer in command at Frere was not an engineer. He was a cavalryman, a lieutenant-colonel of the type who still felt that the army was a social organism, not a fighting unit. His name was Reginald Whitestaff. He was a pale man who kept himself protected from the African sun by wearing a wide-brimmed, non-regulation hat and by wearing gloves.

"Ah, Shannon," Whitestaff said, when Slone had snapped to attention and saluted with a sharp click of his heels. "I think you know Mr. Winston Churchill."

Churchill was in khaki, but with only the insignia of a war correspondent. He was smoking a cigar. Another cigar lay in an ashtray on the colonel's desk. "We've come quite a distance from Omdurman, eh, Lieutenant?" he asked.

"Nice to see you again, sir," Slone said.

"I've been telling Mr. Churchill that he's come to the right place for action," Whitestaff said. "We'll be taking out a train for reconnaissance in the morning, Shannon. I want you to be in charge. Sort it out for me, will you? I'll leave the details to you."

"Sir," Slone snapped. It sounded so simple. "Sort it out for me, will you?" That meant that he would be up most of the night and that he'd be keeping other men awake as well.

"Six o'clock sharp," Whitestaff said, "I'll be accompanying Mr. Churchill, but no special preparations are necessary."

The poker game was still going on. Slone went to his bunk area and strapped on his sidearm, the symbol of being on duty.

"What's up, General?" Hooked asked.

"There's a news correspondent in camp," Slone said, "and the colonel has decided to put on a show for him. I have to have a train.

"I'll give you a hand," Hook said, "as my luck's turned bad."

The compactly built American knew about trains. He set his small crew of civilian advisers to work assembling the train and soon a locomotive was puffing up and down the tracks, switching back and forth to assemble the armoured cars in the proper order. Slone, meanwhile, was making the life of an infantry captain interesting with orders to have a hundred and fifty men aboard the train at 6 A.M.. He knew that many of the men would load into the cars upon receiving orders and sleep there.

Then there was the matter of guns. One was available, a seven-pounder muzzle-loading naval gun mounted on an armoured flatcar. Food. He had to check to be sure that the men had enough to eat, just in case the train ran into trouble and could not steam back to Frere in time for tea.

When all the little details had been taken care of, it was after four. Slone took his own kit to the train, found a place among snoring infantrymen, and managed to get almost two hours' sleep.

In the light of dawn he made an inspection tour. The troops were in place. Enoch Hook was in the cab of the locomotive with the engine crew.

"Topper, this is a military operation," Slone said, climbing up. The firebox was open, and the fireman was shovelling in coal. The heat hit Slone's face, not unpleasant in the chill of early morning.

"Now don't be stuffy, General," Hook said. "I've got men on board with the plate-layers. Wouldn't want to see you get cut off up the line somewhere without a skilled and charming fellow like me to repair the track and get you back."

Slone felt that it would be safe enough. The Boers were quite near, within thirty miles, but they had been sticking to their laagers around Ladysmith. It was obvious that the entire affair had been ordered by the colonel for the benefit of Mr. Winston Churchill. The colonel himself being aboard insured that they would not try to penetrate far. They'd probably go to Chievcley, not quite ten miles to the north, and turn back.

He saw Colonel Whitestaff and Churchill come walking towards the train, and he climbed down from the cab and hurried to meet them.

"Not quite as exciting as a cavalry charge," Churchill said. "But, by God, isn't it a magnificent morning?"

"We're ready when you are, Lieutenant," the colonel said.

"Very well, sir," Slone said. "There's a table for you and Mr. Churchill in the car directly in front of the engine."

He watched them board, ran back to the cab, checked over the train visually. Three armoured cars were in front of the engine, three behind, the last one carrying the seven-pounder. The cars were protected on the sides by six-foot-high boiler plates pierced with loopholes so that the soldiers inside could use their rifles. The locomotive itself was heavily armoured, steel plates limiting visibility from the cab.

"So Mr. Churchill's entertainment is under way," Hook said as the engine hissed and began to chug slowly, moving slowly, moving smoothly to gather speed. He looked at Slone, who was ignoring the comment. "I have heard that the *Morning Post* is paying him two hundred fifty pounds per month, plus expenses."

Now *that* got Slone's attention.

"That's because he's a hero," Hook said. "Personally led the 21st Lancers in their heroic charge that killed all two hundred thousand men in the Khalifa's army. How many did you kill, General, ten thousand? And you're only a lieutenant and I don't think you make two hundred fifty pounds a month plus expenses."

"Topper, you're outrageous," Slone said.

"But we owe this trip to the voters of Mr. Churchill's district," Hook said, "because he probably wouldn't be here if he hadn't been defeated in his attempt to get into the House of Commons."

Up ahead the Tommies in the front cars were alert. They knew full well that armoured trains had been taken before, and that the Boers were quite mobile when they wanted to be. The run to Chieveley was made without incident. The train puffed and hissed to a halt. Slone alighted and ran up to the command car. "Suggest, sir, that the infantry put out patrols," he said.

"It seems quiet to me, Lieutenant," Whitestaff said. "Let's just poke our nose a bit further, shall we? Say into Colenso?" He looked at Churchill as if seeking approval. Churchill smiled and nodded.

"We're going into Colenso," Slone announced when he was back in the cab.

"Wonderful," Hook said. "That's how far from the Boers?"

"We'll have the Tugela river between us and Ladysmith. There are British troops at the river, I would imagine."

"Son, in this war you can't count on anything," Hook said.

Between Chieveley and Colenso the track wound its way up and around a range of hills, and on the relatively steep switchbacks the engine laboured, puffing and chugging with a sound that could certainly be heard for miles over the African wilderness.

Unbeknown to Colonel Whitestaff, he had chosen a time when pressure from the Transvaal government had forced General Joubert to unleash Louis Botha, a vigorous younger commander who was impatient to move. Joubert had agreed to let Botha take four thousand mounted riflemen and five guns across the Tugela River to push towards Pietermaritzburg, which had been virtually undefended when the Boer army first started towards the coast. The overwhelming Boer force had marched south to the Tugela, and advance elements had already crossed the railway bridge lying dead ahead of the Churchill train.

It was one of those advance patrols in force that heard the engine struggle up and around the switchbacks. The Boers, concealed by rocks and bush, watched the train steam past. As soon as it was out of sight, they swarmed over the tracks, placing boulders at the bottom of a long descent. Then the Boers found shelter from the rain that had started to fall, lit their pipes confidently, and waited.

The engineer saw smoke rising from the chimneys of a town ahead. "Lieutenant," he said, pointing out through the narrow vision slit in the frontal armour.

"That's Colenso," Slone replied.

Ten minutes later they were at the outskirts of the town. Slone glanced around nervously and then turned to the engineer, who was already pulling back on the throttle. "Yes, good," Slone said. "We've gone far enough. Reverse as quickly as possible, please."

The engine came to a dead stop, then chuffed into backward motion, retreating from the settlement.

As the engine crested a rise, moving in reverse, Slone scanned a downgrade that lay just beyond. He saw only the incline, nothing suspicious. Nevertheless, he was glad he had passed a warning to the infantry to be alert. As if out of nowhere, the armoured sides of the locomotive began to clang and vibrate with the impact of high-velocity bullets from the Boers' Mauser rifles. A field gun opened fire, and the shell exploded past the train, showering the cars with splintered rock fragments.

"There aren't any Boers this side of the Tugela," Hook said. "Don't worry. It's only hail that's making the noise."

The train had topped the rise and was descending, the engineer using the incline to increase his speed, to gain momentum to climb the next hill. Slone was just about to tell him to slow down when, with a smashing impact, a shell hit the seven-pounder, which was on the car that was leading, since the train was now travelling in reverse. The heavy cannon toppled and fell onto the shoulder of the railway. It was still rolling when the locomotive passed it.

"Brakes," Hook yelped, the instant he saw the pile of boulders blocking the tracks.

The leading cars peeled off one by one as the momentum of the train pushed them into the rocks. They topped slowly and lay beside the track. The engine, puffing and hissing, was at a stop. A hail of fire came down from the hills on either side of the track.

"Where do you think you're going?" Slone asked as Hook started to open the door leading out of the cab.

"We've got to get those tracks open," Hook said.

"You can't go out there."

"I don't fancy spending the rest of what might be a long war in a Boer prison laager," Hook said. "You going to help?"

"Bloody hell," Slone said.

The Boer fire was intense, but thankfully the field gun was silent. Hook's plate-laying crew was in a car behind the engine. When he told them what he wanted, they looked at him unbelievingly. They could clearly hear the peppering of bullets on the armoured sides of the car.

Slone noted that Churchill was out of his car. The derailed cars had spilled out men who were now firing back at the muzzle flashes of the Boers from whatever cover they could find. He saw a man fall, saw blood well up and wet his hair. The remaining soldiers were pouring out of the still standing cars, scrambling for cover, organizing themselves into firing groups.

Enoch Hook and his men moved up the train and began to wrestle the boulders off the tracks. Shots ricocheted off the rocks even as they worked, but miraculously none of the crew was hit immediately. Churchill ran past Slone. "Not quite as exciting as the charge, eh?" he shouted.

"I'd settle for less," Slone called back. He went to work with Hook and his men at clearing the track. If, by some chance, they could clear the engine, speed for a getaway would be important. He went back and unhooked all but one car. The men, if they broke the engine free, would have to crowd into that car, and cling to the outside of the train if there was not enough room inside.

Colonel Reginald Whitestaff was dead. He lay in his own blood, shot neatly between the eyes as he directed the infantry into defensive positions. The captain of the infantry, now senior officer, was busy getting his men under better cover and in directing their fire. Churchill came running back towards the front of the train.

"We're trying to free the engine," Slone told him. "We'll need to have the wounded put aboard the car immediately behind the engine tender."

"Good work," Churchill said.

Within minutes Churchill had organized some men to help remove the boulders. Others were loading the seriously wounded into the car. The entire rout seemed to have taken an age, but Slone's watch said that it had been less than an hour since the train started down the incline and was first fired upon.

"We can push the rest aside with the cow-catcher," Hook said at last. "All of you plate-layers, get aboard."

Slone ran, crouching, Boer bullets singing around him, to find Churchill with men of the infantry, firing upwards at the flash of the Boer rifles. "We're ready," he said.

"Go, then," Churchill said.

"We can crowd most of the men into the car. The others can hang onto the sides."

"They'd be slaughtered," Churchill said. "Get out of here. Take care of the wounded. The other men and I will take our chances here."

There was no other choice but to leave Churchill and the other men behind. The Boer firing increased as Slone ran back towards the engine, but he managed to clamber aboard without getting shot. He told the engineer to go. The train huffed. A regular storm of fire came down on them as it began to move, and then the field gun was opening up again, but missing, and the engine, pulling only its tender and one car, picked up momentum quickly and was soon around a bend and sheltered from the withering Boer fire.

"What about our hero and the men?" Hook said.

"Not to worry," Slone said. "The Boers are humane, in spite of the stories you hear about them. They'll take all of them to Pretoria. Old Kruger is fond of seeing British prisoners being marched through the streets. Keeps up the morale on the home front."

"Well, General, you did all right," Hook said.

"I?" Slone laughed. "I let a war correspondent organize the defence, and I let a civilian, and an American at that, make the decision to clear the track and then do it."

"All the time, though, the general was there a-givin' his orders and inspiring his troops," Hook said. "No, I saw you going back and forth with the bullets dancing in the sand around you. I saw you with the wounded, getting them loaded. You done good, General."

"All we did was lose most of the train," Slone said, "and we left at least seventy-five men behind to be captured. Colonel White-staff is dead."

"I wonder if the *Morning Post* will pay Churchill his two hundred and fifty pounds a month while he's in prison. One thing for sure, he won't have any expenses as a prisoner of war."

"If you don't mind," Slone said, "I've heard all I want to hear about Winston Bloody Churchill." For, he knew, if the war correspondent had not been present, Colonel Whitestaff would not have even sent out the train, much less tried to penetrate all the way to within sight of the Tugela river.

The engagement had convinced him of one thing. He no longer wanted to be in an engineering unit. He was tired of having others do his fighting. Slone had not fired a single shot at the Boers during the ambush, having been too busy trying to move the wounded and to clear the track. At least at Omdurman, when he had ridden with the 21st Lancers in their charge, he had felt alive and had felt as if he were taking part. Somehow, in some way, he would get into this war, really into it.

It was not anger at the Boers or a soldier's lust for blood that drew him on; it was something hard to pinpoint in the space between a quietly heroic sense of personal mission and the thrill of defending the empire.

Since she had joined the field hospital organized by Dr. Hans Van Reenan, Sianna De Hartog had not had to travel far to get into the action. She had still been in her own country, Natal, when she saw her first wounded man. As it happened, he was a British soldier who had been shot through the cheeks by a Boer sharpshooter. The bullet had shattered bone and teeth and there was much blood as Dr. Van Reenen began to clean up the terrible wound. He grunted his orders to Sianna in a low voice. Not far away a firefight was going on, Boers dug in on a low hill, called a *kopje*—a large hill was simply a *kop*—firing down into the attacking British. Sianna had to ask the doctor to speak louder over the din.

'You'll get to the point where you'll be able to read my mind," the old man growled, digging pieces of shattered tooth out of the wound and letting them drop noisily to the top of the metal operating table.

"Ah, no," he said, as he explored inside the ravaged mouth to find that the soft palate had been ripped away, opening the nasal cavities to the mouth.

"Is he bad?" Sianna whispered.

"Better they had let him drown in his own blood," he said. "Now, perhaps, if he is lucky, he will die from shock."

As the situation had become less flexible and the Boer army surrounded Ladysmith, thus immobilizing itself along with the twelve thousand British regulars trapped inside the Boer ring, the hospital moved ever closer to the besieged town. For a time there was little work.

Then, when General Joubert let Louis Botha take his four thousand mounted riflemen and five guns across the Tugela River to push towards Pietermaritzburg, things changed. For a time, there was plenty to do, and as a result Sianna gained a lot of experience. After a particularly brisk clash between relatively small forces, the wounded overflowed the available space in the mobile hospital, and Dr. Van Reenen, fighting against time, was operating only on the more seriously wounded men.

"Sianna-girl," he said, "I can reach for my own knife. You go into the yard and sort out those who have wounds that merely need dressing. Work on them yourself."

They were mostly young, the injured, and they were shy with a woman, but she spoke to them softly, teased them about going home, cleaned and bandaged and gave out doses of morphine. When there were only the seriously wounded ones still needing attention, she was back at Van Reenen's side. She had no time to weep for them until, in the early hours of the morning, the work was done and the living separated from those who had died. Sianna went to her tent, bathed as best she could, shivering in the chill, and then with a woollen sweater around her neck she sat on the edge of her bunk and let the sobs rack her shoulders until she felt cleansed, empty, and very, very tired.

CHAPTER XVII

The Queensland Mounted Infantry, after their one spirited stalking of the Boer laager, had had one or two more successful encounters with the enemy; then they were abruptly recalled to Cape Town, where they were now languishing in camp. Morale was at rock bottom. In their opinion, after having shown their British officers how to fight this war, the Queenslanders were being ignored. Meanwhile, the Poms—British officers—seemed to be intent on losing the war quickly by doing foolish things, such as charging into the muzzles of the good Mauser rifles in the hands of Boer sharpshooters, who could drop a running antelope at a thousand yards.

Though he had arrived too late to witness it, Kelvin Broome had produced good copy out of the Queenslanders' first engagement, and he had seen subsequent operations firsthand and reported them as well. Now he, too, was growing restless, as the war seemed to be moving away from him. The news was all about Baden-Powell in Mafeking and Cecil Rhodes in Kimberley, and now there was a third siege, at Ladysmith in Natal, to hold the attention of the world.

Kelvin saw Matt Van Buren sitting on a rock. The African sun hung low on the horizon, making the western sky a crimson and orange glory. He deliberately kicked a couple of pebbles to let Matt know of his approach. Matt turned and said, "G'day, mate. Pull up a stone seat."

"Deep thoughts?" Kelvin asked, as he sat near the lieutenant.

"Thinking of home," Matt said. "There are parts of the bush much like South Africa."

"But more friendly-like, don't you think?" Kelvin asked. "Or does it seem that way simply because it's home?"

They watched the sun melt and put out horizontal wings as it sank below the horizon. Kelvin broke the silence. "Any hint of orders?"

"None," Matt said. "Kelvin, if we're going to fight in England's wars in the future, someone ought to see to it that we fight under our own officers, not Poms."

"Ummm," Kelvin said.

"We were talking about home, about Australia. There's something about the country that changes a man. Our people went out there as Englishmen—or, in my case Dutch and believe it or not, American in the case of my grandmother—but the bigness, the openness, the bush—Australia—it changed them. I guess we developed more of a respect for life because here were maybe half a dozen white men in an area of some few hundred square miles. These Pommy officers point at a pile of rocks that rises halfway to heaven, with a Boer sharpshooter behind every rock, and they say, 'Gentlemen, have your men take those rocks.' They don't put it into words but they give the impression that it's vital to the continued existence of the Queen, England, and all her imperial possessions that those rocks be taken."

He paused. Kelvin was silent, sensing that Matt wasn't finished. "I think that if Australian officers had been in command at Balaclava, Lord Tennyson would have had to find another subject for his poem. If the 21st Lancers at Omdurman had been Australian, they'd have scouted the flank and sneaked up on the wogs as if they were a mob of kangaroos, and the losses would have been greater on the wog side and less on our side."

"Incidentally," Kelvin said, "have you heard that Winston Churchill has been captured?"

"No," Matt said. "Did he mount a single-handed cavalry charge against the entire Boer army?"

Kelvin laughed. "No. I don't think he can be blamed, after all. He wasn't in command. An armoured train poked through the Boer lines and got cut off."

"There you go," Matt said. "The Poms haven't yet understood that this is a mobile war, that a Boer commando patrol can move fifty miles or more in a night, that the enemy has good, mobile artillery, and that he's not going to stand and let a well-coordinated assault overrun him."

Kelvin laughed. "Some of the officers are dreaming about a

Boer attack on a British square. The wonder is, Matt, not that the British have bad officers but that they have any good ones at all. Wealth and position are still the key to higher rank in the British Army. The army is the path to glory for the pampered sons of the aristocracy—look at Churchill. First he takes part in what may well have been the last cavalry charge, and now he's been captured by the enemy. He'll escape. The Boers don't really care. They're too busy fighting men with guns to worry about a few prisoners escaping. And even though he's nothing more than a war correspondent here, he'll become a hero of the empire, I assure you. You'll hear from that young man in the future, and maybe he's one of the good ones, one of those peers who advance the empire. But for every good one there seems to be an incompetent one, sometimes more than one."

"And still they win," Matt said, "because Tommy Atkins does the job for them. He marches uphill into the strong position. He fights like ten men. He gets killed now and then and that just makes others like him fight harder. They're an odd people, these English."

The sun was down now, and the twilight would soon become an inky darkness until the moon rose. Kelvin fussed with his pipe, lit it, sent clouds of aromatic smoke into the still evening air. Matt heard his name being called over near his tent. He stood, said, "Here." A runner came and saluted with clicking heels.

"The presence of Lieutenant Van Buren is required by the commander."

Matt returned the salute.

"If anything's going on, Matt," Kelvin said, "you'll let me know?"

"If I can," Matt replied.

The Australian colonel was standing in the headquarters tent. An English colonel was seated behind the desk that had been formed by a campaign chest with shining brass corners and bindings.

"Ah, Van Buren," the Australian said. "This is Colonel Roland Streeter, of General Buller's staff."

Matt gave a snappy salute and said, "Sir!" General Sir Redvers Buller was commander-in-chief of all the British forces in South Africa.

"Your commanding officer has high praise for you, Lieutenant," Streeter said. "I've read your reports on the taking of a Boer laager and also your subsequent engagements. I'm interested in your methods. Can't say I like them, because skulking around under cover and creeping up on an enemy is too much like the tactics of the Boers, but I am interested, because they just might well be applied to a little project that I have been asked to undertake."

"At your service, sir," Matt said. This one, he was thinking, was a true Pom. Skulking, indeed. If this one had been in command, the Queenslanders would have formed a front in line and charged into the Boer rifles to die with amazing bravery.

"What I have in mind is a bit hazardous, and you are under no obligation to agree to do it," Streeter said.

"Perhaps, sir, if I knew—"

"No, no," Streeter said. "Can't do it that way. It's a mission for a volunteer."

"And no questions asked, sir?" Matt said.

"Absolutely," the Australian colonel said.

"I'm your man, sir," Matt said, questioning his own sanity even as he said it.

"Ah, good, good," Streeter said. "You Australians seem rather adept at moving through the countryside unnoticed. What we want you to do, Lieutenant, is to take a message to Colonel Baden-Powell, in Mafeking."

"Yes, sir," Matt said, trying to picture a map of South Africa. Mafeking was, he knew, to the north, past the Orange Free State. He wondered why, if it were necessary to send a message to B.P., it wasn't easier to deliver it from the other end, from Rhodesia, in the north, much closer to Mafeking.

"I'll leave the composition of your group up to you," Streeter said. "Needless to say, we can't give you enough men to fight your way through Koos De La Rey's army and then past Cronje's around Kimberley. I'd say no more than four men, perhaps fewer."

'Yes sir, fewer than that will do," Matt said.

"You may draw what supplics and weapons you want. Maps through my office. We had thought about providing you with a Boer guide, but you just can't trust these fellows. They might profess loyalty to the crown and all the while their sympathies are with Kruger. It's pretty cut-and-dried, this assignment, after all."

Yes, it was, Matt decided, after he had studied a reconnaissance map there in headquarters. The British colonel had gone off back into Cape Town. The Australian colonel had left Matt with the maps and one orderly, who was dozing in a camp chair in front of the tent. It was cut-and-dried. Simple. He even had transport for more than half the distance. The rail lines were still open between Cape Town and the Orange River Station south of the Free State border, unless Koos De La Rey had cut them within the last few hours. After that, all he had to do was cross the Orange Free State, get through De La Rey's army, tiptoe gingerly through Cronje's army that surrounded Kimberley, and travel roughly three hundred miles to the north through territory that was ruled by the Boer commandos. Yes indeed. Cut-and-dried.

"Matt," Kelvin Broome said, peering into Matt's tent to see him gathering his kit, "I think there's something you're not telling me."

"Can't," Matt said.

"Ah, now, you're not going to do that to your old mate, are you? I mean, here I am, having to compete with the likes of Banjo Patterson for the readers' eyes back home and no story worth printing for weeks and you're onto something and won't tell me?"

"Kelvin, it wouldn't do you any good."

"Try me."

"Man to man?"

"Off the record."

"I'm off to Mafeking."

"My God." Kelvin brushed back his hair. "How?"

"I'm to skulk past two Boer armies."

"Matt, I'm probably the finest skulker ever to leave the bush," Kelvin said.

"I can take only a couple of men."

"I'm a good hand with a rifle, if it comes to that."

"If it comes to that, if we're spotted, I think I'll spend the rest of the war in a Boer prison laager," Matt said.

"Well, then you'll need pleasant company," Kelvin said cheerfully. "Come on, Matt. I'm drying up down here. The war's at a standstill with the sieges being all the news, and Mafeking's the one

most worthy of copy. An interview with old B.P. will make a name
for me in Australia."

Kelvin Broome, Matt knew, was a product of the bush. He rode
as well and could probably shoot as well as any of the Queensland
Mounted Infantry. He was pleasant, reliable company. "I don't
think we'd better let the brass know that you're going."

"You're the boss."

"When I find out what train we'll be taking from Cape Town
station, I'll let you know. We might have to pretend not to be
together until we leave the train up around the Orange River."

"I won't even know you, son," Kelvin said.

Matt left Cape Town with a letter endorsed by Buller himself,
authorizing him to draw horses and any equipment and supplies
he felt necessary from any British unit. He had decided on one
man, a man he had come to know well and to admire. This was
Sergeant George Wood, a sandy-haired always-tousled man of
smiling mien who stood over six feet and was broad and strong. In
Australia he had been a stock rider for a squatter who was a friend
of the Van Buren family. On the ship coming over, Wood had
recognized Matt and had, as he was fond of saying, "been keepin'
an eye on the lad" ever since.

Wood found a way to enjoy life wherever he went. Although the
cars on the train going north were crowded with British reinforcements, he managed to find a secluded corner, in a car loaded with
weapons and ammunition, where he set up a rather cozy place for
Matt and himself. It was quiet, and private, and a couple of bottles
of good Cape brandy made the trip bearable. Only once did Matt
see Kelvin Broome during the run from Cape Town to the Orange
River Station.

There, far from the brass who knew Matt's orders, Kelvin joined
them, and George Wood handled the details about drawing
horses, weapons, and supplies. When George showed his letter
signed by Buller to a quartermaster, the man pushed back his hat,
his eyebrows went up, and he exclaimed, "Blimey, you've got a
license to steal!" He looked up craftily. "With this letter, mate,
you and I could be rich."

Matt and Kelvin had been going over maps. Directly to the
north the country was infested with Boers. To the northwest, up
the Orange River, was Bechuanaland and the beginning of the

great desert. Matt had no intention of riding out of uniform and thus opening himself to the charge of being a spy if captured, and to the punishment. It would be impossible, or at least improbable, to expect to be able to steal through two Boer armies and get past Kimberley by travelling directly north. There was only one possibility and that was to go west into Bechuanaland, bypass the Boer armies besieging Kimberley, and come back to the railway south of Mafeking.

"Six hundred miles through land we know nothing about," Matt said. "We'll have to guess about water. We'll travel by compass, and if the going is rough, we'll lose a lot of time backtracking, looking for a way to the north. Piece of cake. I'd say that the vultures will be picking our bones before we cover half the distance."

"That makes me shiver," Kelvin said. "Ever since I was a nipper in the bush I've had an absolute dread of being eaten by those filthy birds."

"If you'll have the decency to die first, I'll heap rocks over you," George Wood said.

"You're all heart, mate," Kelvin said.

"Sir," Wood said. "We need a guide, that's all, a man who knows the territory."

"A Boer?" Matt asked.

"A blackfellow, I'd say," Wood said. "Shall I inquire of the Poms, sir?"

"Goodonyer," Matt said.

Wood was back within an hour, trailed by a short, wiry-haired black man who stood no more than four and a half feet high. "Gentlemen, meet Luku," he said.

"I think, Sergeant, that you must have been moving along the lines you suggested before you made the proposal," Matt commented.

"A good noncommissioned officer anticipates the need of his superiors, sir," Wood allowed.

"Couldn't you find a full-sized one?" Kelvin asked.

"Don't judge Luku by his size," Wood said. "I bought him from—"

"Bought him?" Matt asked.

"Manner of speaking, sir. He was working for a Pom scout unit.

I gave the sergeant major two bottles of Cape brandy for him." He paused. "We'll have to requisition replacements for them two bottles, sir."

"Sergeant," Matt said, rolling his eyes.

"The little begger says he's sixty years old, sir, says he's traipsed every foot of that land out there, all the way to the north side of the Kalahari."

The little black man spoke up. "You go, you shrivel up. You no know water holes. You no know way."

"Did you get him a horse?" Matt asked.

"Doesn't want one," Wood said. "Says he'd rather walk."

"He'll slow us down."

"Says he won't. Says he can keep up with any horse."

On the way up the Orange River towards the border, Luku proved his worth by warning them of the approach of a small Boer commando force. From concealment they watched the Boers ride South.

"How did he hear them?" Kelvin asked. "He warned us a full ten minutes before we could hear their horses."

When they had travelled about fifty miles to the northwest, Matt directed Luku to turn northward. The little bushman nodded and pointed. "Good water," he said, and that night there was good water. Next morning they were moving again at first light. The travelling was easy, and they covered fifty miles per day for the next couple of days, passed to the west of Kimberley, and rode into an area of arid hills that slowed them. Somehow Luku was always ahead of them, unless Matt decided he wanted to take a look and galloped his horse, which was seldom. The land was becoming increasingly inhospitable. George Wood kept a close eye on a pride of lion that kept pace with them one day, sniffing curiously but finally deciding, Matt felt, that they either were not hungry or that white men did not smell appetizing.

Matt realized that the trip would have been ten times more difficult without Luku, but he felt that, after all, he could have guided the little group through with only a few unnecessary diversions. Fifteen days after leaving the Orange River Station, they rode onto tracks running east and west, the Molopo Railway that ran from Mafeking to the west. There was evidence that the line was patrolled regularly by mounted men. Luku guided them to a rocky hill, found a place where even the horses were well hidden, and disappeared. He was back just before dark with word that they were only a few miles from Mafeking, and that the Boers were quite lax in their watchfulness.

"In dark," Luku said, "walk through."

It was nearly midnight when the little bushman led them down the hill. They were walking, leading their horses. After an hour's climb up an arid ridge, they could see the flickering lights of the Boers' campfires. They lay in a band below them, yellow and red jewels in the black night.

"It looks to me as if they have the area well covered," Matt said.

"You follow Luku," the little black man said, setting off confidently. "Keep horses quiet."

Once they passed so close to a group of Boers that they could smell meat cooking and hear male voices harmonizing in a romantic song. The words were guttural, odd, but the effect was rather beautiful, Matt felt, as he followed closely on the heels of the little bushman. Ahead was a dark mass, the buildings on the fringe of town.

"Now you lead," Luku whispered to Matt.

"He wants you to get shot if the sentries see us," Wood said. "You fall back, sir. I'll make contact with the Tommies inside."

"Never mind, Sergeant," Matt said. "Stay here with Kelvin."

He eased forward, seeking out the shadows. He could see no lights in the buildings immediately ahead, but occasionally he caught a glimpse of lamplight from a window farther into the town. He was closing within a hundred yards of the nearest buildings when he heard a click. It was pure instinct that caused him to pitch forward on his belly. A rifle round made a thunking sound near his ear as he fell, and the rifleman was so near that he could smell the cordite.

"Hello, the town!" he called out. "Hold your fire. I am a British officer."

There was a flash, a boom, and dirt flew into his left eye. He rolled, seeking more cover. "Blast your eyes!" he yelled at the top of his voice. "Hold your bloody fire, you gormless twit. I told you I was a British officer."

"Advance and identify yourself," a disembodied voice said.

Matt rose carefully, brushed himself off, and walked forward with his hands over his head. The ground went out from under him suddenly, and he fell into a five-foot-deep trench, landing with a jar.

"There's a trench just in front of you," came the voice.

"Thanks a bloody bunch," Matt said, climbing out of the trench and moving forward.

Men closed around him from three sides, rifle muzzles pressing into him. "He looks like an officer," a man said.

"I am Lieutenant Matthew Van Buren with a message for Colonel Baden-Powell from the commanding general. From General Buller himself."

"Gor, they're 'ere to relieve us."

"Where is the army?"

"In Natal and in Cape Town," Matt said. "Look, I have three companions out there. I'd like to call them in. We've had quite a trek."

"Tell 'em to come in with 'ands 'igh."

Matt called his group, warned them of the hidden trench, and waited until they had joined him. "Gentlemen, if you'll just take us to quarters—"

"You don't want to be taken to the colonel?"

"How long have you been here?" Matt asked.

"Too bloody long."

"I imagine Colonel Baden-Powell will be here in the morning," Matt said. "There is no need to wake him."

"What's with the Kaffir?" someone asked.

"This man is with me," Matt said. "He has been of great service to us. I want him fed and given a place to sleep."

"No," Luku said. "You here. I go now."

"Where will you go?" Matt asked.

Luku waved an arm to the northwest. "My people there."

"You have pay coming," Matt said.

"Two rifles, hand gun," Luku replied. "Bullets. Money no good in bush."

Matt gave the bushman his own rifle and told Kelvin to turn over his. To keep from being totally unarmed, he took Sergeant Wood's pistol and belt and gave it to Luku. Thus laden, the bushman disappeared into the darkness.

Matt woke to the sound of a cannonade. Half a dozen rounds fell within the British perimeter and exploded with enough noise to wake the dead, not just the town. He leapt to his feet and looked out of the tin-roofed hut in which he and his two companions had been sleeping. Smoke was rising from the impact point a hundred yards away. Otherwise there was no movement. He was putting the finishing touch to his dressing, trying to brush some of the trail dust from his uniform, when Lieutenant-Colonel Robert Stephenson Smyth Baden-Powell came striding down the street accompanied by two well-appointed officers. Matt met him outside the hut, with Kelvin and Wood just behind him.

B.P. was quite formal, returning Matt's salute and taking the message pouch from him with a nod of his head.

"I trust, Lieutenant, that you've brought word of our relief?" B.P. said, as he opened the pouch.

"Sir, I was not given permission to read the messages," Matt said.

"Good Lord, all the way from the Cape and you weren't curious?" B.P. asked, opening an envelope. He read for a while and then broke into a laugh. "Gentlemen," he said, "there is no promise of relief. We are all to be decorated for our heroism, and we're requested to hold out as long as humanly possible."

"That's it?" George whispered behind Matt. "We came over seven hundred miles for that?"

Matt kicked Wood on the ankle as a signal to be quiet.

"And you, gentlemen," B.P. said, "will you stay with us, or must you return to your command?"

Matt didn't answer immediately. He had no orders to cover the question. He'd assumed that once in Mafeking he would stay, but after seeing the town in daylight he didn't want to commit himself.

Kelvin saved him from answering by saying, "Colonel Baden-Powell, I represent a Sydney newspaper, and I'd like very much, sir, to have a few moments of your time so that I can pass along to our readers your thoughts on the siege."

"My pleasure," B.P. said. "Now?"

"At your convenience," Kelvin said.

"Come along, then. Every day in Mafeking is much the same. The morning serenade from our friends outside, and then hours of watching the flies mate." He turned and looked back. "You may as well come, too, Lieutenant. We'll sort out some tea."

Outside Baden-Powell's headquarters, a commandeered private dwelling, a group of lean, filthy-looking natives were digging frantically in a refuse bin. The colonel took no notice. Inside orderlies fetched tea with British army efficiency. When everyone had been served, it was Kelvin who spoke. "Colonel, have you heard that Madame Tussaud has modelled you in wax, to add your image to those of the immortals in her museum?"

Baden-Powell cocked his head. "By Jove," he said.

"Hear, hear," said an aide.

"I had hoped that some small notice had been taken of our predicament here," B.P. said. "In Cape Town, perhaps. Are you telling me, sir, that they're aware of our little garrison's efforts in London?"

"Indeed," Kelvin said. "In fact, there's a great demand for more news about Mafeking and its gallant defenders."

Kelvin settled back. His bait about the waxworks had served its intended purpose, having put the colonel in a mellow mood.

"Since the fifteenth of October," B.P. began, leaning back, "we have held off at least six thousand of Piet Cronje's fighting men, three hundred white women, four children, and seventy-five hundred Kaffirs."

"You've done a magnificent job," Kelvin said. "But why, Colonel, did you choose Mafeking to fortify?"

"Why, because of its strategic location, of course," B.P. said. "And because it has a symbolic value in multiples of its worth. It's so near the Boers' border, you see. It's a rail junction, but most importantly Dr. Jameson launched his ill-fated raid on Johannesburg from Mafeking. When I saw that the town had not been occupied by the Boers, I immediately began to stock provisions and to fortify it. I built bomb-proof shelters. I had mine fields laid."

He talked on for some time, answering Kelvin's questions in great detail. When Kelvin had all that he wanted, he thanked B.P. and stood up.

"By the way, Broome," B.P. said, "when you want to send your story out, I'll furnish you with a native runner. There's a telegraph just fifty-miles to the north, you know."

"Thank you," Kelvin said, thinking again how much easier it

would have been for Streeter to get word to B.P. via that route than through the Boer lines.

"And both of you will, of course, join us for a picnic tomorrow," B.P. said.

"A picnic?" Matt asked, incredulous.

"It's Sunday, you know," B.P. said. "The Boers don't fight on the sabbath. Gives us a chance to limber up, get some exercise without having to worry about sharpshooters or cannon. Pity, though, that the blighters took exception to our having a bit of polo on Sunday." He frowned. "Hard to understand these Boers, eh?"

There was, indeed, a picnic. Women spread cloths on the grass, children played noisily and the men strolled in full-dress uniform with their arms clasped casually behind them. There were excellent beef sausages and fresh bread. Except for the African sky, vast and hot, and for the less-than-attractive surroundings—the tin-roofed town smelled rather foul as it sweltered under the sun—Matt might have been at a picnic in Australia. The women were well dressed, and one, a captain's wife, seemed to want to flirt with him. He saw Kelvin leave, carrying a sausage and a piece of bread, nibbling as he walked, then turned to the captain's wife.

Kelvin walked out of the white section, past the quarters of the garrison, into the native *kraal*, the collection of villagers' huts. He was still nibbling on the sausage. Small black children, their stomachs distended by hunger, seemed to emerge from everywhere until he was surrounded by imploring urchins. Some had terrible sores on them. Their eyes followed the movement of his hand as he took a bite of sausage.

"Hungry, are you?" he asked.

"Eat, baas, eat," said a boy, moving to stand directly in front.

"Well, there's not enough to go around," Kelvin said, extending what was left of the sausage. The small boy snatched the sausage and tried to run, only to be swarmed upon by his fellows. As he went down, Kelvin saw him stuffing the sausage into his mouth. He looked around. A tiny girl, her legs and arms pencil thin, her belly bloated, was eyeing his bread. He took advantage of the fight over the sausage to give her the bread. She stuffed it into her mouth quickly, coughing, her eyes watering as she tried to swallow it.

He soon came to the conclusion that all was not as well in Mafeking as B.P. would have the world believe. The story he wrote that night was not for Baden-Powell's eyes. He described simply and with economical language the starving native children, the seven thousand or more people who fought daily to salvage scraps from the refuse bins of the whites. He did not bother to write about B.P.'s disappointment over the Boers' telling the defenders of the city that if they persisted in playing polo on Sunday, the Boers would be forced to shell the field. This was true, but it was not the important story.

CHAPTER XVIII

Tolo Mason had inherited his size from his Samoan grand-father. At seventeen, he stood three inches taller than his father. The years of work, of riding alongside the stockmen, or hay-making and cutting wood and doing all the other jobs that go with running a cattle station, had made him muscularly slim. He liked to expose as much of himself as possible to the sun away from the main house; his naturally tawny skin was baked to a coppery red. He had his mother's hair, dark and wavy, and his father's delicate features, the long, aquiline nose, sharply delineated chin, trim eyebrows and alert brown eyes.

Jon Mason was proud of his son. After Dane de Lausenette's death, a series of more competent tutors had given him an education beyond what he would have got at school. And in the last two years before the new century, Tolo had ventured into an area of learning for which there was not much groundwork. He probably knew more about the totemic beliefs of the Australian Aborigines than most men who called themselves ethnographers. Quite often Tolo would notify his father, or his mother if Jon were away, that he would be gone for a few days, and off he would go, on walkabout. On one such trip, when he had just turned sixteen, he travelled as far as Arnhem Land in the Northern Territory. Now his ambition was to take ship to Western Australia and venture into the great outback deserts in search of Aborigines whose habits and customs had not been affected by daily contact with the white men.

Misa, who herself had become interested in the myths and beliefs of the Abo, worried about that plan and urged Tolo to postpone it, at least until after his father's upcoming trip to England. Jon had been appointed to a delegation to London for discussions of Australian unification with Joseph Chamberlain, secretary of state for the colonies in Lord Salisbury's government. Chamberlain's approval and support was vital in the effort to introduce in Parliament a Federal Bill, an act to allow the formation of an Australian Commonwealth, and Jon wanted to see it through.

Though disappointed, for his father might be gone a long while, Tolo agreed to postpone his own trip to Western Australia.

Jon thanked him when Tolo told him the news. "It will make your mother feel better," he said. "And perhaps when I get back, we'll make a family do of it."

Tolo laughed. "Father," he said, "I fear that you've spent too many years in offices to go traipsing around the outback."

"Oh, ho," Jon countered. "The sprout thinks it has outgrown the tree." But he, too, laughed, patting his soft, slightly protuberant belly. "I'll admit, you may have something there. Need to do a bit of riding, what?"

"Maybe some bush cutting?" Tolo asked with a grin.

"Let's not get carried away with this fitness madness," Jon said. "I'll do a lot of walking on the deck during the long trip to England." He put his hand on his tall son's shoulder. "You're the man of the house now. Take care of your mother."

Tolo nodded. He knew that in many ways he pleased his father, and that gratified him. He did, however, have one small area of guilt. From the time he was about twelve years old his father had tried to interest him in the various Mason-Fisher enterprises, and Tolo had honestly tried to find fulfilment and excitement in business. He still accompanied Jon into Melbourne now and then and walked by his side as he toured the shipping facilities, or stood by his desk as he made decisions involving thousands of pounds, and to Tolo it was all an exercise in absurdity. He remembered once, when he was younger, having asked his father, "Why do you work to make more money when you already have more than you'll ever need?"

Preparing for his trip, Jon reflected on his family with complete satisfaction. He had come to recognize Tolo's lack of interest in business early on, and though disappointed, he had encouraged the boy's scientific and scholarly bent. And he had found compensation for his son's disinterest from a surprising source.

One by-product of having had tutors in the house for years was that Misa had absorbed the tutors' teachings alongside her son. The Samoan girl, who had been taught to read and write and do simple arithmetic by the missionaries in her native island, had by now accumulated a library in the station house that astounded Jon, for both its size and its range of subject matter. Of late Jon had been intrigued to see book after book on banking coming into the house from publishers in Australia, England, and the United States.

He had always been in the habit of talking about his business affairs with Misa, and for years he had assumed that she was listening only because she loved him. However, as time went on, she began to take an active part in those business talks, almost without his noticing it, asking questions and making suggestions that, often as not, went directly to the heart of the matter.

So it was that, as Jon faced a lengthy absence from home and his affairs, he felt he could leave certain instructions with Misa and know that they would be carried out. He employed one young man who did nothing much more than keep the road hot between Melbourne and Caroline Station, which over the years had grown to be the home of the Mason family. By using this messenger, Misa would be able to deal with any problem that arose without ever setting foot in Melbourne, and that was the way she wanted it.

There was one situation that bothered him. The Fisher Shipping Company had a branch in Sydney that, for years, had been quite profitable. The original manager of the Sydney branch had been put in place by Jon's stepfather, Marcus Fisher. The manager had been a good, honest man who earned his sizable salary by keeping Fisher Shipping in Sydney competitive with other firms and by putting the company books well into the black year after year. Upon his death Jon had promoted the branch accountant to the position of manager, and five years later the margin of profit was so near the break-even point that if long-overdue renovations were carried out, they would actually push the balance into the red.

Jon, puzzled by the disappointing figures from that branch of the business, had brought home copies of the accounts to study. Although he knew the basics, he was not an accountant, and several nights of poring over the numbers had told him nothing. He walked into his study one evening only a few days before he was to leave for London to find Misa seated at his desk, pencil working, a neat column of figures adding up on a piece of paper.

"The man is stealing from you," she said matter-of-factly. "Here is how he is doing it."

Jon stood behind her and listened attentively. "You see," she said, "there is no proof. He is clever, that one. The business volume has actually grown by a small percentage, thus increasing cash flow, but the profits are smaller."

"I saw that," Jon said. "What I can't figure out, at least from the books, is why?"

"I think you will find the problem here," she said, tapping the book with her pencil.

Jon bent down and read, "Dubbo Meat Packing Company."

"Here," Misa said, pointing again.

On shipment after shipment the Dubbo Meat Packing Company of New South Wales had been reimbursed most of the shipping costs for spoilage. The Fisher companies had only recently become involved in a fast-growing industry, the shipment of meat in refrigerated vessels.

"Why does only the Dubbo Meat Packing Company have spoilage?" she asked. "Other packing companies ship meat on the same ship, but they don't get a rebate for spoilage."

"Blast," Jon said. He shrugged. "I suppose we'll just have to let it ride until I get back. It'll be a delicate situation. The man's been with the company for years. We can't just jump in and accuse him of stealing."

"Perhaps you could send the comptroller from your Melbourne offices to Sydney."

"No. He's a good man, but he's not a diplomatic person, if you know what I mean, Misa. To send him up there would be like tossing a hungry dingo down inside a chicken pen. No, we'll just let it ride. I'll be back in no more than three months and then I'll go up there and have a look at it."

To Jon's surprise, Misa insisted on travelling with him into Melbourne. It had been at least a year since she had been into the city, and then only to shop for clothing and odds and ends for the station. Tolo had said good-bye at home, so the trip turned out to be a pleasant time of privacy for Misa and Jon. They spent two nights in the town house, without servants, acting very much like newlyweds.

Since he had first seen her in a Kanaka compound on one of the plantations owned by his stepfather, Jon had never tired of Misa. He regretted only one thing regarding his relationship with her: that he had lost several years letting her get away from him after that first time he had loved her in a grove of trees, when she was doing a duty, repaying him for a kindness to her people. As he boarded a Mason-Fisher ship for the long, watery way to England, he wished that he could live it all over again, start from the time he had first seen her, from that time when she, dutiful daughter, loyal to her tribe, gave him her body as the only thing of value she possessed. He should, he told himself, have married her then and there, regardless of difficulties. At the time, he had been quite young, with very limited means.

Alone on board ship, Jon began to become acquainted with his fellow passengers, tried to limit his intake of the very good ship's fare, walked the decks for exercise, and came to the conclusion that he was a damned fool. He began to add up the time he'd spent away from Misa since they had moved to the interior. Weeks, no, months out of his life. And he was not getting any younger. Here he was, sailing away from her, to be gone for God knew how long. True, it was in a good cause, and a man did have responsibilities. But he resolved that once this federation thing was settled, he would retire from public life. It might even be a good idea to start selling off some of the far-flung Mason-Fisher properties. What need had he for sugar plantations in Queensland, for example?

Putting resolve to action, he went to his cabin and started a long, running letter to Misa, a letter that would be posted from Cape Town, when the ship put into Table Bay before starting the seemingly endless run up the western coast of Africa towards the North Atlantic and the English Channel.

Misa had not left Melbourne directly after seeing Jon off. Instead she had returned to the town house, dressed in a simple but rather elegant suit, and taken a hansom cab to the Mason-Fisher headquarters, where she asked for Mr. Price Vermillion.

Vermillion did not live up to his colourful name. He was a big, hulking man, grey, a bit stooped from long years bent over a desk.

He entered Jon's office, where Misa waited, smiling pleasantly. He had had a few dealings with the Missus before and had found her to be a solid-minded woman, with surprisingly good business sense.

"Mr. Vermillion," she began, even before he was seated. "I want you to have a look at this." She had brought the books, and her figures, from the Sydney operation.

Vermillion took the books, bent to put his eyes within inches of the inked figures, and started running down columns with his fingernail, which had ink under it and was stained permanently blue. Misa didn't point out the areas of suspicion for she knew, in time, that Vermillion would find them. It took him only fifteen minutes. He did some calculations on scrap paper and looked up at Misa grimly.

"This is my fault, Mrs. Mason," he said. "I should have been paying closer attention to the Sydney operation."

"Nonsense," she said. "We overwork you as it is Mr. Vermillion. You do agree that this Mr.—" She bent forward to see the name she had written at the head of a column. "—This Mr. Mitchell Norton is stealing."

"It's obvious," Vermillion said.

"How do we prove it?"

Vermillion thought for a moment. "Well, perhaps we could . . ." he hesitated. "Yes. One of our reefer ships is due in Southampton within a very few days. With your permission, Mrs. Mason, I shall alert our agents there to hire detectives to observe the operation, particularly the unloading of products from the Dubbo Meat Packing Company."

"Please do," she said. "I'm going to stay in Melbourne for a few days, Mr. Vermillion."

"If there's anything I can do—"

"Thank you," she said. "You can inform me immediately of any findings from England. And please have someone check to see when a Mason-Fisher ship will sail for Sydney."

Vermillion raised one grey eyebrow. For the Missus to go off to Sydney would be an event the likes of which he had not witnessed in all of the years since young Jon had taken over the company.

Misa went from the office to her stockbroker. She had been taking small sums from what Jon called her household money for years and playing the market with them. It had taken her several years to break even. In the past few years, she had been toying with bank stocks, and she was showing a tidy gain, at least on paper. Banks fascinated her. There were times when even a solid, multimillion-pound company like Mason-Fisher went to the Melbourne banks for investment or operating capital, and Misa could not imagine a more painless way of showing a profit than to lend money and get it back increased by interest.

She was by no means a large customer, but the broker knew who she was and he had hopes of bigger things. He met her with great courtesy, gave her a cup of tea, and went over the account with her, telling her that this stock looked as if it were worth buying, that that one should be sold. She gave the broker a draft for a thousand pounds with instructions to buy stock in one particular Melbourne bank, but not one that was recommended by the broker.

She spent one day shopping, accepting the rudeness of white sales clerks with her face set in a little smile, not taking any special pleasure in the look that came over their faces when she began to read from her prepared list and her purchases began to accumulate. Had she been dressed as a household servant, she would have been treated with more friendliness and, because she was a beautiful woman, perhaps with some clumsy flirting from the men behind the counters. Since she was dressed well—Jon often ordered her clothing and when it came to something for his Misa he never questioned the price—and was obviously a woman of position, the clerks were made uneasy. It was seldom that an Australian white had to deal with a darker face, someone from the lesser races, yet also someone from a position of financial superiority. When it happened, there was open resentment.

She learned from Mr. Vermillion that it would be at least a week before they could expect any news about the disposition of the Dubbo Meat Company's shipment in London. Misa sent a message to Tolo, informing him that she would stay in Melbourne for an indefinite period and that she was considering a trip to Sydney. She did not order him to come into the city to accompany her, but from the way she worded the message Tolo got the idea that she would welcome his company. He arrived at the town house a few days later, dressed in the rough clothing of a man of the bush, tall, coppery, impressive with his young, handsome face impervious to distractions from the urban world.

"I do hope you brought some clothes that will be suitable for the city," she said, when he burst into the parlour and lifted her completely off her feet, greeting her as if it had been months and not days since he had last seen her.

"If they're good enough for the station, they are bloody well good enough for Melbourne," he said.

She smiled and shook her head. She knew that he would dress to please her if she took a firm stand. She would not insist until they reached Sydney.

A few days later, when a messenger from the office brought word that Price Vermillion requested that she come to his office, she hurried over. Vermillion had a long cablegram in his hand. After formal greetings, he said, "Mrs. Mason, our ship was unloaded in the usual way, except that the considerable shipment of meat from the Dubbo Meat Products Company of New South Wales was left in the freezers and marked as being spoiled. The next day several unmarked lorries arrived. Our investigator was told that the spoiled meat was being sent to a glue factory. However, upon following the lorries our man saw that the Dubbo shipment was taken directly to an open market where the sides of beef were auctioned along with the remainder of our ship's cargo, bringing quite good prices."

"I see," Misa said. "Not only do we and our insurance company reimburse Dubbo for their so-called loss, thus giving them full price for their beef, there's also the wholesale price of the shipment in England. That means that the supercargo, who should have been attentive to our commercial interests on board, and most probably the ship's captain as well, are working with Mitchell Morton."

"It would seem so," Vermillion said.

"Mr. Vermillion, I think, if it isn't terribly inconvenient, that I'd like you to accompany me to Sydney."

Vermillion considered it for a few moments and then nodded. "Yes, that would be best," he said.

They sailed aboard a Mason-Fisher coastal steamer, Misa preferring the sea voyage to travelling by rail—which in any case would have required them to change trains in Albury, on the border, owing to the fact that Victoria and New South Wales used different gauges of track. Misa was given the captain's cabin, despite her protests, but she appreciated the comfort nonetheless.

In Sydney, when Misa and Tolo checked into a hotel frequented by whites, they received startled looks but no overt discourtesy. Tolo's size and his rugged appearance—he still wore the same clothes he had brought from the bush—and Misa's obviously expensive and tasteful clothing earned them puzzled acceptance.

On the voyage up the coast, Misa and Vermillion had worked out their strategy. Vermillion had pointed out to her that since a good deal of money was involved, money changing hands both in Australia and in London, there had to be a mechanism for exchange. There were two possibilities, Vermillion guessed, for getting money back to Australia from England. The safe and simple way would be interbank exchange.

"If so," Misa said, "then they have a banker working with them."

"That would be splitting the pie into rather a lot of pieces," Vermillion said thoughtfully. "It would mean dividing the take among Mitchell Norton, the ship's captain and his supercargo, and a banker in Sydney. And there are others to pay—the men in England, for example, who drive the wagons that pick up the so-called spoiled meat at the dock and handle its sales at the wholesale market."

"I think we'd better take a very close look at the books," Misa said.

"I get your point," he said. "Mr. Mason and I had put the decline of the Sydney branch down to increased competition. Somehow, Mrs. Mason, they've been bleeding the company for years, because five years ago our Sydney operation netted over forty thousand after taxes. If one presumes that business has not, after all, declined, perhaps even increased, that leaves a pie worth carving, eh?"

"I would like you, Mr. Vermillion, to visit the offices of our branch by yourself. Make it seem like just a simple inspection tour. Don't spend a lot of time looking at the books. Just get an impression of Mitchell Norton, take a look at the bank trans-actions."

"And you, I hazard to guess, will visit the Sydney Merchant-man's and Marine Bank?"

She smiled. "That is my intention, Mr. Vermillion. And I shall also talk to a very good firm of solicitors."

The accountant shuffled some papers. "When you go to the bank, you will want to speak with Mr. Christopher Deakin, president and principal stockholder."

Mr. Deakin was a short, robust man whose hair had fled from his crown, leaving thick, snowy-white fringes that flowed down his temples into a full beard as white as his hair. His mouth was dark and sour-looking by contrast with the beard, and his eyes were shadowed by a simian forehead crested with bushy eyebrows. He was dressed in a three-piece suit with a high white collar and a conservative cravat. When he was told that Mrs. Jon Mason was in the bank and desired to speak to him, he bounced to his feet, his brows knitted, and hurried to meet her.

The instant he saw Misa's dark, Polynesian face he halted in midstride. "Surely there's been some mistake," he said.

"No mistake, Mr. Deakin," Misa said. "I want to talk with you about your transactions with our branch office here in Sydney. I think, to answer my questions, you'll need your account books."

Deakin was not accustomed to being ordered about by brown-skinned women. Yet he felt himself caught on the horns of a dilemma. He was aware of the wealth, and therefore power, of the Mason-Fisher companies. But it was unbelievable that Jon Mason, who was the quintessential Australian gentleman, could be married to a Kanaka. "Young woman," he said imperiously, "can you furnish proof that you are, indeed, Mrs. Jon Mason?"

"Only my person," Misa said.

The look on Misa's face gave pause to Deakin. "You understand why I must be sure? After all, it is the responsibility of the bank to protect the privacy of its depositors' affairs, including those of Mason-Fisher."

"I understand fully," Misa said, acquiescing to his demand. "I will be back, Mr. Deakin, with proof of my identity."

He had a momentary impulse to stop her, but his shock at seeing the Kanaka woman in his bank was more influential than his thoughts.

When next she came, two days later, she was in the company of a distinguished man with an official air. Thinking that perhaps he had committed a grave error, he ushered Misa and Mr. Price

Vermillion—whom he knew by name and correspondence—into his office and looked only briefly at the papers which Vermillion presented.

"I think you've noticed, Mr. Deakin," Vermillion began, "that deposits from Mason-Fisher Sydney have declined in the past five years."

Deakin nodded and started to speak. Misa leaned forward. "Do you handle the personal bank account of our manager, Mr. Mitchell Norton?"

"I'm afraid, madam, that you're asking for confidential information."

"I'm asking for your cooperation," Misa said calmly. "Quite frankly, I expect it."

Deakin bristled. "And why do you make such a surprising statement, that you expect me to violate bank ethics?"

In the forty-eight hours since Misa had been turned away from the bank by Deakin she had not been idle. With the aid of a firm of solicitors, who in turn had hired a private investigator who knew his way around the Sydney business world, she had discovered some interesting things. The Merchantman's and Marine Bank also handled the accounts of the suburban Dubbo Meat Packing Company. It came as no surprise that Martin Dubbo was Christopher Deakin's brother-in-law. Mitchell Norton, Mason-Fisher's manager in Sydney, was a frequent visitor in the homes of both Dubbo and Deakin.

"I expect it, Mr. Deakin," Misa said, "because I don't think you want to go to jail."

Deakin paled and then blustered. But he subsided when Misa spoke again. "I don't really want to have you in court," she said. "I'm sure you could produce a half-dozen clergymen to testify to your good character, and your old mother might even still be alive to totter to the stand and tell the judge what a good boy you are."

"This is insufferable," Deakin said, but he did not move from his chair.

"If a hungry man stole your wallet in a public place," Misa said, "he'd be sentenced to a long, long term in prison, but not before he was preached to by the judge for being depraved. You'd get a slap on the hand and a suspended sentence. So we won't bother with that, Mr. Deakin. Instead, you will, this afternoon, sign over your shares in the Merchantman's and Marine Bank of Sydney to me, personally, in exchange for exactly one pound per share less than yesterday's highest bid on the market."

"You are insane, madam," Deakin said. He leapt to his feet, his face red, perspiration forming on his bald head. "I have no idea what is going on in your heathen head—"

Misa raised an eyebrow.

"—but if you think—"

"Sit down," Misa said.

He started to fume, but there was a look in her eyes that chilled him. Vermillion was hunched forward, his eyes glaring at Deakin.

"Mitchell Norton has made a statement to the police," Misa said. "In that statement he explains in detail how the Merchantman's and Marine Bank, the Dubbo Meat Packing Company, the captain of one of the Mason-Fisher reefer ships, and he himself have defrauded Mason-Fisher of Sydney of over two hundred thousand pounds over the past five years."

Deakin felt a sharp pain in his chest. He had always felt that Norton was the weak link in the chain.

"I suppose, Mr. Deakin," Misa said, "that by taking you and Mr. Dubbo and the others into court we could regain a portion of our loss. In the meantime we'd be wasting valuable time and manpower and spending money on solicitors. I think my solution is neater and less painful all round. I've always had a yen to own a bank, so if you'll draw up an agreement covering the exchange of stock—"

"I am not admitting anything," Deakin said, "but if I do as you say there will be no further accusations? There will be no, ah, unpleasantness for me or my brother-in-law?"

"You will be free to retire to your country house, which I suspect may have been built with my money," Misa said. "Your brother-in-law can continue to steal cattle or whatever he wants to do."

"All right, I'll agree to the exchange," Deakin said, "but only at two pounds above yesterday's highest bid per share."

Misa rose. "Well, then, Mr. Vermillion," she said, turning to her associate, "will you please advise that very efficient captain of the police with whom you talked that we shall be needing his services after all?"

"Wait, wait," Deakin protested.

The price of Deakin's controlling interest in the bank cleaned out Misa's brokerage account totally, and it required a hefty dip into the general funds of Mason-Fisher-Melbourne. She placed the assistant manager of the bank in temporary charge. At the office of Mason-Fisher-Sydney, Price Vermillion was turning out a few men who had been hired by Mitchell Norton. One of the Mason-Fisher ships quickly found itself with a brand-new captain and supercargo.

And Misa Mason had a bank.

"What, exactly, will you do with it?" Tolo asked.

"I had thought," she said, with a straight face, "that I'd turn it over to you. It would be a good place for you to start learning about the business world."

"Not a chance," Tolo said, with quick alarm.

She laughed and took his arm. "No, Thomas, I will not try to shut you up in a bank."

"You had me a bit frightened," he said.

"Well, I wish I could turn it over to you," she said, "but even if you were willing, I couldn't, because you have no experience in banking and I've got a rather substantial sum of my husband's money invested. No, I have to have a manager, an experienced and competent person, and I'm at a bit of a loss to know where to find one I can trust."

Tolo smiled. "Run it yourself," he suggested. "I believe you've read every book on banking that's ever been written."

Her smile was the shy smile of her youth. "I wish I could. I really do."

"Another suggestion," Tolo said. "Father has always intended bringing us to Sydney to visit his old friend and his family. Perhaps Mr. Gordon could help you to find a good bank manager."

Misa had considered contacting the Gordons, but past experience had made her wary of social meetings. Tolo's suggestion, however, made sense. Jon and Sam Gordon were not only old friends, but quite often ventured into trade together.

To the delight of his teenage daughter Sam Gordon had installed a telephone both at his office and in his home. He had not yet purchased an automobile, much to the girl's disappointment and to his mother-in-law's, both of whom had ridden in a

Lanchester *and* a Daimler. Like the Prince of Wales, both Java and Magdalen preferred the Daimler. There were several of them in Sydney, the original German models and those made in England under licence. When Sam called home and Java answered, speaking loudly to be heard over the line noise, her first thought was that, at last, her father had given in to the subtle pressure being exerted by the youngest and oldest members of the family, for Sam said, "I have a bit of a surprise for you all."

"Oh, wonderful," Java said, for with the single-minded optimism of youth she just *knew* that her father's mind was in tune with hers and that he was going to announce the imminent arrival of a new Daimler.

"I've just had a telephone call from Mrs. Jon Mason," Sam said. "She wants to see me on a matter of business and I insisted that she come to dinner tonight."

"Oh," Java said, her voice low.

"Tell your mother that there'll be three," Sam said. "Mrs. Mason has her son with her, and she wanted to bring along one of her associates, a sort of business manager, I take it."

Tolo had consented reluctantly to wear what Misa called civilized clothing. He looked rather magnificent in a smartly tailored cream serge suit. The light colour of the suit offset his sun-bronzed face. He helped his mother out of the carriage and followed her and Price Vermillion up to the Gordons' pathway, which passed through a lovely flowering garden. Jessica Broome Gordon opened the door and said, "It's so good of you to come, Misa!"

Misa, responding to the warm greeting with a smile, took the offered hand and let herself be ushered into the entrance hall.

"We have so wanted to see you again," Jessica said. "It's been so long! When was it?" She waved a hand. "Never mind, I don't care to remember that many years ago, but you and Jon had just returned from Samoa."

"This is Mr. Price Vermillion," Misa said. "And my son, Thomas."

"You were just a little nipper when I saw you," Jessica said. "You have become quite a handsome young man."

"Thank you," Tolo replied politely.

"Well, come," Jessica said. "The others are eager to meet you."

Java and her grandmother, Magdalen, were in the parlour. Java saw a very pretty brown-skinned woman at her mother's side, but her eyes were even more attracted to the coppery face of a tall young man with an impressive spread of shoulders. She felt her heart miss a beat, and she drew in a deep breath. Magdalen was on her feet, advancing towards Misa with both hands out. The introductions were just finishing when Sam Gordon, who had been delayed, came in. Postponing any further socializing, he immediately took Misa and Vermillion off to his study to talk business.

Tolo, left alone with three women, each in her own way a shining representative of a different generation, felt big, awkward, and far too ruddy-brown for their fair company. But being well educated, he had no difficulty in giving concise, polite answers to their interested queries regarding his father's health and their life on the cattle station in Victoria.

Magdalen, obviously impressed with the youth, talked politics and about his father. "I'm very much pleased that he is a delegate to London," she said. "I know of no man better qualified than Mr. Jon Mason to present the case for federation."

"Thank you." Tolo smiled broadly. "I, too, think highly of my father."

"You resemble him very much," Jessica remarked. "You have his nose."

"But not his fair skin," Tolo said, with a confident laugh.

"Do you find that to be a handicap?" Java asked, speaking for the first time since the introductions.

"Not in the bush, not in my chosen field," he said.

"Java, that was a very personal question," Magdalen corrected her.

"Please, Mrs. Broome," Tolo replied, smiling. "I don't mind at all." Magdalen returned the smile, and then Jessica and she slipped discreetly from the room to see about dinner, allowing the young people a few moments of private conversation.

"You mentioned your chosen field," Java said.

"What do you know about the Aborigines?" he asked.

Java put on a thoughtful expression making her look quite fetching, which was not lost on Tolo. "Ummm," she said.

"They're rather pitiful here in Sydney, mostly beggars, living in horrid little shacks."

"A vanishing race, eh?" Tolo asked. "Doomed to the scrap heap of history?"

"So they say," Java agreed.

"I intend to show, when I write my book," Tolo said, "that after reaching a low, perhaps in midcentury, the numbers of the native race are increasing."

"Lord," Magdalen said, "don't tell Henry Lawson that."

"Ah, Mr. Lawson," Tolo said. "The spokesman for White Australia."

"Do you know him?" Java asked.

"No," Tolo responded.

"You're making a study of the Abo, then?" Java asked.

"I first became fascinated by their stories," he said, "on the station when Mother and I, and sometimes my father, would sit around the fire with the Aborigines at night and listen to the old ones talk about the Dream Time and the spirits. Their religious beliefs are rather original."

"Perhaps I should do some reading," she said.

"Hard to do, since there's little in print. Even the scientific community feels that the Aborigines are dying out, and therefore not worth the bother of study."

"And you're going to change that?"

"I'm going to try." He laughed. "At least the field is wide open, and there'll be nothing to compare my writings with." He leaned forward. "As soon as my father gets home from England, I'm going off to Western Australia. In the outback, across the deserts, the natives live much as they lived before the white man came to Australia. I think it's important that their beliefs, their way of life, be recorded before we alter it beyond recognition with our niceties of civilization."

"That sounds so exciting," Java said. "Sometimes I wish I were a man so that I could do exciting things."

"That would be too great a loss," Tolo said. "I meant to have you as a man. But I'm sure you could study and learn about the Aborigines."

She flushed and looked up at him. He was smiling, sitting comfortably across from her. They were of almost identical ages, he having been born in 1882, she in 1883.

"I think we have something in common," she said.

"I hope so," he replied.

"I was born on a tropical island, Java. So were you."

"Yes, that's true," he acknowledged.

She cleared her throat. "Will you go to the war?"

"No," he said.

"I think that's wise of you."

"I have no desire to kill people I don't know. I have my plans. Besides, I'm not sure that Britain is justified in trying to subdue the Boers who want, it appears, only the right to run their own lives."

"Good Lord," she said, "I hope you don't say things like that in public."

He grinned. "Mrs. Mason didn't have any stupid children." Then he put his forefinger to his mouth and flipped his lips while making a blub-blub sound. "Only Tolo," he said.

Java laughed delightedly.

"How long will you be in Sydney?" she asked.

"I don't know. A few days at least, maybe a week. Mother's bought herself a bank, and it'll take some time to get it sorted out. Probably we'll go home for the holidays, then come back afterwards. We always spent Christmas at the station, for all our people there. But then it's back to business. In fact, Mother's here tonight to ask your father if he can recommend a suitable bank manager."

"I'll take the job," Java said lightly.

"It's yours," he responded.

"But I'll want thousands in pay."

"That's fine with me."

"You're far too agreeable. I've never trusted a man who was too agreeable."

He stared at her. "I am entirely untrustworthy," he said. "Underhanded, conniving . . . and bold in my admiration for what is beautiful."

She cocked her head at him. "I think, at times, that you're mocking me."

He let his eyes feast on her pale, pretty face, on the glory of her abundant hair, gathered so neatly on her head. He ran his eyes down her slim, long neck and across the beautiful developing female curves of her figure. "Never," he said. "Be assured. Never."

Sam Gordon had a couple of suggestions for Misa and Price Vermillion. He had been associated with a young banker for some time and felt that the man would make an excellent manager. Price wrote down the name and the man's present place of employment. Sam then asked questions about the decline of Mason-Fisher in Sydney and was astounded by the brazenness of the ring of thieves. He looked at Misa Mason with new respect when he learned how and why she had purchased the Merchantman's and Marine Bank.

Dinner was pleasant, but Misa could not help but note that there were no other guests, only Tolo, Price Vermillion, and she. Both Jessica and Magdalen were warm and friendly, but she was relieved when the evening ended and she and Tolo were back in their hotel suite. She had been in her room only half hour when a knock came at the door. She had finished her bath and toilet and was propped up in bed reading last year's financial statements of what was now *her* bank. A bellman was at the door with a telegram for her. She opened it eagerly, for she knew that it was from Jon. She held the cable to the light, yet her world collapsed in darkness around her.

> *Regret to inform your husband killed 2 December stop street accident stop details follow*

She could not breathe for long, long moments, and then she sucked air into her lungs so forcefully that it burned and came out in a wail of anguish that brought Tolo running from the adjoining room. Later they would learn how Jon Mason, husband and father, walking in a light rain on the way to a conference of delegates, perhaps with his mind on them, and on his home so far away, had stepped from a curb into the path of a motor car. Although the automobile had been travelling at low speed, the impact had panicked the driver who turned the wheel suddenly and crushed Jon between the front of the automobile and a metal lamppost.

Jon Mason's embalmed body was shipped to Melbourne in a sealed coffin placed inside a freezer room on a Mason-Fisher ship.

He was buried in the place he and his family had come to love so well, the station, on a little knoll looking down on the gardens. Evan Bainbridge, a bush priest who had known Jon from the time of his first venture into wool-buying, spoke a few words at the graveside. Bainbridge had aged and withered from his years in the sun. He seemed to be entirely dried-up, thin, tanned like leather, but spry as a young joey.

"He came to this country as a child," Bainbridge said in a dry voice. "He fought in a faraway war in the name of Australia and the mother land, and he grew up with our nation. He travelled the wide oceans of the world and found love far away. To that loyal wife we say, grieve, as you must, but at the same time rejoice, for Jon Mason was a good man who genuinely cared for his fellows and gave of his substance and wealth in their care. To his son we say, be proud, for you have grown tall and manly, like your father. And be assured, both of you, that one day you will be reunited with Jon, as surely as God's grace reigns forever and ever."

Misa's weeping had been done in the privacy of her room. Tolo turned his face away, for great tears were wetting his cheeks and there was a pain of loss so great in his chest that he wanted to bellow out his rage. His mother moved to his side and took his arm and leaned against him, knowing that it would be a distraction for him, causing him to turn his attention from his own loss to hers.

The letter that Jon had posted in Cape Town on the voyage across to England had been waiting for Misa when she returned to Melbourne from the trip to Sydney. In it there was a sweetness that was cause for more weeping, for he had promised her that never again would he let either business or politics take him far away from her. He had said that he intended to sell off many of the Mason-Fisher holdings and to drop at long last the name Fisher from any of the remaining companies.

And so one thing became clear in her mind, even as she buried him so belatedly. She would carry out his plan. She would begin the careful liquidation of the widespread Mason-Fisher holdings, and she would consolidate all in two areas: the ever-profitable shipping business and in banking.

Nevertheless, the letter brought many questions into her mind.

What if he'd made that decision before going to England? What if, what if . . . It was a long time before the echo of that question disappeared.

CHAPTER XIX

As a century creaked towards its end, the British forces in South Africa were at peril. Half of the British strength was besieged in Mafeking, in Kimberley, and in the Natal railway junction town of Ladysmith. The rest were scattered thinly over hundreds of miles of frontier and were subject to being destroyed piecemeal. In the engagements fought thus far, British losses exceeded Boer losses, often by staggering numbers. The policymakers in London had two answers to the problems. First, they poured fifty-eight thousand men, nine thousand horses, and mountains of supplies into Cape Town in forty days. That such investments and movements were not the ultimate solution was illustrated by simple facts: the new khaki drill uniforms were too thin for South Africa's cold nights and abrasive environment; soldiers' boots that had looked splendid in England came apart at the soles in the dry African climate; there were more horses to feed than there were saddles to ride them; and even if all of the pontoons for building bridges that were in Africa were strung together, they would not have bridged the Orange River.

The man initially chosen to be the British commander-in-chief in South Africa, General Sir Redvers Buller, had seemed to be an excellent choice, but one of his first acts had been to split his forces, sending one group to Natal to make an effort at relieving Ladysmith, then dividing the rest into three unequal groups in the Cape Colony, where Boers outnumbered English settlers. He himself accompanied the Natal contingent, leaving his headquarters in Cape Town without its commander-in-chief.

In one week in December that threatened to make the mighty British lion the laughing-stock of the world, the Boer farmer-soldiers smashed the British in three separate engagements. They defeated Sir William Gatacre and four thousand men on a ridge

called Kissieberg Kop, near Stormberg; they outfought Lord
Methuen and eight thousand men advancing towards Kimberley
near a hill called Magersfontein; and they humiliated General
Buller himself so badly on the Tugela River in Natal, near Colenso,
that Buller advised the war office to abandon the attempt to relieve
Ladysmith. Buller sent a message to the troop commander in
Ladysmith, ordering him to burn his codebooks in preparation for
surrender.

In a very British way, the commander of the Ladysmith
garrison, Sir George White, indignantly repudiated any idea of
surrender, and Buller's very un-British behaviour inspired the
policymakers in London to take strong measures to alter the
course of the war in South Africa.

On December 18 it was announced that Frederick Sleigh
Roberts—Field-Marshal of the British Army and created Baron of
Kandahar for his brilliant long march to defeat the Afghan army
under Ayub Khan in 1880—would take over as commander-in-
chief in South Africa, replacing Buller, who would remain as
commander of the forces in Natal. In addition, the hero of
Omdurman, Kitchener of Khartoum, would be sent to South
Africa as Roberts's chief of staff.

When Slone Shannon heard that Kitchener was coming to
South Africa, he sat down immediately and wrote to the general,
reminding him that he had been one of the "boys" in the Sudan,
asking that he be reassigned to a fighting unit immediately.
Recalling ruefully the unhappy incident involving Churchill—in
which he had fired not one shot—Slone was more than ever
determined to get into this war in an active way. Churchill had
since escaped his Boer captors, and no one knew exactly where he
was; if he succeeded in eluding recapture, he would cover himself
with glory. Slone did not want glory, but he wanted his part, and
with Kitchener coming, perhaps he stood a chance to get it.

Koos De La Rey, whose revolutionary battle tactics were
making him famous, had taken Vryburg, on the Bechuanaland
border, and had formally annexed it to the Transvaal. Then,
moving rapidly, he had overcome scattered resistance in southern
Bechuanaland, and he now held the railways all the way to the
Orange River Station.

Dirk De Hartog and his commando unit—grown a bit smaller now with several men dead, others sent home with wounds, and still others missing because they simply decided to return home to work their crops—scouted deep into the northern Cape Colony and came back to De La Rey's headquarters to report that the road to Cape Town was open.

"General," Dirk said, "give me five thousand men and we'll make the Cape Colony a Boer Republic in ninety days. We'll gather men as we go south. The British are weak and scattered. The Boers in the Cape Colony are waiting for a sure indication that we're going to win this war. Let me put a force into Cape Town. Let me capture those British stores that are building up there, and the men of the Cape will rise to fight with us."

De La Rey nodded and enjoyed Dirk's vision for a moment. There was nothing he would like better than to drive south. He knew that the way was open. A force of two or three thousand could brush aside the British forces at the Orange River Station and use the Englishmen's own rails to move the army south. But it was only a dream. "My boy," he said regretfully, "I don't have five thousand men, and there is no way I'm going to get five thousand men."

"General, in God's name, we have thousands of men tied up in the sieges. Let Baden-Powell have his glory at Mafeking. Give me the men who are sitting there doing nothing."

"I have suggested that," De La Rey said. "I have begged for an invasion of the Cape Colony. We have a citizen army, Dirk. There are many who would not leave their own countries to travel so far from their families and their fields."

"General," Dirk said, "if our commanders continue their present tactics, we're going to lose this war, you know."

De La Rey's face sobered. He nodded. "We could have won. We could have taken Durban, had the army not halted at Ladysmith to surround a force that would have been impotent against us in the field. Joubert should have pressed his advance earlier and sooner, thus forcing the British to come out and fight against superior numbers and be destroyed. He did let Botha take four thousand men and some guns across the Tugela—but it wasn't enough." He paused, shaking his head. "And now, as you say, Dirk, with five thousand men we could be in Cape Town. But here we sit with thirty-five thousand good men tied up in the sieges, lobbing artillery shells into Kimberley, Mafeking, Ladysmith. And the might of the British Empire is gathering. We are as strong as we will ever be. Their strength grows daily."

"Then there's to be no invasion of the Cape Colony?" Dirk asked.

"Oh, we'll raid sporadically into the colony and make things interesting for the British—true to Boer style—but there'll never be enough men here in the south to do the job completely."

Dirk looked into the southern distance, and hopeless anger grew in him. He had not wanted this war. Some of the men in his unit still did not understand why they were fighting. One of the younger ones, though, had hit the crux of the matter when he boiled it down to this: "I guess I'm fightin' this war to see if I tip my hat to the Brit, or he tips his to me."

"General De La Rey," Dirk said sadly. "My commandos struck what might very well have been the first blow in this war. I left Natal with thirty-eight men. I now have nineteen. I'm going to take them home."

De La Rey nodded. "All right," he conceded. "I can't say I blame you." It was that kind of army. A man fought as long as he thought it advisable to fight, and then he went back to his own turf.

"When the British gather their strength," Dirk said, "and begin their drives into our states, I want to be fighting to protect my own property."

"I understand," De La Rey said. "God be with you."

In Mafeking, Matt Van Buren sought out Kelvin Broome in the hut that they had cleaned up for their use, following their clandestine arrival in the besieged town.

Broome was writing busily, but when Matt came in, he paused, put down his pen, and wiped dust and sweat from his brow with a soiled handkerchief.

"Kel," Matt said, "I have no desire to spend Christmas here."

"Now that's a cheery thought," Kelvin replied. "Surely relief will come before Christmas."

"Not a chance," Matt said. "Look, native runners come and go through the Boer lines all the time. It's not far to Bulawayo, in Rhodesia."

"We'd certainly be out of the action in Rhodesia," Kelvin said. "I came here to write about a war, Matt."

"There's a railway in Rhodesia, through Portuguese East Africa to the coast. From a Portuguese port we can get a boat down to Durban."

"Well, it does get so exciting here I can hardly stand it," Kelvin said mockingly. "And old B.P. has just about squeezed the last drop out of tongue-in-cheek stories about dogs and chickens getting killed in the regular morning bombardment." His true feelings were deeper than that. He was Australian, and like most Australians he believed in the superiority of the white race and especially the superiority of the Australian branch of the white race, but his heart was hurting for the native population of Mafeking. He had seen enough sickness, malnutrition, and out-and-out starvation, enough human misery to last him a lifetime. He had written about it, and once it got published he doubted that he would be particularly welcome among the sterling-white heroes who were defending Mafeking.

"If you're set on leaving, I'm your man," Kelvin said. "Especially if there's a telegraph at Bulawayo where I can get my dispatches out."

CHAPTER XX

When Bina awoke, the sun was already high. she opened the curtains in her bedroom, and the light poured in so strongly that she recoiled and flung one hand up to shade her eyes. It was hot in the room, and a fine sheen of perspiration dampened her upper lip. She stood in front of her dressing-table for some time and looked at her naked body, curvaceous, aglow. She rang a bell, and a solidly built Samoan woman entered almost immediately, bobbing her head.

"Draw my bath," Bina said. "Ask the girls to strip the bed completely. Wash and iron everything."

"Yes, missy," the servant said.

Now Bina met her own eyes in the mirror. There was a mocking tone there, a twisted smile on her lips. What she was seeing was a whore.

It had come about so easily. She had given her body to Clive Taylor in exchange for something of value. At first she had told herself that what she did with Clive was not prostitution, but deep down inside her, solid Irish horse sense kept saying, "Call it what you will, missy, you're trading flesh for money, even if indirectly, for by bedding Taylor you purchase the right to continue your business."

"Bath ready, missy." The Samoan handed Bina a clean towel.

She sat in the tub, brought especially for her all the way from Sydney, and tried to clear her mind, but she could not. She realized that it bothered her only in the mornings, and especially on those mornings when her bed had a masculine smell, when she felt soiled inside and out, and the servants were driven to do a thorough cleaning job on her entire suite in the fine house in Cloncurry. It would be all right soon, when she had finished her bath and felt cool—for a few moments—and clean. And, after all, the price she had collected for a few evening hours of her time matched the earnings of her best girl for an entire week.

And that made it worse, for money was the main incentive. It had been money, a sum that to Ellie, Dolly, Nancy, and the other girls would have seemed princely, that had led her to smile, nod at a suntanned, rawbone squatter who had taken a fancy to her, and to find that in bed he was a simpering, awkward boy. After the first one there were others, until it was common knowledge in northern Queensland that if a man had the money—and that meant an amount that would impoverish a small landholder—he could buy a long evening of the closest thing to heaven on the Australian earth at Bina Tyrell's house. It became a symbol of a man's high status if he could afford the madam of the house instead of one of the girls, and only a few could.

The members of the exclusive group of men who had spent the evening in Bina's private suite—she would not allow them to spend the night—had not yet reached a score when Henry Lawson, tiring of the political bickerings of Sydney, went walkabout with the aid of a good horse and fine companions and ended up riding into Cloncurry.

Lawson was a man doing battle with the world in which he lived. He had considered going to London, but he had given that up when he thought of having to parade down a street in London in top hat, gloves, and "those other gloves the swell folks wore over their boots"—spats. He was sick of the "drivel and claptrap" surrounding the federation squabble, and he sought ease for his troubled mind in the bush that he loved.

Cloncurry suited him well. It was full of swashbucklers, miners, drovers, and bushmen of all types. He heard about Bina's House on his first day there, and on his first night he was in the parlour, watching and listening as a truly beautiful woman played the piano and sang. His companions were taken in hand by Ellie and the still childlike Dolly and soon disappeared, but Lawson waved off the attentions of first Nancy and then several others and, with a drink in hand, kept his attention on the woman he had been told was the madam, Miss Bina Tyrell herself. He could tell that the liquid in the glass that she touched to her lips between songs was water. The glass was kept filled by a dark Kanaka woman, but he was not disturbed at seeing a member of the lesser race firmly in her place as a servant.

Bina was aware that the house had a rather famous guest. When she finished a particularly sad love song and the parlour was quiet, she glanced over at Lawson, planning to go to him and welcome him. He beat her to it, arriving at the piano even as she closed the lid and started to rise.

"Charming, absolutely charming," he said. "You sing beautifully."

"Thank you. Since it comes from you, Mr. Lawson, I particularly value the compliment."

"Ah?" He smiled. "I had hoped to travel incognito."

"Whatever for?" she asked. "All Australia loves you."

No mere whorehouse madam, this one, he was thinking. She had the looks, the manner, the instincts of a true courtesan. Fit to be the mistress of a king, but there were no kings in the Australian bush.

"You overstate," he said, smiling, "but I am flattered."

"Will you read for us?" she asked, her face showing such suppressed excitement that he couldn't say no.

"Well," he said, with a wry grin, "it would be a first, wouldn't it?"

Bina stood, rang a little bell that she kept on top of the piano. When she had the attention of everyone in the room, perhaps twenty people, most of them men, she said, "Mates, here's Henry Lawson."

That simple introduction brought a stomping of feet, whistles, shouts, clapping.

"Any of you blokes care to hear Henry read some of his verse?" Bina shouted.

There was wild approval, which subsided when Henry stepped out in front of the piano, put his hands in his pockets, and looked up at the ceiling. "What'll it be, mates?" he asked.

In the hubbub of voices he stood, smiling gently, at peace for the moment with men he knew naturally—even if he did not know their names.

" 'Our Andy'," were the words heard most often.

"All right, cut the yabber," Lawson said smilingly. "I won't talk long, maybe ten minutes, and then each of you can grab your girl and go have your naughty to your heart's content. But one of you bushrangers is going to have to shout me a beer."

The men vied for the honour, but were moved off by Bina who said, "On the house, Mr. Lawson."

"You jokers know that I've written a few poems other than 'Our Andy', don't you?" Lawson grinned. "How about this one:

> 'My father's picture hangs on the wall, and
>   father-in-law's as well.
> One was a bushman and one a Norse from the seaport of
>   Arundel.'

There was energetic applause when Lawson finished, and a man shouted, " 'Our Andy'."

Lawson sighed, drew back his shoulders:

> 'Our Andy's gone to battle now
> 'Gainst Drought, the red marauder.'

A hush greeted the end of the story. These were men who knew the harsh dry country for what it was, an enemy, a killer at times. Lawson had caught the spirit of the struggle.

Bina seated Lawson at her table in a corner of the room, shielded from the view of most by a garish oriental screen. "Beer, or something stronger?" she asked.

"Beer," Lawson said. He was content. He wrote his poems for men like those out there in the parlour, men who worked hard and braved the loneliness and the sandstorms, the floods and the droughts. To be accepted by them, to be praised by them was, for the moment, all he needed.

"Are you hungry?" Bina asked.

"Not for food," Lawson said.

She laughed.

"I can't afford you, Bina," he said. "I'm no rich man. I'm just a writer, and not a hard-working one at that."

"Let's say that we're working on the barter system tonight," Bina said.

"Then I am pleased to have sung for my supper and for dessert," Lawson said.

For the first time since Lester had disappeared she was treated tenderly, treasured and cherished. In the dreamy aftermath, she lay uncovered on the sheets, exposed to the cool night air coming in through the open windows. After concerned questioning from Lawson, she found herself telling him the story of her life from the time she began to realize that there was more in the world than the seamy life of the east end of London. Lawson cursed under his breath when she talked about Joseph Van Buren.

"God, I love this country," Lawson said, after Bina had fallen silent. "While I deplore men like your squatter, I can't help but admire him, too, because this country belongs to the tough. The first ones, the convicts, had to be tough to survive, and I guess they passed something down to all of us, even if we're not directly of their blood. Individuals here and the country as a whole get rich by defying the conventions of the old world. We're building a new breed of men in Australia, and the world is going to hear from us one day, mark my words."

Bina made no comment. It was past midnight. A fresh breeze was at last banishing the heat of the day. Oddly, she did not ache to get Lawson out of her bed, as she had the others.

"Take yourself," Lawson said after a long pause. "You're a member of this new breed, Bina. A regular Australian success story."

She made a sound of denial.

"No, truly," he said. "From failure you have brought success."

"Ah, yes, I am the queen of Cloncurry night life," she said with a chuckle.

"Don't disparage it too much," he said. "And don't look back, Bina. A very wise man who lived around the time of Christ wrote what I take to be the finest advice. His name was Hillel. He said, 'Live well. That is the best revenge.' "

"I've given up thinking of revenge, after all," she said. "For a while I burned with it, wanted to fight all the squatters. The burn began to ease, and then I realized that one woman could do nothing against them."

"It doesn't matter. It will all sort itself out, one way or the other. Unification is coming, and with it there'll be changes. The voice of the people will be stronger then."

"I suppose so," she said. She yawned deeply. "G'night, then."

"Leave me?" he whispered, gathering her in his arms.

"I think it's customary to sleep at least part of the night."

"We can sleep when we're dead, beautiful Bina." He began to caress her, and in spite of her sleepiness she responded.

"Come to Sydney," he said, later, when there was a faint light at the window.

"To do what?"

"To lift my spirits now and again," he said.

"I'm not, as you said, some fancy rich woman."

"You could be the finest thing in Sydney, in all Australia. All you have to do is sit at the piano, demure and ladylike, and sing."

"Oh, ho," she said sarcastically.

"Truly. The stage would welcome you."

"What, and ruin my reputation?" she asked, with a giggle. "You know what terrible things people say about actresses."

"All that, and wit besides," he said fondly. "My dear Bina, I am not just yabbering. For example, you could open a cabaret, with good food and your singing and playing, and also some dancing. You could be successful in Sydney, in spite of its Victorian front," he said. "You could be successful there as well, if that is what you want."

"Henry," she said, "except for an overwhelming case of sleepiness, this morning I like my life just the way it is. Good night."

"Well, that's Sydney's loss," he said. "You could be the freshest, biggest thing to hit that old town. We diggers have always made heroes out of rebels. We've built the bushrangers—who were, after all, outlaws and killers—into imitation heroes like the American train robber, Jesse James. You could be the female version of Harry Redford."

"Who?" she asked.

"Harry Redford. He stole a herd of one thousand cattle and drove them almost two thousand miles through the outback to Adelaide. They caught him there and tried him, but the jury acquitted him because of the marvellous audacity of the wonderful droving feat. Whenever men talk of daring and the bush they'll mention Harry Redford. It would be the same with you. I warrant that you'd be invited to the houses of the elite because they would secretly admire you for doing what was necessary to escape a pretty grim life. Bina Tyrell, rebel, heroine."

For three more nights Henry Lawson graced the parlour, reading his verse each night by popular demand, and for three nights he was in Bina's bed. When he left, there were no tears in Bina's eyes, only a glow of warmth all around her body. She had had her permanent man, even if Lester had been ripped out of her life after so short a time. She knew that she would see Henry Lawson again some day. She had no idea when, or how, but there was that certainty in her. For a short time, again, she would fill some need in him, and he would fill her and, for brief hours, make her forget what she had become.

It still seemed odd to Bina that Christmas came during the summer in Australia. It was hard to get excited about the holiday when the temperature soared into the nineties each day with the maximum summer temperatures still to come after the turn of the new year, in January. The girls decorated the parlour, and clients and girls alike joined in with Bina to sing the old songs of the season, but what had always been a glad holiday seemed here quite gloomy. There was no work on Christmas day or Christmas night. Some of the girls needed a day of rest to recover from the riotous Christmas Eve party. The residents of Bina's House gathered for roast goose, trimmings, and all the side dishes. For a while, at table, with the girls chattering on about their private affairs, their desire for a new dress, what a certain cattle rider had said about a certain hairdo, Bina could forget herself and smile at their sometimes childish ways that blended so smoothly with their womanly profession. She was fond of all of them, especially her three original friends, Ellie, Dolly, and Nancy. When the meal was over, she retired to her room, and sent her servant to ask the three to come to her.

Ellie was first, rubbing her stomach and groaning that she had eaten too much; then the others came, too.

Bina had laid a table with a Venetian glass decanter set, four tiny glasses with gold and silver trim beside a decanter filled with a fruity liqueur. "I just wanted to have a few minutes with you," she said, "the four of us together."

"Bless you, luv," Ellie said.

"A toast to us then," she said, pouring the liquor and handing a glass to each.

"Never did get used to drinking out of these dinky things," said Nancy with a smile, but she lifted the glass to her lips.

"To us, then," Bina said. "To Bina, Ellie, Dolly, and Nancy, the original four."

"Long may we live," Dolly said, tossing down the liqueur in one gulp and then making a face at its sweetness. "Gor, Bina, are you trying to poison us?"

Bina laughed. "We've come a long way," she said. "Do you girls have any idea how much money I've put into your bank accounts for you in just these few months?"

"I see the amount in the little book, and it scares me," Ellie commented.

"It shouldn't," Bina replied. "You said, Ellie, that you wanted to open a dress shop in Sydney. I told you that you would be able to do it in just a few years. I'd say that you have more than enough now, if you're ready for it."

"That's what scares me," Ellie said. "For years I've dreamed of that, and then I look and see pounds in four figures, and I say, Ellie, girl, there's your dream, and it gives me the cold shivers."

"I don't understand," Bina said.

"Luv, since I was a girl in pigtails, I've had someone looking out after me. When I ran away from home, I found my first fancy man. Then you. I think of being on my own, of being responsible for a building and a business, and all I want to do is run to my room and hide my head. I think I'll just let the money accumulate, thank you, let it grow for the time when I'm too old to make a man want me. Then maybe I'll open up a boardinghouse for old whores, and we'll all sit around on winter nights, comparing the men we've known."

"As for me, I'm going shopping tomorrow," Nancy said. "Anyone want to come? Dolly saw a red dress that she said would just fit me."

"Lovely," Dolly said. "Just your thing, Nance."

"Well, cheers, luv," Nancy said, finishing her drink and standing.

"Will you stay a moment, Ellie?" Bina said, as the others left. Alone with Ellie she said, "You're not getting any younger, Ellie."

"They still come for me and ask for me," Ellie said stiffly.

"Of course you're still attractive. I didn't mean that. I just thought that we might talk. How about if I went with you to Sydney, Ellie, if I helped you get the dress shop established?"

"Now that scares me even more," Ellie said. "It makes me think you're planning on leaving us."

"I was thinking of our going together, you and I."

"And what about Dolly and Nancy?"

"Nancy has a good head," Bina said. "Haven't you noticed that I've asked her to do the books lately? She's smart, Nancy is. She can handle the business end of it. And little Dolly is tough. She can keep the girls in line and keep the constables happy with free samples now and then."

"We wouldn't be gone a week before some fancy man would move into this suite," Ellie said. "I don't want to see that happen to the girls."

"All right," Bina answered. "I'll keep that in mind."

Christmas afternoon. She took off her dress and put on a peignoir, then sat in front of the mirror to brush her hair. She was thinking of the child that had been born in the bush station and how it had mewled so plaintively as it died, and of the lyrebird that had been a devil to torment her. When a knock came on the door she said, "It's open."

"Christmas present," Clive Taylor said. He was in civilian clothing, looking quite smart in suit and tie. He carried a gaily wrapped package.

"Why, how nice, Clive," she said, rising. The peignoir, not chosen for modesty, showed a startling length of leg as she walked to him and kissed him on the cheek. She was glad to see him, actually. It had been a melancholy day so far, and her effort to establish common ground with Ellie had failed. She opened the package and thanked him for the tortoise-shell combs. He began to remove his clothing, throwing his coat aside and unbuttoning his shirt.

"Not today, Clive," she said, smiling.

"Not in the mood, eh?" he asked, pausing.

"Well, not on the Saviour's birthday," she said.

"Oh, come along now," he said casually, removing his shirt, "everyone knows that December twenty-fifth was chosen rather arbitrarily. No one knows when the lad was really born."

"Clive," she said, her voice firm, "if you don't mind, not today."

He let his shirt fall to the floor and looked at her, his face hard. "I do bloody well mind," he said. "I rode over here with the intention of having you, and that I am going to do."

She backed away, holding up her hands. As he tried to seize her, she slapped him with all her strength, the blow resounding in the room like a pistol shot. He looked at her coldly for a moment, and then, calmly, deliberately, he slapped her back with his huge hand. She reeled sideways, bounced off the bed, and hit the floor. Even as she fell, she was trying to crawl away, the hem of the peignoir ripping as it caught under her knee.

"Now, let's get started, Bina," he said, speaking so calmly that it chilled her.

She pulled herself to her feet at the cupboard door, supporting herself on the knob. Then she threw the door open, seized a shotgun from inside, and whirled, both barrels pointing at his middle. "*That* was the last time you will ever strike me, do you understand?"

"Put that bloody thing away before someone gets hurt," he said.

"If anyone gets hurt, it will be you," she warned. "You'd better go now, Clive. I don't like what you've done. No man has ever struck me."

"There'll be something similar again if you don't use your head," he said.

"Get out."

His eyes widened in recognition of her seriousness as he saw her finger tighten on the trigger. He held up both hands to placate her and backed away. "All right, I'm going."

The look in his eyes frightened her. She knew that he would be back, and that when he came there would be trouble.

"I know that you killed a man in the bush," he said. "Don't think you can get away with it here."

She was trembling. "Can we talk?" she asked, her voice cracking. Even with the shotgun in her own hands, he still had all the advantages. He was a man who would not hesitate to use his greater physical strength. He was the law in Cloncurry, and at any given moment he could put Bina and all of her girls behind bars.

"I'm listening," he said, his voice cold.

"I refused you only because it's Christmas Day." Bina was recapturing her courage.

"Goodonyer," he said sarcastically.

"But now that you've struck me, if you ever touch me again, in any way, I will kill you."

He sneered. "I think you're going to enjoy prison. Just who the hell do you think you are?"

"I know who I am and what I am, and I know that as long as there's breath in my body, I will retain the right to say no to you, or to anyone else," she said. She turned and put the shotgun back into the cupboard. He was still standing near the door. "Sit down," she said. "I want to make you a proposition."

He sat, his face still dark. He had pulled on his shirt and he was buttoning it.

"I have two thousand pounds invested in this house, what with the original cost and the improvements. There are, as you know, ten girls working here, and I think you can estimate their productivity and the money they bring in. The house takes ten percent of their earnings, and the house does their bookkeeping for them—honestly. I'm offering you the house for what I have in it. Your investment will be returned in less than six months. Are you interested?"

"You know I don't have that kind of money. And I don't know anything about handling girls."

"Ellie and Dolly will handle the girls for you. Nancy will help you with the book work. You can forward five percent of the gross to me until you've met the purchase price."

He was looking at her with interest. "That's a generous offer. But why, and how do you know you can trust me?"

She laughed. "I don't think you'd steal, not even from a whore."

"Look, Bina, maybe I was a little out of hand a moment ago. There's no need—"

"I've been thinking about leaving for some time now," she said. "I want to get out of the business before I lose all sensibility and start taking all comers like the girls."

"Yes," he said. "I can understand that. Where will you go?"

"I don't know," she lied. "Do we have a deal?"

"We need to talk about it some more. I'm surprised, but, yes, it sounds interesting."

"At least you won't have to cut into the profits by bribing the chief constable," she said, smiling.

"There is that," he acknowledged, grinning.

Bina employed a solicitor to put it in writing. At the signing she said to Clive, "The original three are partners in this enterprise. Treat them well, and they'll be loyal. I suspect that in spite of their crocodile tears at my leaving they're secretly relieved to have a man in charge of their lives again." She touched him on the hand. "Don't look down on them, Clive. Don't steal from them. And don't let some fancy man come along and talk them out of the money that I've saved for them from their earnings."

"I think I should have married you," he said.

She raised her eyebrows as if in mock shock.

"I'll take care of them," he said. "Drop us a line and let us know what you're doing?"

"We'll see," she said, but Bina had no intention of ever keeping in touch with anyone in Cloncurry. She left without a backward look.

By the time she had reached the coast at Townsville and had luxuriated in a hotel bathtub big enough to hold a small ocean of hot water, her life in Cloncurry seemed unreal. When she got out of the tub, she wrapped a huge towel around her and stood in front of a full-length mirror. She felt and looked cleaner. And she looked younger. More than good enough. Ready for a fresh start.

She wondered if it wouldn't be wise—she was not wealthy, but she had enough money to provide a modest living for herself for many years—simply to find a little town somewhere by the sea and settle in. She'd become a churchgoer. God forgave, didn't he?

But there was something that drove her to book a passage on a coastal ship leaving almost immediately. Henry Lawson's words kept coming back to her. She thought it would be rather nice to be "the freshest, the biggest thing" ever to hit Sydney, even nicer to follow the advice of old Hillel. To live comfortably with a little style was the goal she set before her.

PART TWO
1900

CHAPTER XXI

The Aborigines, having no calendar, regarded the first day of a new year and even the first day of a new century as just another day. Their ceremonies for newness had to do with season, not a printed number on a piece of paper hanging on the wall. Tolo Mason spent the morning of January 1, 1900, helping the stockmen move a small drove of cattle to better grass. With the cattle in the new pasturage he rode back to the house.

His first personal experience with death had come to him at the station. He had never forgotten the sight of the Aboriginal girl Daringa lying on the straw-littered floor of a barn; he carried in his mind a permanent picture of her in death, her neck broken and her features twisted. Soon afterwards, he had watched the painful, wasting demise of his tutor, Dane de Lausenette, another type of death and one that aroused in him questions that continued to this day.

The loss of his father had at first been more of an abstraction than either of the two deaths he had witnessed previously. He had not been able to believe the news of the telegram, the cold words printed on paper. He had experienced no feeling of loss, only a numbness, which was denial. It could not be, he had felt. Jon Mason was too real, too vital, too much a part of his life to be dead. Jon was there, somehwere, in England or on the sea, alive, and coming back to his wife and his son and the land that he had come to love.

When Jon did come home, in a sealed coffin, the fact became a bit more real for Tolo, but it was only at the funeral itself that his tears came, the ceremony bringing to the surface all the pain and rage of his loss.

Reaching the house, he dismounted and handed his horse to an Abo boy, beat the dust from his trousers with his floppy-brimmed bush hat, and entered. The front rooms were insulated against the day's heat by closed draperies; thus they retained a residual of the night's coolness. He heard the clatter of pans from the kitchen, pressed on to see that the door to his father's office was open. Misa was at the desk, her dark hair drawn into a loose bun, dressed in black for mourning, as convention required, but in a frock so well tailored that it seemed almost as if she had chosen it expressly for Jon, who had always enjoyed seeing her well and expensively dressed.

"Ah," she said as her son appeared at the door, "you've come at a good time. I was going to send for you."

Tolo sat down, crossing his long legs. He knew that she had been spending many hours in the office in the past few days.

"I gave you a copy of your father's will the other day," she said. "Did you read it?"

He made a face. He had not read the document.

Misa laughed. "Your lack of greed is commendable. Your lack of interest is not. Don't you care what we own, what will someday be all yours?"

"Here I can ride the land, move the cattle, and watch the water supply rise and fall with the season. I can't ride the lands of a station in northern Queensland."

"As you know," she said, "in the last letter your father wrote to me, he told us how he had decided to sell off the stations and sugarcane plantations in Queensland. I intend to carry out his wishes."

Tolo shrugged.

"I must go up to Sydney again."

The tone of her voice put him on guard. He was perfectly content to say on the station, at least until the time was right for him to travel to Western Australia to begin his field study of the Aborigines of the Great Sandy Desert and the outback. She was, he knew, going to ask him to go to Sydney with her. Tolo immediately felt a push and a pull. Here, on the station and in the saddle, while working with the stockmen, he had no worries. It was a life he loved. In Sydney he might see Java Gordon again, and he wondered about the magnetism he sensed drawing them together.

"I'd like you to go to Queensland," she said.

He looked up frowning.

"Through the estate agents, I have received estimates of the worth of the Mason-Fisher holdings in Queensland," she said. "I've never seen the properties themselves." She paused and felt the tears sting in her eyes as she remembered that she had in fact seen one of the Fisher stations, the one where she had first met Jon. "Well, at least I've not seen all of them," she said. "I'd like your opinion as to the asking prices."

"How would I know?" he asked.

"You have eyes. You can see the condition of the buildings and whether there is water. You can observe and describe the places to me. We can travel to Sydney together, and you can go on from there."

Tolo sighed. He did not like the idea of leaving her, not with the loss of his father so recent and so raw, and this venture into Queensland would take months. However, perhaps it was all for the best. Her newly acquired bank in Sydney seemed to be occupying her interest, taking her mind off her grief. He himself was most content when he was working, and it was most probably the same with her.

"Mother, we won't sell this place, will we?"

"No," she said, smiling. "I know how you feel about it. It can be yours now if you like. We can have the deed transferred into your name, although I'd be your legal guardian until you're twenty-one."

He laughed. "I'm happy with the way things are. If I allowed you to put the station in my name, next thing you'd be trying to push off your shipping firms and banks on me," he said. "You're the business head in this family."

"I'll be looking for a house in Sydney," she said. "Before you leave for Queensland, I'd like your help in choosing one."

He felt a sadness begin then, for he suspected that their lives would be forever changed by her decision to buy a house in Sydney. That sadness grew until, as he stood beside the carriage that would take them into Melbourne, a carriage towing a loaded wagon with all of Misa's books and papers, all her clothing, and many personal things that she did not want to leave behind, he felt again the full weight of the loss of his father. Jon Mason and the station where Tolo had grown up were linked in the young man's memories with a poignancy that made his eyes water as he stepped up into the driver's seat and clucked to the horses.

He had taken only a few things of his own. He had his books, those dealing with Australian history and the Aborigines, his riding boots and bush clothes. He had left behind such things as the boomerang fashioned for him by old Colbee, the telescope that had been a Christmas gift from his father, his rock collection, all the toys and distractions of his youth, for he considered the station his permanent home. He would be coming back.

As he drove away from the station, everything overwhelmed him: the death, the loss, the change. He drove with his head held high, but tears were streaming down his cheeks. If Misa saw, she made no comment, gave no sign that she was aware that her big, strong son was weeping.

"Someday," Misa said, as she and Tolo strolled the deck of the Mason Company steamer that had left the rough waters of the Bass Strait behind and was rounding the southwestern tip of Australia into the Tasman Sea, "the Australian states will work out their differences about railway gauges, and there'll be an easier train service between Melbourne and Sydney."

"The blood of your fathers is in me," Tolo said. "I rather enjoy the sea, the smell of it, and the movement under foot."

"Until the storms come," she said.

He laughed. She seemed to have left behind her mourning, although she still wore black. "When I come back from Queensland, Mother, I want to prepare for my trip to Western Australia."

She nodded. "I've been thinking of that," she said. "Wouldn't you be better prepared for what you want to do by spending a year or two in university?"

"To study what?" he asked. "The learned men in the colleges are still arguing about Darwin's theories. Their primary concern with the study of man and his cultures, for the moment at least, seems to be what to call it. The French are arguing over whether it should be called *anthripologie* or *ethnologie*. I don't care for that sort of academic debate. I simply want to search out and record the beliefs of the Aborigines wherever I can find them, getting the stories of the people and their past before they're irreversibly altered by contact with the white man."

Misa Mason was very proud of her son. In Sydney she enjoyed the looks they got when they walked together through the lobby of the hotel. She knew they made a striking pair: the neat, pretty Samoan woman and tall, broad-shouldered, bronzed young man dressed in a suit of the latest cut.

With an estate agent, they inspected a dozen houses, none of them at all suitable. Misa was grateful for Tolo's patience in looking at each one. Almost eighteen years old now, he was a young man with a dream of his own, and she was proud and pleased that he loved her enough to postpone his dream and help her as she had asked.

True to his background, Tolo asked the agent about the availability of a country house near Sydney.

"No, Tolo," Misa objected gently. "You won't be here much. I'm the one who'd have to make a daily drive into the city if we bought a place in the country." And in the end Misa selected a town house, a semi-detached building not far from the Broome-Gordon house.

When Tolo said his good-byes and boarded ship for Townsville in Queensland, Misa was still living in the hotel, making daily excursions to the bank and to the house to check on the decorators, also visiting art galleries and buying pictures by Australian artists to hang in the new house.

Although Misa had the comfort of a few of her personal items in the hotel room, most of her things were in storage until the house was ready. The hotel was clean and new, the rooms very quiet and a bit barren and sterile, all too conducive to periodic waves of utter loneliness that took her by surprise and drove her nearly to panic. She tried to bury herself in her work. The days went rapidly by as she delved into every aspect of the workings of the Merchantman's and Marine Bank.

One morning she held a long discussion with the bank's new manager and its board of directors, considering a shift in direction of the bank's business.

"Australia is changing," she told them. "Whether we like it or not, there is going to be a definite change in the pattern of land ownership in the coming years. We lend money to squatters; I see this in the books. But we hold very few small mortgages."

"The large landowners, the squatters, are the ones with a solid

financial history," commented Daniel Moore. He was the young
man whom Sam Gordon had recommended to Misa for the
position of manager of her bank. In his early thirties, Daniel had
dark hair that he combed straight back, and he was clean-shaven,
perhaps to display his strong chin and pleasant mouth. He had a
solid look about him, dressing well and quite conservatively, and
Misa had already developed confidence in him as an excellent
choice for her bank.

"But how does a man acquire a financial history and build some
standing unless some bank makes that first loan to him?" Misa
asked.

Dan Moore smiled and spread his hands. "Mrs. Mason, if a
smallholder applies for a loan at this bank, his application is, of
course, considered. I haven't been with the bank very long, but I've
seen a few such applications. I'm sorry to say that it's usually the
opinion of the loan committee that the applicant hasn't a chance of
paying off such a loan."

"I want this bank to operate on sound business principles,"
Misa said, "but to humour me, Mr. Moore, will you please appoint
someone to make a study of land sales and purchases in that part
of New South Wales that could be served by our bank? I may be
wrong, but I have an intuition that we are missing out on a good
source of business. Perhaps I'm just being idealistic, and if so, then
it is up to you gentlemen to tell me so, but I think that I'd like to
have a part in this change that's coming. I think I'd like to be able
to look back in my old age and say that this bank and I had helped
in the formation of a new segment of society in New South Wales,
a new and growing group of small, prosperous landowners."

She was still thinking about the day's discussion when she
finished changing into a smart, dark gown designed for evening
wear and stood before a mirror in the hotel suite to examine
herself. She saw a woman who was still young and vital, dark and
comely, with a thick black mass of hair piled on her head in that
deliberately sensuous style that had swept the world of female
fashion from America and the pen of Charles Dana Gibson,
creator of the Gibson Girl.

She chose a rose from a vase of the fresh flowers that she had
ordered to be delivered to her room daily, and trimming the stem
to the right length to stick into her hair at the side, she smiled. For

years she had done everything possible to divert attention from her brown skin. Oddly enough, since Jon's death, she had undergone a change of attitude. Admittedly, the fortune that had been created by Marcus Fisher, Jon's stepfather, and increased by Jon was enough to give any woman a certain confidence. Yet it was not only the fact that she had enough money to live anywhere in the world, to buy anything she wanted, to be totally independent of people and their prejudices that caused her to start wearing a flower in her hair day after day. Though the words remained unspoken, Misa made the declaration again and again: *Look at me, I am Samoan.* A gesture of defiance and of personal pride it was, and with the rose in her hair she walked regally into the dining room.

"Your table is ready, madam," the headwaiter said with a bow. Generous tips bought the overt respect of that sort of man, even if they did not entirely erase his covert presumption of superiority and his resentment at having to show deference to anyone with dark skin.

Misa nodded and started to follow the headwaiter's lead, but their path was blocked by a small, pretty, black-haired woman in a gown that was the height of fashion.

"Here, here!" the woman burst out. "I've been waiting for half an hour and you're seating *this* lady immediately?"

"Madam Mason has a permanent table booked," the head-waiter said. "I'm so sorry. You shouldn't have to wait much longer. Now, if you please?" He stared at the woman, but she made no move to get out of his way.

Misa was smiling, admiring the woman's outburst, but wondering if it came from the fact that a woman of brown skin had been given priority over a lady of very white, very creamy, very British skin. She decided to find out. "I think I might have a solution to this problem," she said. She fastened her large brown eyes directly on the eyes of the other woman. "My table is quite large enough for two, and I would enjoy having company. Would you care to join me?"

"I'd love to," the woman said without hesitation, just a trace of bush in her accent. "If I don't eat soon, I'll perish right away."

Misa held out her hand. "I'm Misa Mason."

"Bless you, luv," the other said, taking Misa's hand. "I'm Bina Tyrell."

Neither woman could help but notice that numerous male heads turned as they walked behind the waiter to Misa's table in a quiet corner. Bina looked at Misa and winked, smiling wryly. The gesture made Misa smile spontaneously. She felt a surprising warmth for this woman with whom she had exchanged fewer than a dozen words. She took her usual chair, and Bina sat opposite her, perusing her with frank curiosity.

"You're Samoan?" Bina asked.

"Yes."

"Lovely. Very lovely indeed."

"Thank you," Misa said, smiling with genuine pleasure, "but I think it was you that they were admiring."

Bina laughed. "It's all in knowing how to dress, how to use makeup, and how to swing your hips when you walk, isn't it?"

A laugh burst out from Misa. "Are you so frank and honest about everything?"

"Everything except my age and my bank balance," Bina said. "And speaking of the latter, yours must be impressive. I priced material like that in the dress you're wearing just last week." She wrung her hands to express the asking price of the material. "Not that I'm being nosey, mind you."

"I detect a bit of Ireland, a lot of London, and a bit of the bush in your speech," Misa said, changing the subject.

"Right on all counts," Bina said.

"My son and I have lived on a station in Victoria until quite recently," Misa said.

"I'm down from Cloncurry," Bina said. "But before that my husband and I had a small station in central Queensland."

"Really," Misa said. "It happens that I'm interested in learning about smallholders and how they operate."

"Whatever for?" Bina asked quizzically. "It's a losing game. If the floods don't get you, the drought will. Or you'll be gobbled up by some squatter who sits on all the good grass and the only water that's available during the drought."

"Did that happen to you?"

Misa listened as Bina, who had warmed to Misa as much as Misa had warmed to her, told about losing her husband and then her land. Misa felt even more drawn to the pretty, lively little black-haired woman, for they had the loss of a spouse in common.

"If you had been able to borrow money at a good rate of interest from a bank, would you have been able to hold out?" Misa asked.

"Perhaps, if the rains had come," Bina said. "But I've talked to a lot of people since then. Many of them borrowed money from a squatter; then when it was time to pay, the only way out was to have their land taken. A bank? They'd do the same thing, wouldn't they?"

"Well, a bank must operate in a businesslike manner. If a loan is made with land as the security and the loan is defaulted, the bank must take the land. You see it isn't the bank's money that is at risk. The money belongs to depositors and investors."

"You sound as if you know something about banks," Bina said.

"Not as much as I'd like to know," Misa said.

Bina laughed. "I need to learn a bit about banks myself," she said. "I came to Sydney with the proceeds from the sale of my business in Cloncurry to open a fine restaurant and take Sydney by storm with my fabulous talent. The only problem is that my estimates of the money needed were based on life in the bush and in Cloncurry. Sydney property doesn't come cheap."

"I know," Misa said. "You had a restaurant in Cloncurry?"

"Actually, it was more like a boardinghouse," Bina said guardedly. "You might say a boardinghouse and nightclub combined, perhaps."

Their conversation rambled elsewhere amiably before and during the meal, and with relaxed ease afterwards as each of them sipped a glass of white wine. Then Misa returned to the subject of property. "You say you are having trouble finding a suitable building in Sydney?"

"I've found one that's perfect," Bina said. "It's large enough to have an orchestra stand and a dance floor, and it's in a respectable location. But I simply can't afford it with my available funds."

"In the meantime?" Misa asked.

"In the meantime, I'm going to work," Bina said. "I do hope that you don't feel brought down when you find that you've been dining with an entertainer."

"We brown-skinned folk have few prejudices," Misa replied.

"If you're interested, you can see me at the Sydney Palace,

starting tomorrow night, as a matter of fact. I'll be on before the trained dogs and after the comedy team."

"Well, I'll just have to come to see you," Misa said.

"Sorry, I don't have any passes yet. If you want to wait a couple of nights I can get you one."

"No, I'll come tomorrow," Misa said.

"Don't sit in the front row," Bina cautioned. "Too close. You hear the dancers' feet pounding on the boards, and you smell the sweat of the acrobats."

When they parted, Misa had a strong feeling she had made a friend. She looked forward to seeing Bina's performance, and the next day seemed long and her table quite empty when she went down for an early dinner.

Liking Bina as she did, Misa was curious about her. She had discovered quickly that the bank had certain ways of getting information about people, so while waiting for the evening's entertainment, she asked Daniel Moore to find out what he could. He sent a telegram to a bank in Cloncurry, addressed to a man he knew there. By the time Misa had taken a hansom cab to the theatre that night, she knew a lot more about Bina Tyrell than she had expected.

Misa, suspecting that the Sydney Palace would not be exactly the meeting place of the elite, had dressed plainly, and once inside the theatre, the composition of the audience showed that she had assessed the situation correctly. The audience was mainly middle- and working-class folk and the programme was a mixed bill of typical vaudeville acts, beginning with dancers and singers. When at last the curtain went up on what the barker said was the most sensational new act to hit Sydney for years, Misa leaned forward to see her friend sweep from the wings dressed in a flamboyant silver gown.

Bina turned when she reached the piano and bowed. She was, as she arranged her gown and seated herself, the epitome of the lady, her face stiff, brows raised, eyes narrowed and looking down her nose pensively.

"I have been told," she said in a haughty voice with an exaggerated Pommy accent, "that the fair city of Sydney lacks culture, and so I have come from that seat of culture, Cloncurry, to enlighten this benighted town with certain classical selections."

She poised, lowered her hands, and began to play Chopin's "Minute Waltz". The audience stirred restlessly. Misa held her breath, knowing that agony of embarrassment one feels when a friend or a member of the family is making a fool of himself.

"This," Bina said in that haughty tone, still playing softly, "is called the 'Minute Waltz'." Then she grinned and rolled her eyes. "In Cloncurry, however"—suddenly now she was talking bush—"we are so advanced that we play it in thirty seconds." She began to put a ragtime rhythm to the piece, and her audience chuckled appreciatively. Then, without a pause, she moved into a slightly bawdy, fast-moving London music-hall song, about a young lady in an old and lucrative profession who decides to become a virgin once again. The audience roared. Bina's voice was at times growling, rowdy, but always a very feminine and very musical contralto. She knew how to use it to best advantage. When she had finished the song, she began to play Bach and spoke again of the high culture of Cloncurry until, without warning. she once again launched into a rollicking number. When the curtain closed, it had to be opened five times for Bina to acknowledge the applause, and she had to perform two encores before the audience was finally satisfied.

Misa decided against trying to visit Bina in her dressing room. She had ordered flowers to be delivered there during Bina's performance. It was also a simple matter, with the help of a pound note, to arrange for one of the ushers to deliver a note to Bina. She wrote: "Wonderful! I am so impressed. Must talk with you. Meet me at"—she gave only the address of the bank—"one o'clock tomorrow afternoon. Ask for me by name."

Bina arrived a few minutes early at Misa's office the next day. When a secretary announced that Miss Tyrell was waiting, Misa leapt from her chair and opened the door herself.

" 'Ere," Bina said, looking puzzled and affecting a strong Cockney accent, "wot's this, then? 'Ave they pinched you for writing bum cheques?"

"Come in, come in," Misa said, taking Bina's hand. "Oh, you were so good last night. So very good."

"You work here, is that it?" Bina asked. "That's why you were asking questions about bank loans to smallholders and all?"

"I work here," Misa admitted. "Come, sit down and we'll have some tea. And then I want you to tell me about this place you've found that you think would be suitable for your restaurant."

Bina sat, looking around at the rich wood of the furnishings. The panelling on the walls had originated somewhere in the Indian subcontinent and had made the long trip to England to be handcrafted, then back across the oceans to Sydney. She began to describe the building she had found, and before she realized what was happening, she was in a cab with Misa and then they were going through the building with an estate agent. He was appropriately polite to the white woman and not so polite to the brown-skinned one until, with a flush on his face, he realized that the brown-skinned one was the one who was helping finance the enterprise.

"These rooms would be kitchen and service areas," Bina said.

"How much to equip the kitchen?" Misa inquired.

"Expensive, perhaps a thousand pounds."

"The main dining room would have to be decorated," Misa added.

"And a dance floor installed. Hardwood. Expensive," Bina commented.

"How much would you need to do it all, with what you have already?"

"Fifteen thousand pounds."

Misa turned to the estate agent. "Will you accept a cheque on the Merchantman's and Marine Bank to bind purchase?"

"That would depend, madam," he said, "on the signature on the cheque."

"Would the signature of the owner do?" Misa asked coldly, reaching into her purse for a cheque book.

Bina began to smile. She was still smiling when they were in the cab going back to the bank. "I thought you just worked there, that maybe you were on the loan committee. And you own it, all of it?"

"I married well," Misa said modestly.

"Goodonyer," Bina said. "And you're going to lend me the money to buy the building and open my own place?"

"I'll make you two offers," Misa said. "I'll lend you the fifteen thousand at the current rate or I'll invest fifteen thousand and be half owner."

"But you don't even know me," Bina said.

"I know more than you might suspect," Misa said.

"For example?"

"I know that you're a very solid businesswoman, that you ran a very profitable establishment in Cloncurry."

"Do you know what kind of establishment?"

"I do," Misa said, avoiding eye contact.

"Perhaps Henry Lawson was right," Bina said.

"I beg your pardon?"

"Nothing," Bina said. "I'll tell you someday. You know what sort of business I've been in and you still want to be a partner with me?"

"I feel that those of us who are slightly outside the pale, out of the mainstream of respectability, should stick together," Misa said. "You came from hunger, from poverty, and you did what you believed had to be done to overcome it. Long ago, I was brought to Queensland as an indentured worker, a Kanaka. The man who became my husband helped me and my people, and I, too, did what had to be done to overcome the limitations of my background." She did not explain to Bina that she had given herself sexually to Jon in payment for his help, which had enabled her father to lead his group of Samoans to freedom. "We have much in common, Bina, and I'd like very much to be in business with you. I won't interfere. The running of the place will be left to you."

"Goodonus," Bina said, holding out her hand. "Partner."

Bina had signed a two-week contract with the Sydney Palace. She fulfilled it, and before the end of the period her name was well-known in Sydney. Her seductive wardrobe, her flirty, husky, musical voice, the way she had of looking through her long, black eyelashes at the males in her audiences started men talking all over town. Soon the new girl who sang and played the piano at the Sydney Palace was acclaimed as the freshest, rowdiest thing to hit Sydney since the original convict had come ashore.

CHAPTER XXII

In South Africa the arrival of a new century was greeted from a wide variety of viewpoints. Boer manoeuvres and minor victories had exposed the eastern part of the British Cape Colony all the way to the seaboard, and in Cape Town itself the New Year's parties were subdued by rumours of a general uprising by the majority, the Boers.

Kit Streeter did not attend a party to see out the old year but stayed at home with her mother. The ominous thing that was growing in Evelyn Streeter's head brought on excruciating headaches. At times it seemed to Kit that her mother's left eye would burst from its socket, and when the pressure from inside was at its greatest, Evelyn's mind wandered. On New Year's Eve she came out of her bedroom, a bit dazed by the laudanum that Kit had given her for the pain, to ask imperiously just who was the strange woman in her home—that was Kit—and where was her little girl, meaning Kit at some early age. Kit took her mother by the arm and gently led her back to the bed, sitting with her and talking soothingly until Evelyn looked up suddenly and said, "Kit, where have you been?"

Kit had had only two letters from Slone since she had seen him last. They had been good letters, but not as warm as the ones she had received in Cairo. She sensed an unspoken reserve in his written words, and at times she would let tears drop onto the letters as she read and reread them. Each night she prayed for his safety, that he would come back to her, and she vowed silently to do whatever he asked when next he came to her. If he wanted to take out a special licence and get married as quickly as possible, then so be it.

And yet there was her duty to her mother and to her father. Her mother's desperate illness was beginning to tell on Roland

Streeter. The lines on his face were deeper. He was noticeably less energetic, less interested in life, wanting only to be with his family. On Sundays, when off duty, he would sit for hours, holding Evelyn's hand, talking to her in a low, soft voice. Kit was not included in those largely one-way conversations, but now and then she would overhear and would feel his pain, for her father was going over old memories, reliving the days of his courtship of Evelyn, going into great detail about their honeymoon trip to India. When he talked of such things, Evelyn's discomfort seemed less severe. She lay with her eyes closed, her hand clutching Roland's, apparently drinking in every word, for she smiled when she was especially moved.

Under such circumstances it was understandable that Kit did not put Slone's solitaire ring on the third finger of her left hand, that she did not defy the wishes of her mother and father and formally announce her engagement to the young Australian. She could only wait and pray, and live with her conflicted feelings. Repeatedly Kit wondered whether it would not be easier if her mother died, freeing herself from her pain, and, not too incidentally, freeing Kit to write to Slone saying, "My darling, we will be married the very next time you are able to return to Cape Town."

Sianna De Hartog spent New Year's Eve with the man she knew as her father. Dirk was alone, since the men of his commando unit had gone home to their farms near Pietermaritzburg. He had found Dr. Van Reenen's hospital unit on the approaches to the besieged town of Ladysmith, where it had been for some weeks, and his reunion with Sianna was a warm and joyful one. He was pleased to see that during her short time at war she had come to no harm; on the contrary, the experience had, it seemed, benefited her, matured her into confidence. She had lost the tentativeness that had once been the natural way of a teenage girl. It pleased him that his niece was evidently a bit more shapely, more womanly, but it pleased him even more when Dr. Van Reenen praised her work.

While waiting for his commandos to return, Dirk spent time with the Boer units, who lazed on the heights overlooking Ladysmith, rather enjoying the long, hot summer days. Supplies had been requisitioned from nearby Boer farms, so there was plenty to eat. During the holidays wives and families came in ox wagons to visit their men. To entertain the visitors, the Boers fired their good German cannon into the town. The obliging British in Ladysmith returned the barrage in a halfhearted way and thrilled the visitors, who were hurriedly led to shelter while the British artillery riddled a couple of tents and injured a horse.

"How long will we be encamped here?" Sianna asked Dirk one evening as they sat in front of the hospital tent and watched a spectacular sunset. "You said, Father, that we had to capture the ports. But there's no effort towards that. It was said that thousands of Boers would rise up to revolt, in the Cape Colony, that Cape Town would be a Boer port."

The news was indeed discouraging. During what the British were already calling Black Week, in December 1899, the Boers had defeated the British on all fronts, inflicting three huge defeats against the best British generals and leaving the roads open to the coast. But only Koos De La Rey had moved to take advantage of these victories, and now he, too, was stalled-up against a vastly superior force in the south. And still the Boer leadership continued to squander Boer strength in the opening sieges of the three towns—Mafeking, Kimberley, and Ladysmith.

"Things will change soon, and perhaps quickly," Dirk said. "The British have new commanders now. Lord Roberts will soon be in Cape Town and in command. Kitchener is to be his second-in-command. We'll see a change in strategy, but I suspect that if Kitchener is placed in command in the field, it may seem slow. He's known as a careful man. In the Sudan they say he never made a move until everything was in his favour."

"I have heard officers here say that there will be a strong effort to relieve Ladysmith soon," Sianna said.

"Yes, I expect that. That's why I'm here instead of with De La Rey. The British will move northwards. This is my country, after all, and I want to be here to help defend it."

Sianna shuddered. It was more than the evening's chill that caused the shivery feeling. She had seen only small engagements, but she knew now how terrible war could be. Modern weapons could make horrors of a man's flesh. To think of her father, who was very dear to her, being involved in battle frightened her. There was, however, one consolation. She had not fallen in love. She did not have a young man that she loved to worry about. Dirk was such a capable man, such an experienced man, that she felt he could take care of himself.

The new year found Matt Van Buren and Kelvin Broome back in the war zone. Having made their way easily through the lines around Mafeking, they had made a quick journey by rail from Bulawayo through Portuguese East Africa to the coast. There they had the luck to catch a coastal ship immediately and land in Durban in time to join the New Year's Eve party in the officers' mess at headquarters.

On New Year's Day Matt began to sound out the officers who worked in army headquarters in Durban, to get a picture of what was going on. The imminent change of British command was the most popular topic of conversation, but there was also word that Buller, the man who was to be relieved as commander-in-chief but left in charge in Natal, was waiting not for specific orders from Roberts and Kitchener, but was actively moving on his own to relieve Ladysmith.

Buller had assembled an army of thirty thousand men south of the besieged town. The 5th Division, General Sir Charles Warren commanding, was at Chievely. It took little skill on Matt's part to have himself assigned to the 5th, as a platoon commander in one of its regiments, the Middlesex. He told Kelvin Broome of the new developments, and the newsman decided that a front where thirty thousand British troops were concentrated just might produce a newsworthy story or two.

Slone Shannon did not have to wait for Kitchener to reply to plea to be assigned to a fighting unit. He found a local personnel officer who gave orders for him to join General Warren's 5th Division near Chievely, and he travelled north with a supply train to join his new unit. Rain had come to the African veld. Wagons were bogged down in the mud, and the efforts of huge teams of oxen and mules merely succeeded in tangling harness and half drowning some of the animals. Slone left the train strung out for miles, the wagons hopelessly stuck, men wet and out of sorts, and rode into the main encampment of the 5th Division.

The first thing he heard when he reported to his assigned unit—a

mounted brigade under the Earl of Dundonald—was that
Winston Churchill was back at the front. Following his escape,
Churchill had, with assistance, made his way safely through enemy
territory to the coast and sailed to Durban, where he had been
received as a hero. Slone smiled and shook his head, half in
astonishment, half in admiration for the arrogant, plucky, and
exceedingly fortunate young man.

Slone's unit was on the move the next morning. As the sun rose,
Dundonald's mounted brigade rode ahead of the army to climb a
hill on the south side of the Tugela River. At the top Slone
dismounted and looked around. He could look north across the
Tugela to a ridge of higher hills, the highest being a peak called
Spion Kop. Beyond the hills a flat open plain reached all the way to
Ladysmith.

At this moment General Buller himself rode up the slope to
confer with his subordinates. Curious, Slone sidled quietly to
within eavesdropping distance of the generals. "General Warren,"
he heard Buller say, "there is a road on that hill to the left of Spion
Kop. It traverses the right shoulder of the hill and passes to the
back of Spion Kop. You will take that road, General, and then
advance with all haste across the open plain to Ladysmith."

Like all military orders, it sounded quite simple.

Kelvin Broome had been unable to find a horse with which to
ride with Slone and Dundonald's mounted brigade. He found
himself moving with a unit of foot soldiers reinforced with field
guns and Maxims. The unit was proceeding quickly towards the
river when scouts reported mounted Boers ahead. Soon Kelvin
could see the Boers riding slowly away from a rocky, tree-covered
kopje and traversing the column's line of march. British gunners
set up their cannon, and a cannonball was sent winging towards
the Boers, who were fully three thousand yards away. Cheers went
up.

"Give 'em another," a man shouted.

A second gun roared.

Kelvin was composing a lead line for a story, something about
the high sport of potshotting at human game with cannon over
three thousand yards of rugged African countryside. The British
were moving forward again, keeping an eye on the mounted Boers,

who seemed to be in no hurry to get out of sight.

Suddenly Kelvin heard a bullet whine past his ear. The sound was a thin, shrill whistle, like that of a strong wind blowing through a small crack.

"Take cover, take cover," an officer was yelling.

A foot soldier near Kelvin said, "Gor, the Poms have done it again."

"Return fire," came the order. "Horses to the rear. Keep the cannon firing."

While concentrating on the mounted Boers, the unit had marched within range of Mauser rifles manned by Boers concealed on the kopje. The bullets were coming thick and fast now. A man near Kelvin grunted as if in surprise and sank helplessly to the ground, blood spurting from his throat.

"Artillery!" an officer was shouting. "Artillery!"

The men at the British guns worked with robotic precision, and shells began to fall onto the kopje, but the Boer rifles continued to return the fire, taking a heavy toll. British stretcher-bearers were kept busy, carrying their bloody burdens to the rear.

The British officers had led their men into a nearly perfect ambush. Kelvin, taking cover behind a friendly rock, heard a heavy-calibre slug ricochet off the stone less than a foot from his head. He had to agree with a soldier who sought cover behind the same boulder.

"Bloody officers," the man said. "Don't know what they're doing. It's going to be a bloody long war, mate."

CHAPTER XXIII

A young messenger found Dirk De Hartog having breakfast with Sianna. Sianna had set up a small table outside her tent, and on it steamed a fresh pot of tea and bowls of hot porridge enriched with fresh milk from a cow that had wandered near the hospital area. Dirk accepted the message, read it, and sighed.

"Something important?" Sianna asked.

"I'm to report to Louis Botha," he replied.

"Pray God that means the army is going to move at last," Sianna said.

Dirk finished his porridge, gulped down the last of his tea, and rose. "I'll get word to you," he said. He bent and kissed her on the cheek.

General Louis Botha met Dirk outside his tent and returned his salute. "The war brings us together, my friend," Botha said. "May God bless that which we must do together." He indicated a map table set up in the open and stood before it with his hands behind his back while Dirk leaned and examined the fresh markings on the map. Nearby a pair of tomtits twittered in a bush. A large, colourful butterfuly flew low over the map table, so near that Dirk's attention was drawn away from the map for a moment.

"The Natal Army left their camps around Frere on January tenth," Botha said. "Twenty-four thousand men. It appears that Buller intends a crossing of the Tugela at Potgieter's Drift." Potgieter's Drift, a ford of the river, was fifteen miles upstream from the Boer headquarters at Colenso, just below Ladysmith. "Oom Paul has telegraphed me, asking me to take command of our forces on the Tugela."

Dirk nodded, encouraged. Botha, at least, was a general who was willing to move.

"I'd like you to take your commando unit here," Botha said,

stabbing the map. He was pointing to the hills north of the Tugela. Dirk knew the area.

"I have only twenty-five men," Dirk said, "and only nineteen of those are experienced. The others are new and must be trained in the field."

"I understand," Botha replied. "You will be my eyes, as you were with Koos De La Rey. Avoid contact with the enemy as much as possible. He moves ponderously and carefully, this General Buller, so it should be easy enough to keep track of his position and to keep me informed."

It was not difficult to find the enemy. The British were arrayed along the south side of the Tugela, their forces stretched out between Potgieter's Drift and another ford, Trickhardt's Drift, three miles upstream. Dirk relayed word back to Botha that in his opinion the British would probably try to advance soon.

He was right. On January 16 and 17 Buller crossed to the north side of the Tugela, using both fords, and prepared to march on the hills to the north. Botha ordered his troops to begin their offensive movements.

Slone Shannon, attached to the Earl of Dundonald's mounted brigade, had been riding hard. Dundonald, after crossing the river with Warren's forces, had been ordered to try to outflank the Boers by moving his men to the west, around the hills north of the Tugela.

Slone was impressed, for the earl had been moving his brigade as if they were Boer commandos, fully mobile, living off the land. Slone was not privy to the councils of the high brass, but he was enough of a student of warfare to know that if Dundonald could get his men around the hills, he could, with proper reinforcements, be in Ladysmith in a matter of two to three days.

When, on a lovely morning, with the sun glowing red over the kopjes, Slone heard the bugle sounding officer's call, he fully expected to hear news of the reinforcements and fresh orders to take his squad of men as quickly as possible and make for Ladysmith.

After Slone and all the other officers had gathered, the Earl of Dundonald addressed them. "Gentlemen," he said, "here is a message from General Warren. I read it to you as received." He cleared his throat. " 'The general officer commanding as far as he can see finds that there are no cavalry whatever round the camp and nothing to prevent the oxen from being swept away. You are to send five hundred mounted men at once to be placed round the camp.' "

A groan went up from the assembled officers. Each man held his breath as a staff officer began to call names and units for the necessary but unexciting assignment of moving to the rear, to guard the fifteen thousand oxen of the army's baggage train.

Slone's name was not called, so later that morning he rode ahead with the remaining force of one thousand men. They ambushed a small Boer patrol as Dundonald seized a hill at the western edge of the ridge and moved his troops into position, ready to move across the plain to Ladysmith. From this point, Dundonald sent back request after request for additional men and weapons and permission to advance. Permission was denied. "I want you close to me," Warren replied.

Immobilized and frustrated along with the rest of the mounted infantry, Slone stood looking up at the rugged slopes of the hills. He could clearly see Spion Kop, the highest point in the area.

General Warren had meanwhile sent other units against Boer positions in the hills, as a sort of dress rehearsal for the major action. Buller, at the rear, sent messages threatening to withdraw Warren completely unless that major action got under way at once. Warren considered Buller's ultimatum, and then, looking around, saw the imposing heights of Spion Kop. *There* was the high ground, he decided, and since it was a military axiom that the highest ground should always be taken, Warren quite casually ordered an assault on Spion Kop.

Early Boer Trekkers had climbed Spion Kop to look down on the rich and verdant land of Natal. They had given the hill its name, which in English meant Scout Peak. It rose nearly fifteen hundred feet above the Tugela to a plateau flanked on three sides by higher ridges. The south side of the plateau was open for an advance by British troops.

Under Warren's new orders, Slone and a detachment of dismounted cavalry, commanded by Lieutenant-Colonel A. W. Thorneycroft, headed towards Spion Kop at eleven P.M. on the night of January 23. A light drizzle was falling, and Slone got a chuckle from fellow officers and blank looks from his men when he said. " 'It was a dark and stormy night.' " Apparently, unlike their officers, British mounted infantry men did not read Mr. Bulwer-Lytton, the popular novelist famous for his melodramatic opening lines.

The drizzle and low clouds shut off any light from moon or stars, and the mist thickened as the men stumbled, clawed, and felt their way up the steep slopes on the south side of the kop. Slone, leading his group in a darkness so total that he had to instruct his men to stay within hand's reach of one another, hoped that all the noise of movement would not carry, in the still South African night, alerting the Boers camped in the surrounding hills.

At first there was good-natured whispering among the men, but as the night wore on and one hour became two and then three, the exertion of the climb made it unnecessary for Slone to order silence. He could hear only the sounds of boots on rock, an occasional thud as a man slipped and fell, and hard breathing. They climbed for four hours, with only two short rests, and then the slope began to lessen. Slone turned and whispered to the man behind him, "Fix bayonets. Pass the word."

He heard the clink of metal on metal. An officer came stumbling through the darkness, giving the password, "Waterloo."

The officer ordered Slone to stop while the rest of the assault force caught up. "Some of the older officers had to have assistance," he explained.

Slone welcomed the rest and told his men to relax as best they could. He peered ahead through the dense mist but was unable to see anything. Finally the word was passed to move on. He felt the grade becoming more gradual and was able to move forward with less effort.

He froze when a voice speaking in Afrikaans came out of the fog—a challenge from a Boer sentry. He felt immediate pride in his men, for he did not have to give the order to charge.

"Waterloo!" cried several of the men, giving the password in answer to the Boer sentry's challenge, and they ran forward, bayonets pointing. The Boer picket fired his Mauser without effect, and then he scrambled away.

Slone judged from the terrain underfoot that they had reached the top of Spion Kop. Senior officers came to the same conclusion.

Since the assault force had not brought a field telegraph, they announced their bloodless capture of the high ground with three rousing cheers.

Slone distibuted his men, and while they were digging in, he made a circuit of his position and encountered other officers doing the same. The ground sloped away on all sides. The troops were digging a trench in the shape of a flattened V, the point of which faced north towards the probable Boer line of advance. The digging was difficult, for the ground was extremely hard and full of rocks. The engineers had been allowed by their officers to discard some of their equipment during the difficult climb, and no one had thought of bringing a supply of sandbags, so when the troops had scraped out a shallow ditch only a few inches deep, they had to complete their meagre defences by stacking small stones to a height of about eighteen inches in front of the trench.

The Boer picket who had been sent running by Slone Shannon's unit soon had his message spread through several Boer laagers. Louis Botha immediately ordered a counterassault, for if the high hill went to the British, the entire Boer line would be in danger of being breached. He sent Dirk De Hartog to have a look and report on British strength on Spion Kop.

Dirk climbed the north slope of the kop with his commandos. As the mist began to lift from the height not long after dawn, Dirk could not believe his eyes. The British troops had halted and dug in on a plateau below the highest ridges of Spion Kop. Meanwhile, hundreds of Boer snipers, having left their horses at the foot of the slope, had begun to ascend the hill behind Dirk.

He knew he had no time to report to Botha, not if the Boers were to take advantage of the incredible blunder by the British officers. Dirk began to send messengers to the climbing Boers, taking command of the situation without a second thought, ordering the men to position themselves on the various high points that overlooked the plateau—Three Tree Hill, the Northwest Knoll, and Aloe Knoll.

At eight o'clock, with the mist lifted completely, the Boers unloosed a storm of fire from the high ground into the shallow, completely indefensible British trench.

Slone was near one end of the trench, studying the surrounding ground. His blood was chilled by the sight of encircling ridges above his position—grey, rocky heights that dominated the trench from a distance of no more than a couple of hundred yards.

"God help us," he whispered to himself. Just then his uniform was sprayed with blood and splattering brain matter as a high-velocity round from a Boer's Mauser rifle struck the head of the man next to him. Then he heard the shattering roar of rifles fired by the hundreds: it sounded like a hailstorm on a tin roof. Men were falling with incredible swiftness. From one of the high knolls—he would learn later that it had a name, Aloe Knoll—the Boers raked Slone's position with a storm of uninterrupted fire.

Slone lifted his carbine and began to fire back at the flashes of the Boer rifles. Looking to either side of him, he saw man after man in the trench take direct hits, most of them shot through the head by the accurate rifles of the Boers. And then the big guns began to fire.

The pom-pom, used by both sides, was a particularly inventive new horror. It was a fully automatic, thirty-seven-millimetre cannon. Carriage-mounted, it was easily moved, and the Boers soon had one in position. The explosive pom-pom shells began to rain down on the British trench.

With the day now completely clear, the heights were bathed in a lovely morning light. For the British the clear sky was deadly. The Boers moved up six more cannon, to pound the British-held positions, and another pom-pom joined the fire.

In the trench Slone Shannon saw one grizzled old sergeant to his right lay down his carbine and begin to build a protective heap of dead bodies. Slone felt a flush of revulsion. Around him the men who were still alive hugged the bottom of the trench, only a few of them making any attempt to return the devastating Boer fire. Slone tried to swallow but found that his mouth was too dry. He looked down the trench again. The experienced sergeant, having built a rampart of bodies between him and the deadly Boer Mausers, was resting his carbine across the back of a dead man, taking careful aim at the flash of rifles on the high knoll. Frantically Slone began to pull the dead to him, struggling with their weight, placing body on top of body to make a bulwark three bodies wide and three deep before he was satisfied. A bullet thudded into the heap with a sound like a cleaver hitting a thick slab of raw beef.

"Bloody bastards!" Slone yelled defiantly, his voice scarcely audible above the frighteningly swift blasts of the two pom-poms, the throaty roar of heavier shells exploding, the shattering roar of rifles. He braced his rifle on the dead and began to fire as rapidly as he could. He cheered, and heard others doing the same, when British shells began to explode on the high ground in the Boer positions.

"Blast them, blast the bloody bastards!" he yelled, as he fired back at the flash of rifles.

The sun was now high, already hot, and Slone's throat was so dry that his voice was hoarse. To his right two more men had built a protective pile of bodies to cut off the incoming fire.

He looked ahead. A small force of British had boldly advanced, and the Boers came to meet them. The British fell back under the withering fire, many of them dying before they reached even the doubtful protection of the trench.

Suddenly he thought of Kit, saw her in a white dress, smiling up at him, lips parted for his kiss, and a vast wave of loss swept over him, for he was sure at that moment that he would not descend Spion Kop alive. Even as this black mood hit him, he noted with dismay that the shells that had been falling on the Boer positions on the heights had ceased. But the thunder of Boer fire went on and on.

Kelvin Broome was with General Warren that morning. Warren's headquarters had been set up in a valley two miles southwest of Spion Kop. From headquarters nothing of the action could be seen. No cable had been laid for a field telegraph, and the available heliographs on the heights had been smashed early on by Boer fire. Warren had to depend on foot messengers to know what was happening on the hill.

Kelvin could sense that all was not right. First of all, there was no direct communication with the troops on Spion Kop, not even by messenger, for the runners went first to Buller, who had a good view of the overall scene from the top of Mount Alice, across the river from Spion Kop.

A contingent of British sailors, recruited to man two huge naval guns positioned on Mount Alice, saw Boers on Aloe Knoll and opened fire. General Warren—who had thought that the entire summit was in his hands—panicked and sent an order for the artillery to cease fire. The guns fell silent.

Dirk De Hartog had gathered his men in the heights overlooking the plateau and had placed them in position to fire directly down into the British main trench. The necessary slaughter sickened him. They were protecting themselves with dead men down there, and still his men poured methodical rifle fire into the trench.

By midmorning some of the Boers had moved forward, reaching the trench, and Dirk watched as the fighting became hand to hand. From his vantage point he could tell that the British were doing more than merely dying. He had never doubted the courage of the British soldier, and he saw it proven time and time again as the British fought back with determination. Boers were dying, too, and Dirk, who knew his army well, realized that if the going got too rough—if too many Boers were killed—the rest would simply melt away, leaving the field to the enemy.

The sun passed the zenith on that endless day. Slone's sense of smell at first had been outraged by the stench of the dead, then deadened. Vultures soared overhead but had the sense not to try to descend into the gunfire. Slone saw an embattled group of British throw down their weapons and surrender, to be driven from view by the drably clad Boers. He had used up all his ammunition and almost all that of the dead nearby, and he was down to just a few rounds and was saving them. Recovering from his black despair, he was no longer certain that he was going to die. His hopes grew stronger when, at about one o'clock, reinforcements ascended the south slope of Spion Kop, out of view of the Boers, and arrived to take their baptism of fire.

Dirk, sickened by having to shoot into the dead bodies that now packed the main trench, moved his men from the high ground to reinforce the Boers' front line, which was close to the trench and was now threatened by the British reinforcements. He positioned himself next to a commando he knew, Deneys Reitz.

"They are so close we can toss biscuits to them," Reitz said.

Dirk forced a laugh. "Some of the camp biscuits I've eaten might be more deadly than bullets."

"They are killing us," Reitz said, spreading his arms to indicate the ground, which was littered with dead bodies.

"But, my friend," Dirk said, "while our own dead are among us and quite evident, you cannot see into the trench from this point. We are killing more of them."

"The men don't see the British dead," Reitz said. "All they know is that we're already taking heavy losses. Many have left the field. By tomorrow morning the British will be pouring across the plain to the relief of Ladysmith."

Matt Van Buren, leading his platoon of the Middlesex, was among the British reinforcements reaching the summit of Spion Kop around one in the afternoon. Before reaching the British trench, his unit took part in an abortive attack on a Boer position to the right, the charge losing its aggressiveness and disintegrating in the face of withering rifle fire and the ceaseless pounding of the pom-poms. Matt ordered his men back.

As he took a fresh look at the situation, Matt could see the main trench ahead and to the left, and he observed that Boers were forming for an attack on it. He realized that if the main position fell, the entire plateau would be lost to the Boers. He began to shout encouragement at the men, his and others. With the help of a good sergeant, he pushed and pulled the men, formed a wedge, and then, leading the way himself, charged towards the trench to the aid of his overwhelmed comrades. The whistle and thud of Boer rifle bullets flew past his ears. The Boers were charging, too, from the opposite direction. The two forces would meet head on at the trench.

In the trench only a few men were firing at the attacking Boers. Matt picked out one active area where at least two men were pumping bullets from their carbines as fast as they could, and he steered his men in that direction. Next to him a man fired on the run, and one of the charging Boers went down, skidding on the rock. With the Boers only yards away Matt leapt into the trench, fell heavily on top of a body, rolled, and put his rifle into action. His men followed, and in an instant the fire slaughtered the charging Boers, the last of them falling so close that Matt could see the dark stains of blood under their rough brown clothing.

Matt discharged one final round but missed a Boer who was diving over the rim of the plateau towards safety. He looked to his left and saw the British dead heaped randomly in the trench. Apart from the men who had come with him, the nearest living man was yards away. To his right a young officer with a smudged face and dazed, staring eyes grinned and said, "Goodonyer, mate. Nick of time. Have you some spare ammunition?"

"No worries," Matt said, handing over a cartridge belt. "British insignia, Aussie voice, right?"

"Right. Slone Shannon, Queensland."

"Matt Van Buren, likewise."

"Small world," Slone said.

"Big enough war," Matt said. "Next time, I'll have Australian officers, thank you."

"Not nearly as much excitement with Aussie officers," Slone said. "Australians would have crept around the hill and hit the Boers from the rear. No glory at all in that."

"Our blood, their glory," Matt said.

One of the pom-poms shifted and began to send explosive shells screaming into the trench. Matt, seeing Slone snug behind his pile of bodies, began frantically to build a similar shelter, all the while fighting nausea. The steady, deadly fire from the high knolls continued like an incessant pelting rain. In the heat of the afternoon, however, Matt's main attention was on his unbearable thirst.

Dirk knew that the inevitable would happen as soon as darkness came to cover any movement. In the twilight he saw some of the Boers begin to leave, backing off like shadows down the hill. He had lost men, and once again his commando force was far under strength. He had no choice, so he drew his remaining men together, and they descended the hill, found their horses, and rode off to report to Botha.

"We must not let all our troops leave the hill," Botha said after listening to Dirk. "It is the key to this battle. If they leave, the way is open to Ladysmith."

"I'll go back," Dirk answered, "but I can't guarantee that

all of my men will."

On the British side confusion had been compounded by Buller's having relieved Warren of command in the middle of the battle without word of this passing officially to all those concerned. More reinforcements, meanwhile, had continued to climb the steep south slope of Spion Kop, so that by nightfall twenty-five hundred men were jammed on the hill, exposed to the Boer fire, and another two thousand were trying to join the fight. In the growing darkness Colonel Thorneycroft, senior surviving officer on top of the hill, ordered the plateau to be abandoned. On the way down he met Lieutenant Winston Churchill, who had a message from General Warren to hold on to Spion Kop.

"I have done all I can, and I am not going back," Thorneycroft replied.

Kelvin Broome had been aware of the presence of the more famous correspondent at Spion Kop, but it was not until evening that he encountered Churchill and introduced himself. Together, in the growing twilight, the two men climbed the hill. Streams of wounded were being evacuated. Men who showed no signs of wounds staggered as if they were quite drunk. Some fell and lay where they had fallen in a stupor of shock and exhaustion.

"Do you suppose General Warren knows the true conditions?" Kelvin asked.

Churchill grunted in derision. "There are thirty thousand men within ten miles of this position, and not one general who has the capacity to put any portion of them into effective action."

The Boer guns were still pounding the hilltop. Kelvin was intimidated, but when Churchill continued to climb and reached the plateau, Kelvin followed. He could see a line of deep shadow extending across the open area and he walked towards it, and realized with a lurch of his heart that the line of shadows was death, men piled in heaps in a long, flattened V extending for two hundred yards. And among the dead the exhausted survivors rested, some fast asleep.

Slowly, slowly, the hilltop was emptied, so that the Boer guns now exploded their shells only upon the already ravaged bodies of the dead. In the darkness Kelvin saw neither Slone Shannon nor

Matt Van Buren as they followed the evacuation down the hill. Churchill and he were among the last to leave, Churchill looking over his shoulder to see the darker shadows that represented that long trench of death. Below, the two correspondents found a mess tent and sat together to eat, Churchill perched on a boulder and Kelvin, who was very, very tired, sitting on the ground with his legs stretched out.

"Banjo Patterson wrote that you and the Duke of Marlborough drink a bottle of beer for breakfast every morning," Kelvin said.

"An arrant lie," Churchill said with a snort. "In this God-forsaken land one can't find beer every morning."

"He also said that you told him you were going to plaster the pages of your newspaper with the name Winston Churchill, so that the next time you stand for Parliament you'll fly in."

Churchill chuckled. "Are all you Australians so quick to violate a confidence?"

"Being the topic of conversation is the penalty for being famous, Mr. Churchill."

Churchill nodded. "Yes, I'm making Winston Churchill as famous a name as I possibly can. I bless the Boers who took me prisoner when they ambushed that train. That incident did more for my political career than I could otherwise have done in a decade." He fell silent and ate heartily for a while. "But mind you, Broome, it's for a reason. Laugh if you must, but I have sensed from the time I was very young that a special destiny awaits me. I don't know what will come. I only feel that it will come, and I will be prepared to bear up under it. Everything that has happened— everything that is happening and will happen until that moment— is merely preparation for that destiny."

Kelvin Broome did not laugh. Perhaps it was the growing chill. After the heat of the African day the chill came on suddenly and severely. Perhaps it was sheer exhaustion, but with Churchill's visionary words he felt a tremor go through his entire body.

With dawn the white flags of armistice were displayed by both sides, and from the two sides of Spion Kop men climbed to see three hundred and fifty British bodies, mostly clustered near or in the main trench. It was not possible to walk along the trench without stepping on a leg or an arm, and these members were not always attached to a body. On the Boer side medical squads had to handle three hundred bodies.

That day, stunned by his defeat at the hands of mere commandos, General Buller ordered a retreat to safety—back to the south side of the Tugela River.

CHAPTER XXIV

For a man-boy not yet eighteen, but approaching fast that lofty age, there was interest in almost everything—in the way the crew moved efficiently about their duties on the Mason ship that took him to Townsville in northeastern Queensland, in the old city itself, and in the land that had been his father's. Tolo Mason had no way of knowing that the first station he visited was the site where his father had first seen his mother among a group of indentured Kanakas.

Over the years Jon Mason had managed to secure good managers for all five of the properties in Queensland. At the station near Townsville Tolo was greeted with curiously effusive respect by the manager, who had been told by letter that the Queensland properties would be going up for sale. Tolo assured the manager that he would be highly recommended to any buyer. He felt some pity for the man, for he had been loyal to the station for a number of years and now faced an uncertain future.

Three of the properties were within riding distance of Townsville, and Tolo spent the better part of two weeks in looking them over. All three were in excellent condition. Armed with a letter of introduction from his mother and the manager of the Merchantman's and Marine Bank of Sydney, Tolo visited the bank that handled the Mason-Fisher accounts in Townsville, and was greeted with more pomp and circumstance than his seventeen years would have won him had he not been representative of—and heir to—one of Australia's great fortunes. He left Townsville with three estimates of the worth of the properties, all within a few hundred pounds of each other, and with a feeling of satisfaction. Already interest had been expressed towards the purchase of two of the holdings.

Once again on a Mason ship, he requested that the captain make

an unscheduled stop at the sugar port of Bundaberg. He hired a
horse and rode into the cane fields stretching out from the town
and saw that the first of the Mason-Fisher sugarcane plantations
was among the largest in the area and that the fields were in
excellent condition, foretelling a bountiful and profitable crop.
The second sugarcane plantation, two days' ride away, was much
like the first. He made an appearance at the bank in Bundaberg,
where the family business was looked after, got his estimates, and
telegraphed his mother that he would be heading home as soon as
he could catch a ship, with only one more stop along the way, in
Brisbane.

He bought a ticket to Brisbane on another company's ship,
planning this stop because of his dead father. He missed Jon very
much and was not yet ready to let the memories of his father slide
back into the far reaches of his mind. Near Brisbane lived a man
whom Tolo had not seen since he was a boy, the man who was
Jon's father, Adam Colpoys Vincent, known as Adam Shannon.
Separated from the Masons for years by the fact that he lived in
New Zealand, Adam and his wife Emily had retired to a farm
outside Queensland's capital.

Brisbane, third largest city in Australia, lay spread over dozens
of low hills from the shores of Moreton Bay up the Brisbane River
Valley almost to the foothills of the D'Aguilar Mountain Range.
Having arrived late in the morning, Tolo spent an hour before
lunch in a cab, seeing a few of the sights. Luckily he had picked a
driver who knew the local history. He was shown the spot where
John Oxley, under orders from the governor of New South Wales,
first landed on September 28, 1824, to find a site for a new penal
colony. He was shown buildings that had survived from the first
decade of convict settlement, and the balcony from which Sir
George Bowen had read the declaration that separated Queensland from New South Wales.

After lunch Tolo hired a horse and rode out of the city, passing
along narrow streets lined by original wooden cottages with tin
roofs, decorative iron lacework, and newly painted fences, then
into more modern neighbourhoods until the city had been left
behind and the track sloped upwards towards the rolling foothills.

By midafternoon he was at a wooden gate that marked the
entrance to the Adam Shannon station. A sign gave it a name, The

Shadows. Tolo rode down a lane that wound through a lovely little valley, where a sparkling creek gurgled over well-worn rocks.

The house itself was quite impressive. It lay in a grove of gum trees on the side of a gentle hill. Cast-iron balustrades framed a double-curved set of entry steps leading to the second level, the living section of the house. The patterned tin roof, painted to resemble Mediterranean tile, was in perfect repair. Behind the wrought-iron rails roomy porches looked cool.

As Tolo mounted the stairs, he caught the scent of cooking emanating from the lower level of the house, and he suddenly felt quite hungry. He used an ornate brass knocker to announce his presence, and the door was opened by an Aboriginal woman in livery.

"Is Mr. Shannon in?" Tolo asked.

"Who calls?" the servant asked, looking at his bronzed face suspiciously.

"Thomas Mason."

He turned his back to the door, having doubts now. He had last seen his grandfather in Samoa, and if Jon Mason had not had a picture of Adam Shannon, Tolo would have forgotten the man's face entirely. Over the years he had heard his father talk of this Adam Shannon, and he knew that at least once Jon had visited Adam in New Zealand, and more recently in Brisbane after Adam had retired from the army and purchased his place in southern Queensland. Misa and Tolo had not accompanied Jon on these visits; Tolo speculated that the old man might have feelings about people of colour.

He heard strong, rapid footsteps behind him and turned. The door burst open, and Adam shannon was there, a smile on his face, both of his hands extended. With his own face stiff, Tolo extended a hand.

"My God, little Tolo," Adam said, looking up into Tolo's face. The boy stood a full four inches taller than he.

"I was travelling from Bundaberg to Sydney," Tolo said.

"Well, boy," Adam said heartily, "I'm so pleased that you decided to stop." His smile faded. "I wanted to come when I first received word that your father was dead."

"I know," Tolo said. He had, in fact, discussed the matter with Misa, contending that Adam Shannon had a right to know that his son was dead. Misa had said, "He has not set foot in this house in all these years. Why should he come now?"

"Well, boy, come in," Adam said, taking Tolo's arm. Inside the door he bellowed, "Emily, Emily, come and see who's here."

Emily Carmichael Shannon appeared, an erect woman who, Tolo thought, was holding her years well, for he could not guess her exact age. Her hair had silvered, but she was shapely, if matronly; she moved easily and her smile was genuine as she gave Tolo her hand. "It's so nice to see you after only hearing about you all these years."

"Well, we have a lot of catching up to do, my boy," Adam said.

"If you'll excuse me, I'll see about some tea," Emily said.

They sat on a porch on the second level, Adam rocking easily in what was obviously his favourite chair. The view was of rolling pasture sloping down to the creek. Tolo, soon at ease, answered questions, spoke of his life on the station in Victoria, of his ambitions to go to Western Australia to make the first definitive study of the Aborigines, of his mother and her business ventures.

Adam chuckled when he heard that Misa had bought a bank in Sydney. "She'll have a real challenge there," he said. "I fear that the Australian male has rather primitive ideas about a woman's place."

"They don't know my mother," Tolo said.

"Well, I wish her the best. She was a lovely thing as a young woman, Tolo, lovely."

"She still is."

"I'm sure she is." Adam was remembering, and the look on his face caused Tolo to fall silent. His grandfather, he guessed, was in his sixties, and he was still straight and robust. He had gained a bit of weight, which helped to keep the wrinkles at bay, so that he looked no older than perhaps fifty-five.

"Forgive me, Tolo," Adam said. "I was travelling into the long ago and the faraway."

"I guessed that, sir," Tolo said.

"We have many things to regret in this life," Adam added.

"I've always thought that regret is good only for wallowing in," Tolo replied quietly.

"A commendable way to think." He looked up at the blue sky.

"From the time I saw your father in Samoa, he and I kept in touch, you know."

"He mentioned you."

"We saw each other, oh, three times I think it was. He was damned proud of you."

Tolo shrugged.

"He knew that you would have certain things to overcome, living in Australia."

"My brown skin."

There was a silence, during which the older man reached for a pipe, which he slowly and deliberately filled with tobacco, fussing with the lighting of it. Tolo sat and waited while Adam performed this ritual, musing on the significance of his own mixed origins, the contrasting strains of blood and bewildering array of names in his family's past. His great-grandfather was the Earl of Cheviot. His grandfather's name was Adam Colpoys Vincent, but because of a youthful indiscretion he had changed his name to Adam Shannon. His father, bastard son of a married woman by Adam Vincent-Shannon, had been adopted by the mother's third husband, Marcus Fisher, whom Jon had hated so much that he had changed his name from Jon Fisher to Jon Mason. With all these names, Tolo wondered, what should his own be? Thomas Vincent Shannon Fisher Mason?

"Your father has achieved his goal, it seems." Adam Shannon's words startled Tolo.

"I'm sorry, sir. You mean—"

"I mean his goal to make things easy for you. He told me that he was working to make himself so bloody rich that when he died you and your mother could either buy respect or force it down the throats of white people with sheer power and money." Adam's eyes pierced Tolo's. "I wanted to be a part of your life, Thomas. Told Jon so. He said that I had a life of my own to lead, a family of my own. I suppose that after all he never quite forgave me."

"I suspect, sir, that my mother had something to do with it. She was always content to be alone with me, with the servants and the stockmen at the station, with my father when he was at home. I think that if he had suggested asking you and . . . ah, Mrs. Shannon to visit, she would have protested. After the first few rejections that Mother suffered in society, she decided that the best course of action was to stay totally aloof, never to put herself or me into a position where anyone could reject us."

"And what happened to make her venture into Sydney, into the field of business?"

Tolo grinned. "I haven't quite worked that out, sir. Perhaps she's simply angry at the world for taking my father from us. Sometimes she gives me the impression that she has girded herself for total war against any white face that passes, against anyone who stands in her way."

"It could happen that way," Adam agreed. "Strike back at bereavement by achieving and acquiring—by telling the world, 'Curse you, you have taken something irreplaceable from me. Now I will take something from you.' "

"I think she'll be all right," Tolo said. "I'm on my way back to join her. I'll postpone my trip to Western Australia until I'm sure that she's really over losing my father."

"Good, good," Adam said. He took time to light his pipe again, and just as he had it going well Emily came out, followed by a servant bearing a tea tray.

"You see, boy, what happens when you stay married too long to the same woman," Adam said. "She senses when you're being naughty." He tapped out the contents of the pipe and put it in his pocket.

At tea Emily invited Tolo to have dinner with them and stay the night. Tolo accepted, and after tea Tolo accompanied Adam on a leisurely tour of the grounds.

They dined at dusk in the formal dining room. Conversation at the table was light. Adam bragged a bit about the place and about his cattle, and Emily was intensely curious about Misa's business ventures. After dinner Adam led Tolo into the study, where both enjoyed a fine brandy and Adam managed to smoke another full pipe before Emily came to join them. The talk was truly familial and intimate, Tolo asking questions and listening with respect as Adam talked about his career in the army, yielding to Emily in modesty to allow her to describe his medals and how he had been promoted to brigadier before his retirement.

Before Emily yawned and insisted that they all should go to bed, Tolo felt that he now knew his grandfather well, and could be quite proud of him. And he knew that he had an uncle, Slone

Shannon, who was in the British Army, fighting the Boers in South Africa.

The good-byes next day were warm. Adam went to the stables with Tolo and supervised the saddling of his horse. When it was ready and the stable boy was leading it outside, the old man took Tolo's hand.

"There's one thing that you might remember," he said. He touched Tolo's arm. "It isn't what is here, on the skin, it's what's here and here." He tapped his head and his heart. "You have the blood of kings in you, boy, both from your mother and from your father." He chuckled. "I'm not sure that you have much to brag about from my side, but for what it's worth to you, boy, never forget that your great-grandfather was the Earl of Cheviot, Major-General the Earl of Cheviot, and he was with Wellington at Waterloo."

"Thank you, sir," Tolo said. "I'll remember that."

But as he stood at the rail of a ship coming into Sydney Harbour, remembering his visit and his grandfather's words, Tolo wondered what a certain young girl and her family would think of his lineage. Would they consider his Samoan blood cancelled out by the blood of a peer of old England, or would they believe, as most Australians seemed to, that the allegedly inferior blood of the brown races was so potent that one drop of it in a man's veins overpowered all other redeeming qualities?

He laughed. There was Sydney. For the first time as he looked at the city he felt the worth of the fortune that his father had inherited and breathed expansively. "Yes, Father," he whispered into the wind, "we will have respect, even if we have to shove pound notes down their throats."

CHAPTER XXV

The coastal steamer on which Tolo had taken passage from Brisbane was secured by its thick braided ropes to the Mason docks shortly after noon.

In accordance with her dead husband's wishes, Misa had gone ahead with dropping the name Fisher from the family company's name, and Tolo noted that a new sign, Mason Shipping Company, now adorned the building behind the wharf.

He had not informed his mother of his impending arrival. He took a cab to her new town house, was admitted by the Chinese housemaid, washed away the musky scent of burned fuel oil acquired during the voyage, and dressed in city clothes. He then proceeded to the bank, where he was informed that Mrs. Mason was with a business partner at a particular address.

Teams of workers were swarming about the building when Tolo found it—painters, carpenters, masons, and a crew of sign-makers who were erecting a tastefully printed but slightly enigmatic sign that read only *Bina's*. Tolo made his way around a wheelbarrow full of mortar, dodged a hod carrier, and managed to enter the front door without causing the glaziers to drop a precariously wide pane of glass that they were trying to mount. Inside there was more chaos, but he finally found Misa across a newly installed parquet floor of incomparably smooth and beautifully finished hardwood.

Misa had abandoned the black of mourning, and he approved. She looked quite young and gay in a powder-blue suit. Beside her stood an attractive, black-haired lady of petite but rounded shape.

He approached. The two women were concentrating intently on a diagram of the arrangement of tables and fixtures in the main dining rooms.

"Hello, Mother," Tolo said from a few feet away.

"Oh, yes, Tolo," Misa said, hardly raising her eyes from the diagram as the woman with her suggested changes. Then, with a huge smile and a cry of happiness, she exclaimed, "Tolo! You're back!" She came to embrace him.

The other woman waited until mother and son had completed their greetings; then she approached Tolo and gave him her hand. "I can see why you're proud of this young man, Misa," she said. She smiled up at Tolo. "My, my, with you around, we won't have to hire a man to keep order."

"This is my dear friend," Misa said. "Miss Bina Tyrell."

"All the family members call me Bina," she said.

"As for being your doorman," Tolo said, "I'll be far too busy enjoying the surface of that wonderful dance floor."

"Oh, do you like it?" Bina asked. "I had so many doubts. It was so expensive, but your mother said that we should not skimp on the parquet."

"She was right," Tolo replied. "Look, Mother, I've had nothing but ship's food for the past few days, and believe me, it wasn't the cuisine of a passenger liner. Have you had lunch?"

"Sorry, darling," Misa said, "we have, and we have so much to do here. Will you forgive me?"

Tolo nodded with a smile. It was good to see his mother so interested, so alive again.

"I'll bring Bina home with me," Misa said, "and we'll all go out to dinner tonight."

"When shall we go over my findings about the Queensland properties?" he asked.

"Darling, would you please talk to Price about that?" Before the sentence was finished, Misa was concentrating again on the dining-room layout.

Price Vermillion greeted Tolo with a warm clasp on the shoulder and made extensive notes as Tolo spoke of what he had seen and concluded about the Queensland properties. "Actually," he said, when Tolo stopped talking, "it's not the best of all times to sell."

Tolo had learned enough during his trip to understand at least in part what Vermillion meant. For six years the Great Drought— Henry Lawson's "Red Marauder"—had plagued the land. The Mason holdings, located near the coast, had not suffered as much as properties farther into the interior, but they had been affected

nevertheless. Throughout Australia men had been simply walking
away in exhausted disgust from their parched holdings. And these
had been not only the small landowners: for many wealthy
squatters, too, it had become cheaper just to give up.

"Now's the time to *buy* land, not sell," Vermillion suggested.

"Who would want more land?" Tolo asked.

"The government."

Tolo looked puzzled. Vermillion explained. "Unification is
going to come sooner or later, Tolo, and my guess is sooner. When
that happens, there'll be pressure for more land reform. My best
guess is that the government will be in the market for land and that
they'll subsidize small farmers. You know the old saying: God
only made so much land, and he's not making any more. When the
rains come again, some of the land that's nearly useless now—such
as the land in the western part of New South Wales—will increase
in value again considerably."

"I wish us all the best of luck dealing in land when that day
comes round," Tolo said indifferently.

Vermillion smiled. "Still determined to go off and live with the
Abos, eh?" he asked, the land issue tabled for the present.

"Yes." Tolo brushed his hand over his thick, black hair. He
sensed Vermillion's scepticism and instinctively changed the
subject. "My mother seems quite interested in this project with
Miss Bina Tyrell, whom I've just met. How has Mother been? In
good spirits?"

"Oh, yes, certainly, though I'm not sure whether to consider
Miss Tyrell a tonic or a distraction," Vermillion said. "They have
become fast friends, and Mrs. Mason is fascinated by the
preparations for the opening of Miss Tyrell's restaurant. However,
your mother has been spending so much time with Miss Tyrell that
another project she had begun is gathering dust."

"Anything I can do?" Tolo asked. He was hopeful that his
mother had now recovered fully from the loss of his father and that
he could begin to make his plans to go to Western Australia.

"No, no," Vermillion said. He paused. "Unless—"

"Unless what?" Tolo asked.

"Unless you'd like to travel a bit in the outback."

"Doing what?" Tolo inquired, this time quite interested. He
much preferred the bush to the city.

"Checking out applications for loans, evaluating the land offered as security, talking with the applicants."

Tolo laughed. "Now you're joining my mother in trying to make an honest businessman of me."

"It was you who asked if there was anything you could do," Vermillion said, spreading his hands.

"Don't worry," Tolo replied. "I do need something to occupy me."

Later he had second thoughts. At dinner that night Misa listened as he talked about his journey to Queensland, asked interested questions about the properties, then shrugged when Tolo repeated Price Vermillion's statement that it was not a good time to sell. "I leave it to your judgement," she said. "If you and Price want to hang on to the lands . . ."

Little by little he was being drawn into the Mason affairs of finance. He opened his mouth to protest, but then stopped himself. It was too good to see his mother smiling again, and he wanted to oblige her. The stations and plantations all had good local managers, and if the Red Marauder didn't move to the coast and thereby destroy the whole of Australia, the profits would continue to rise. Fortunately the holdings in northern Queensland and the cane fields near Brisbane had not yet been hit—as had New South Wales and areas to the west—by the devastation from hordes of rapacious imported rabbits, nor were they being overrun by the quickly spreading prickly pear, first brought to Australia as a potted plant, then used as a hedge.

Bowing to his mother's wishes, Tolo agreed to travel west to inspect properties, and this gave him an opportunity to see at firsthand the results of introducing plants and animals into an environment where they had no natural enemies. He boarded a Sydney-Melbourne train and rode it as far as Goulburn. While still close to the coast, where the rainfall was adequate, he saw that the succulent prickly pear was rife; a fellow passenger told him that it had infested some ten million acres, causing despair to farmers and new settlers eager to tame the land, for there seemed to be no way to control it.

At Goulburn Tolo bought a horse and turned his way west. Now, in this drier country, he could see the devastation of the rabbits, which had moved up from Victoria, where they had first entered Australia. They were now moving through New South Wales at the rate of about seventy miles a year.

Tolo observed how trees had been cut down for firewood and for building, and sheep had nibbled away the grass. Behind them the rabbits had completed the destruction, eating even low-growing bushes, denuding the ground of its natural cover. Now, during the Great Drought, the sun had baked the thin layers of topsoil into a powder that was easily shaken loose by the westerly wind into vast dust storms.

The conditions presented Tolo with a moral dilemma. It was obvious to him that if the bank should lend money to the smallholders and even the squatters—hard hit by the impact of drought and pests, their problems compounded by a drop in world wool prices—these loan-holders would never be able to repay the principal, not to mention the interest. The Merchantman's and Marine Bank of Sydney would become an impotent holder of vast tracts of land for which there would be no immediate market. He found that several of those who had applied to the bank for a loan had already given up, their lands lying idle, the sheep sold off.

Tolo had reached the conclusion that he might as well turn back, tell Price Vermillion and his mother that he strongly recommended no land loans. But there was peace in the bush. He enjoyed his solitary camps, the sound of night birds, the feel of the wind on his face as he rode leisurely to the west. Here and there a squatter had the fortitude and the means to do battle against King Drought, and at such stations he was greeted with courtesy and given lodging, usually in a building that housed station workmen. He learned that not all squatters were selling or abandoning their lands. Some of them were buying, often at ridiculously low prices.

He continued to the west, coming into the little town of Hillston on the Lachlan river. There he saw something that interested him very much.

It was wheat. Where once sheep had run on the flat, featureless plain, there were now fields of green. Wheat. And what made it possible was irrigation ditches. He talked with the editor of the local newspaper, an older man who liked a good rambling chat.

"Wheat," the old man said. "In the last six years New South Wales has doubled its wheat production. It beats the hell out of sheep, young man. Wheat builds the land, doesn't tear it down like sheep. And the 'cow cockies' are learning a bit as well."

Tolo had not heard the term and questioned it.

"Dairy farmers," the editor said. "Don't use as much grass as meat-growers. Return good nourishment to the soil through manure. Use a minimum of water."

"A friend of mine in Sydney thinks that after unification the government will begin to buy land and distribute it in some fashion, highly subsidized, to new chums and others who have no land."

The old man nodded. "That's a good guess," he said. "Free selection certainly didn't work. Squatters and drought killed off most of the free selectors, didn't they? In fact, I've heard a new term: 'closer settlement'. Don't know who came up with it, but local politicians are talking about it. Government buys up large holdings, cuts them up into small tracts, and sells them off on easy terms as smallholdings. They say that with irrigation and proper planning, one unprofitable sheep station can provide a living for three thousand settlers."

"And wheat?" Tolo asked.

"As I said, it's the coming thing," the old editor replied.

Tolo could not have explained why he pursued the faint idea that was beginning to form. Perhaps it was only that he had to have something to do while he waited for the proper time to leave his mother alone for a matter of months, perhaps even years. The facts were that throughout Australia there were lands that could be purchased for very low prices, and that new ideas were sweeping the interior. Sheep were falling more and more into disfavour. The questions were many. For example, when would nature relent and bring rain on a regular basis? If the six-year drought continued much longer, most of the land in Australia would be unproductive wasteland, worth almost nothing. Would unification come? If it came, would the government subsidize land for settlers? And what in the name of heaven did the Mason family need with more land or more money anyway?

It was a day or two after his return to Sydney before Tolo realized that he might use his questions about land reform as an excuse to see the Gordons again—and particularly Java. He began by paying a visit to her great-uncle, Johnny Broome, at his newspaper.

Johnny listened intently to the young man for half an hour, for his curiosity was piqued by Tolo's observations about wheat-growing and irrigation.

"Tell you what, Tolo," he said at last. "Now and then a politician comes to the little 'debating society' at the Gordon house. And if the politicians aren't there, you'll find that there's a good range of business people. I think they'd be interested in hearing your thoughts on what you've seen out there in the bush, and maybe you can get a glimmer of what the politicians have in mind for the country after unification."

"You think unification is coming, then?" Tolo asked.

"Oh, certainly," Johnny said. "This year, next year, the year after that. It's coming."

"You've been very kind, sir, to give me your time."

"Not at all. I'll invite you on a night when there's going to be someone at the table who might be able to help you in your quest for a glimpse into the future."

To Tolo's surprise, only a day later he had a message from Johnny Broome asking him to dine at the Gordon house that very night. Tolo, dressed quite formally for him, a boy from the bush, and cutting a rather impressive figure, was at the door five minutes before the appointed time. Java opened the door to his knock, and all thoughts of business or of gathering information went straight out of his head.

She wore white. Her Scots-red hair was a glory, her eyes sparkling. "It's been so long, Tolo," she said. "I'm eager to hear all about your travels."

It quickly became evident why Johnny Broome had invited Tolo on that particular night, for the guest of honour was Edmund Barton, a persistent and outspoken advocate of unification and an influential member of the New South Wales Legislative Assembly and Legislative Council.

At first talk was of the war in South Africa. Johnny excitedly reported the news, received that day, that Kimberley had been relieved, and Roberts and Kitchener were pushing Cronje's forces hard in the vicinity of a place called Paardeberg. And General Buller seemed to have recovered from the disaster at Spion Kop, for his forces were moving again, in yet another attempt to relieve Ladysmith. Baden-Powell was hanging on in Mafeking, with no immediate relief yet in sight.

Java had seated herself next to Tolo Mason. She listened to the war talk intently, so intently that Tolo began to feel that she was giving him the cold shoulder. In Java's presence he seemed to lose some of his self-assurance, and he felt oversized, awkward, and young. He tried to concentrate on the conversation, but he had eyes only for Java, her delicate hands, her bewitching way of cocking her head as she listened to the talk.

It was Johnny Broome who brought up the subject of unification and land reform. He glanced at Tolo and winked as Edmund Barton obligingly, almost automatically, began to pontificate on the possibilities, promising unification soon, then expanding on ways to put land into the hands of deserving settlers.

Java turned her face to Tolo and in a whisper said, "Oh, dear, Uncle Johnny's got him on his favourite subject."

A flush of pleasure came to Tolo. She had not, after all, forgotten his presence. But then a hint of resentment towards her for having ignored him for almost half an hour—plus his genuine interest in what Barton was saying—caused him to put his finger to his lips and say, "Shush."

Barton was advancing the very possibility that had been advocated by the old newspaper editor in Hillston.

"But will the people stand for using public money to induce settlers into the interior?" Sam Gordon asked.

"They'll have no choice," Barton said. "The well-off Australian, Sam, is going to have to realize that he has civic duties beyond donning formal dress to attend Anglophile club gatherings and receptions in Government House. I fear that the majority of the people don't feel—as do our rich, especially the country gentry, the squatters—that maintaining a fine stable of racehorses is a public service."

Sam Gordon laughed. "I'm not exactly in that class, Mr. Barton, but, after all, the races do provide a certain amount of entertainment for the ordinary Australian."

"I agree," Barton said, joining in the laugh. "Like the Roman circus they distract the attention of the poor from their misery. But consider this: the races are entertaining city workers, every one of whom considers himself to be a gentleman. Two-thirds of the trade unions have won an eight-hour day. The level of unemployment is at an all-time low. But we lack one important ingredient in our national stew, and that is an independent Australian yeomanry. We must build a class of yeoman farmers and rural homeowners. To do this, I will recommend taxes on the huge estates. I will see to it that banks make money available cheaply for improvements on farms and homes."

"So you're going to use public money to buy success in land reform," Johnny said.

"Isn't that what you've been preaching for years, Johnny?" Barton asked.

When it was time for the sexes to separate—this after-dinner custom was still observed in the Gordon household—Tolo rose and started to file into Sam Gordon's library, where, so often, Sam's father-in-law, Red Broome, had participated in talk of current conditions and the possibilities for the future. He felt a soft, warm hand on his arm and turned to look down into Java's smiling face.

"You haven't told me about your trip," she said. "If you feel that you must have a cigar, I can provide one for you on the front porch."

He flushed with pleasure at her subtle touch, then laughed. "I don't smoke."

"Good, then you won't foul the air," she said, leading him confidently towards the front of the house.

Java's actions had not been unobserved by Jessica Gordon. When she saw how her daughter was looking up smilingly into Tolo Mason's quite handsome but decidedly brown face, a chill went through her. She raised one hand as if to intervene and opened her mouth, but she was standing in the midst of a group of ladies and, after all, Java was a responsible girl of seventeen years. She did, truly, like to hear stories of travel anywhere in the world, especially Australia. That's all it was, Jessica told herself for reassurance, just Java's fascination with the varied landscape of Australia.

Java perched herself attractively on the porch rail, leaning against a pillar. Each of her graceful curves caught the light. Tolo stood looking over her shoulder at the lights of the city. "Nice view," he said.

"Yes," she agreed. "I never tire of it, really, but there's so much else to see—in Australia, in the world, too, I haven't even been to England."

"Nor have I," Tolo said.

"Would you like to go there?"

"Not really. I think I'd rather see Ayers Rock." Ayers Rock was an immense boulder in the middle of the desert, well-known as a site sacred to the Aboriginals.

"Are you still thinking of doing the definitive study of the original inhabitants?"

"Absolutely."

"How did you find conditions among the Abos when you were out in the bush recently?" She was, he sensed, merely making polite conversation, for suddenly he heard a tenseness in her voice, as if she were uneasy in his presence. He, too, felt ill at ease.

"Well, I didn't see any wild Aborigines," he replied, to answer her spoken question. "In times of drought they travel to better hunting grounds and better water. They can cover fantastic distances. The ones who have allied themselves to the white man, droving his sheep, working his stock, are in no worse shape than most of the whites."

"Is it bad?" she asked.

"It's sad enough for the people," he said, "for those who have to give up their land, especially, but I think it's sadder for the land."

"Oh?"

He shrugged. He had been on the point of telling her things that he had not mentioned to anyone else.

"Please go on," she said, after a long pause. "Tell me why you're sad for the land."

"The Aborigines have lived on it for thousands and thousands of years," he said. "I imagine that since the time of the Dreaming, when the first Aboriginal was set down upon the land, there've been many droughts, some worse than this one. But the Abo didn't drove sheep into areas where the grass was dying for lack of water. The native animals didn't pull up grass by the roots, the way sheep do in bad times, and the native people didn't import an animal for which there are no natural enemies to complete the devastation that the sheep had begun."

"Rabbits?"

He nodded. "They've stripped all the cover away, rabbits and sheep. The topsoil blows away and leaves barren rock, and I can imagine the Aborigines standing out there on top of some hill looking down on what we've done and shedding a tear or two."

"That is sad," she said.

"People are starving. When it gets too bad, they just walk away. Even some of the big squatters are leaving."

"When will it end, this drought?"

Tolo shrugged. "There are those who have found ways to survive." He told her about the irrigated wheat fields, about the squatters who, instead of leaving, were buying up more land at the depressed prices.

"If I had money, that's what I'd do," Java said. "I'd buy, buy, buy. I'd buy every acre I could afford, because the drought can't last forever. People are still moving into Australia, and people are still having children. The land may be mistreated, and it may take years for some of it to recover, but it will. It will be there, the land, and, oh, heavens, would I love to own a huge parcel of it, acres and acres, hundreds."

"Thousands, if you want to be a big landholder," Tolo advised.

"Thousands, then." She slid off the rail and stood facing him. "Is it greedy to think of owning thousands of acres of land when there are so many people who own nothing?"

"I don't know," he said. "You surprise me."

"Because I'd like to own land?"

"I suppose so," he said. "I had a different impression of you. I thought you were more concerned about political matters, unification, and perhaps culture in the cities."

Her voice rose a bit. "Oh, I see. Little lady, stick with matters that pertain to you. Take a light interest in political things, for your concern is harmless, since you're excluded from the smoke-filled library after dinner and from the voting booth."

"Hold on," Tolo said, alarmed. "I didn't mean that at all. I just meant—"

"Sorry," she said. "I don't usually jump down a man's throat with so little provocation."

"I just meant—" What had he meant? She looked at him expectantly. "I respect you very much," he said, "and I enjoy your company. You know I wouldn't willingly do anything to upset you."

"Don't get annoyed," she said.

"I'm sorry if it sounded that way."

"Bloody hell," she said.

He looked at her quickly.

"Shock you?" she asked. "I'll say it again. Bloody hell. Why are we—why am I—sniping at you?"

"I don't know," he said. He had never been more excited by a girl and never more confused. "Perhaps we need more time to get to know each other. Are you allowed to go to dinner and to the theatre without a chaperone?"

"Hardly," she said, a note of frustration showing through. After a pause, "My grandmother and I often go to the McNamara reading room."

"I don't know it," Tolo said. She gave him the address, said that she'd be there the following afternoon, and added that she was sure that her grandmother would agree to the three of them having tea together.

"I'm sorry, dear," Magdalen Broome said the next morning, when Java asked her to go to the reading room with her that afternoon. "I've told your mother that I would go shopping with her."

"Oh, dear," Java said. "But you can shop any time."

"And we can't go to the reading room any time?"

Java flushed. Magdalen could see that there was more on her mind than merely listening to more political talk at the reading room. "As a matter of fact, Grandmother, I told someone I'd be there."

"Ah, I see," Magdalen said. "Then we have a serious conflict, don't we?"

"Grandmother, please," Java said insistently. Her feelings were transparent to Magdalen, who immediately suspected a young man would figure in her granddaughter's story.

"And who is it that you've told that you'd be at the reading room this afternoon?" Magdalen asked.

"Thomas Mason."

"I see," Magdalen said. "And what is the urgency? I would

imagine that Tolo, being Jon Mason's son, would be on the side of the angels regarding matters philosophical and political, so it isn't a matter of converting him."

"There's no urgency," Java said. "It's just that—"

"That you want to see him?" Magdalen asked. She was a bit concerned. She had, of course, noted that Java had pulled Tolo away from the men after dinner the night before and had spent some time with him on the front porch. She had also seen her daughter's uneasiness as Jessica kept glancing at the front door during the interlude before the men came from the library to rejoin the ladies.

"No, not really," Java said. "I mean—" She looked thoughtful for a moment. if there was one person in the world to whom she could be totally truthful it was her grandmother. "I suppose I do want to see him," she said, a note of puzzlement in her voice.

"Do you think you can get Sarah to go with you?" Magdalen asked, after a moment of thought. She winked at Java.

Java's eyes sparkled. "I'm sure I could."

"Now, not a word," Magdalen said softly, rising to walk into the kitchen, where Jessica was giving instructions to the Chinese cook. "I told Java," Magdalen explained, when Jessica had finished, "that we'd drop by the reading room and pick her up when we finished shopping."

"Oh?" Jessica replied. She didn't remember the matter having been discussed.

"She and Sarah will be together," Magdalen said. "They'll take a cab to the reading room and wait for us there."

There were times when Jessica was just a bit jealous of her mother's relationship with Java. Mother and daughter got on well enough, but daughter and grandmother were friends. Mostly, however, Jessica blessed God for having given her a mother who was so understanding of a young girl's sometimes frivolous but often melodramatic crises. With her mind focused on the shopping expedition she did not think of questioning Magdalen further.

Java, standing just around the corner from the kitchen door, listening, clasped her hands together, did a little dance, and grinned.

Magdalen came into Java's room later. She had dressed in a comfortable town gown and was wearing sturdy shoes that were good for walking. Java had put on a mauve dress with white lace at the collar, a combination that set off her hair and eyes well.

"We're off," Magdalen said. "I take it that Sarah's answer to your distress call was in the affirmative."

"She'll be here within an hour," Java said. She took Magdalen's hands in hers. "Thank you, Grandmother, for being so understanding."

"I suppose I'm reverting to childhood," Magdalen said, "conspiring against the adults."

Java giggled. "It's rather fun, isn't it?"

"It is," Magdalen said, "as long as it's done in good spirits, and as long as the results don't get—ah, uncomfortable."

"Please," Java said, "if you're concerned about what I think you're concerned about, you need have no worries at all. He's a nice boy, that's all. And I think he needs a friend."

Those last words of Java's worried Magdalen more than anything that had happened to date. She knew her granddaughter to be a warmhearted, caring person. In a girl such as Java, innocent pity, innocent sympathy, whatever she was feeling for her "friend", Tolo, could easily blossom, and quickly, into a much more powerful emotion.

CHAPTER XXVI

The cab that took Java and Sarah to McNamara's reading room had to brave a tropical downpour during the first part of the drive. When the rain slackened off, the wheels of the hansom cab sloshed through puddles with a gritty and sucking sound, and the horse's clip-clop was deadened by the wetness. Sarah pointed to a motor car that was stalled in the middle of the street, so that the cab had to wend its way around.

"And you want your father to buy one," Sarah said.

"Sarah, you'd be happy living in a cave, like the Abos," Java said.

A wet, disgruntled man was bending into the motor cavity of the automobile, his rear sticking up. Sarah giggled.

They dismounted, holding their skirts daringly high to avoid the wet, but there was no one on the street to see the display of high boots and calves. The reading room, musty and warm, was occupied by only three young men, one of them the pimply-faced boy who tended the room in the absence of William Henry McNamara. He was the son of a Sydney union official, one Roy Wilburn. When he saw Java and Sarah come in alone, he looked expectantly behind them for the grandmother, Magdalen. Concluding that the girls were alone, he stopped talking to the other two men, bush types, and approached the table where Java and Sarah had seated themselves.

"G'day," he said. "Hope you didn't get wet."

"No, thank you," Java said.

"Just made a pot o'tea," Roy said.

"No thank you," Java said. She and Sarah had already decided that as soon as Tolo showed up they would adjourn their not-so-political meeting to the little tea shop nearby where the cakes were truly wonderful.

"There's some new material, just in from jolly old England," Roy said, smiling to show crooked teeth that were a bit yellow for want of cleaning.

"Thank you, Roy," Java said. "We'll look at it next time."

Roy shifted from one foot to the other, obviously reluctant to leave the two attractive girls and hoping to continue the conversation. "It's Sarah, isn't it?" he asked, grinning at Sarah and shifting his weight towards her.

"Miss Bladen, thank you," Sarah said, lifting her head and looking at the youth down her nose. "Will you excuse us, please? We came here to read."

Java had to suppress a giggle that was half amusement, half embarrassment. She, herself, would never have given Roy such a severe put-down, but at least Sarah's rudeness served a purpose. Roy left, went back to the two bush types, and now and then all three of the men would cast a look in the direction of the two girls.

Tolo stood at the entrance to the room for a moment, surveying the scene. The place smelled of old cigars and beer. He saw the two girls, and his eyes were drawn to Java's reddish hair, and then he examined the three men who sat across the room, one of them with his feet up on a table. It wasn't exactly the sort of place he would have picked for a romantic meeting, but then he had not been the one to pick it, had he? There were shelves filled with books, papers, and magazines; there were several chairs and a few tables at odd angles. He walked to the table and could not help but notice that both of the girls were watching his approach, Sara with her eyes wide and sweeping once up and down his tall frame.

"Mr. Thomas Mason," Java said, "I'd like to present my friend, Miss Sarah Bladen."

"Charmed," Tolo said.

"I've heard so much about you," Sarah said.

"Java," Tolo whispered, as he sat down, "you didn't tell her about my opium habit, did you?"

"I couldn't bring myself to reveal such an intimate secret," Java said.

"And certainly you didn't tell this nice young lady about my

Aboriginal harem back in Victoria."

"Oh, tosh," Sarah said. "Harem, scarem! I know all about you. You're called Tolo, you're half Samoan, and you're very rich."

Tolo grinned and leaned towards Sarah. "Which of those things do you like most about me?"

"What makes you think I've decided to like you at all?" Sarah retorted, but she was answering Tolo's smile.

"I compliment your good taste in friends," Tolo said to Java.

"Now don't start buttering me up," Sarah said. "I have this ability to see through all subterfuge to the heart of a man's character."

"Then I'm doomed," Tolo said.

"Tolo," Java said, "all the talk is about a Polynesian boy who rode some kind of a board on the waves at Manly Beach. Do you know about it?"

"I've heard of it, but I haven't seen it done. It's the custom in those islands—but I left the islands when I was quite small."

"Well, you're not much help," Java teased. "What good does it do to know someone who's part Polynesian if he can't teach you the Polynesian sports?"

"It sounds exciting," Sarah interjected.

"Actually," Tolo said, "riding the board is in the blood of all Samoans. The skill is innate." He gave them a superior look. "Which way is the ocean?"

Sarah giggled.

Across the room Roy Wilburn had not seen Tolo enter and join the young ladies. He had not had a good look at Tolo's face until Tolo was seated. "I say," he said in not-so-hushed tones to the two bush types, "is that a nigger?"

One of the bushmen spat in the general direction of a spittoon. "Kanaka, more likely," he said.

"What's he doing here?" Roy growled.

"Dressed like a right toff," the other bushman offered.

"I don't care how he's dressed," Roy said. He rose, then hesitated.

One of the bushmen laughed. "He does have the size advantage doesn't he, Roy?"

The other man dropped his feet off the table. "Go on, boy," he said. "The Kanaka gives you any trouble, we're here."

Sarah was in the midst of describing the cakes at the tea shop when Roy swaggered resolutely to the table. Tolo and Java were laughing as Sarah pretended to gobble up a plateful.

"Here," Roy said as he came to stand beside them.

"Where?" Java asked, and Sarah giggled.

"I'm going to have to ask you to vacate the premises," Roy went on, his voice cracking a little as he looked at Tolo.

"Whatever do you mean?" Java asked, still smiling, thinking surely that Roy must be joking.

"You ought to know better, Miss Gordon," Roy said pleadingly, looking at her. "You know how Mr. McNamara feels about wogs."

Java's face stiffened, contorting with her swift anger. "Roy Wilburn, I do not believe this. You dare come to my table and ask my guest to leave?"

Tolo was watching the two bushmen. They were standing now, listening and waiting for trouble. "Thank you, sir," he said to Roy. "As a matter of fact we were just discussing leaving."

"Yes, we were," Sarah said nervously, pushing back her chair.

"Sit down, Sarah," Java said in a heated voice. "We will leave when we are bloody well ready."

"No need to use profanity, Miss Gordon," Roy said. "But rules is rules."

"I have rules, as well," Java said, her face flushed with outrage. "One of them is to feel free to be with my friends anywhere I bloody well please."

The two other men were closing in on the table now.

"Java, it's all right," Tolo said, standing. "Let's go."

"Mr. McNamara himself is going to hear of this," Java said. "And my father as well. Nor will you ever see any Gordon money donated to buy literature. I am more than angry, Roy Wilburn. How dare you—?"

"This brown boy giving you trouble, Roy?" one of the bushmen asked.

"Seems more like the little lady," the other one said, moving to stand beside Java's chair. "I think the Kanaka has been told to leave, miss. Now, if you don't like that, why don't you just go with him?"

"That's enough," Tolo said, his voice calm and low.

"Why, it can talk," said the bushman closest to Tolo.

Sarah rose from her chair, her face twisted in fright, and began to back towards the door.

"Of course, if you'd like to stay for entertainment," said the bushman who stood beside Java's chair. "I'll be happy to show you that this brown boy has nothing a white man doesn't have."

Back on the station in Victoria, Tolo had been known to lift a yearling calf from a bog all by himself. Now, to his own surprise, his strength seemed to be multipled as the bushman's words heated his blood. With a swipe of his left arm, he sent the man nearest to him flying into a table and sliding to the floor. Then he brushed Roy Wilburn aside as if he were a piece of cardboard.

As the bushman by Java's chair threw a punch at Tolo's face, Tolo seized the man's wrist in a vicelike grip and stepped to one side, jerking the man's arm up behind him. Using his free hand to grab the man by the seat of his trousers, Tolo threw him bodily through the air to land on the other bushman, still slightly stunned on the floor.

"Thank you for your hospitality," Tolo said, giving Roy Wilburn a slight nod. "Our business here is finished. We are leaving now."

Java, her eyes wide, allowed him to take her arm, raise her from her chair, and guide her towards the door.

A rainbow had formed in the west. Blue sky was showing through the clouds. No one spoke as they reached the pavement and halted for a moment. Then, suddenly, Sarah laughed, clapping her hands in delight.

"It is not at all funny," Java said, still enraged.

"But you didn't see that man's face as he flew through the air," Sarah said. She looked up at Tolo. "You're very strong. A point in your favour."

"Java, I'm so sorry," Tolo said.

"You have nothing to be sorry for."

"Let's go and have tea," Sarah suggested.

"Java?" Tolo asked.

"Yes," she said. "Yes, damn them." But she was moodily silent, letting Sarah do the talking, as they walked to the nearby tea house. And she cringed a bit as they entered and the hostess, a nice, grey-haired little widow of a sea captain, escorted them to a table. She had been asked to leave a place where she had previously been welcomed. She tried to tell herself that it was only stupid Roy Wilburn, but in her heart she knew that if William McNamara had been there, the invitation to leave would have come from McNamara himself. And if Henry Lawson had been there, what then?

When all three were seated and Sarah was excitedly ordering an array of cakes for them, Java looked at Tolo's bronzed face, studying it. His nose was cleanly moulded, his features fine, very English. Only the extra depth of what she wished were just his suntan and the dense mass of his black hair spoke of his Samoan blood. His shoulders were large under his jacket, his wrists thick and powerful as they extended from faultless linen cuffs. His hands were calloused and big, and yet she knew from his touch on her arm as he guided her from the reading room that they could be gentle. She remembered the ease with which he had manhandled the two bushmen. He had seemed so calm and had shown no anger until one of the men insulted her. When she was with him—and at that moment it seemed quite natural to be with him—she knew she would never lack for protection.

"Tolo, if we can arrange it," Sara was saying, "could you really teach us how to ride the waves?"

Tolo smiled ruefully. "If, first, I can find that Polynesian boy and get him to teach me."

"Oh, well," Sarah said. "Then you're only a fake Samoan, and I shall have no further faith in you."

Java could not immediately return to the light, bantering tones the three of them had been using before Roy Wilburn interrupted at the reading room. She was still studying Tolo's face and wondering how many times he had had to face insult and rejection. How could he stand it? If someone insulted her because of the colour of her skin, or because of anything else, she would be hysterically angry, doing her best to match injury with injury. But Tolo had been so magnificently calm. His poise and his strong but gentlemanly behaviour had put the crude, fair-skinned types to shame. She felt proud of him, and, at the same time, her heart opened easily to him in sympathy. Without fully realizing it, she determined that if she had her way, no man—or woman—would ever hurt him again.

CHAPTER XXVII

Jessica Gordon met Sam on the front veranda as he came home for the midday meal. The summer weather was magnificent and the view from the veranda inspiring. They stood there for a while, hand in hand, and looked out over the harbour. A sailing vessel, all canvas spread, masts tall and straight, was leaving the harbour on a favourable wind. Sam's eyes were on her.

"Do you miss it, the sea and the sails?" Jessica asked.

He laughed. "We had our moments, didn't we?" Sam replied. For a few years Jessica had lived with him aboard the *Cutty Sark*, the swiftest and most beautiful of clippers. "No, I don't miss it, really. It's more comfortable to sleep in a dry bed. But she's a beautiful ship, isn't she?" He inclined his head towards the sea.

Jessica nodded. There were still full-rigged sailing ships in service, and the one before them now was one of the so-called "windjammers," built of steel and several times the size of the old clippers. Even in the age of steam, windjammers were useful for carrying large cargoes at little cost over long sea lanes where coaling stations for steamships were absent. But how long could they last before the world progressed and steamers took over entirely?

Jessica sighed. "Sam, I'm not sure I'm going to enjoy the twentieth century," she commented.

He chuckled. "Considering the alternative, dear, I think I'll like it just fine."

"Telephones!" Jessica exclaimed. "Why in heaven's name did we allow ourselves to be put at the mercy of anyone who is near another instrument? People can intrude into our lives at any time they wish—at mealtime, after bedtime, on Sunday afternoon."

"It's the price of progress," he said. He himself found the telephone to be a valuable business tool.

"And you can't walk the streets anymore without being almost run down by a stinking, sputtering, roaring motorcar."

Sam turned her so that he could look down into her face. "I think I see someone who's having a bad day."

She smiled ruefully. "Sorry, didn't mean to give you that idea."

"Something's bothering you."

"Come," she said. "Lunch is ready."

They were alone for the meal, eating at a small table in the green room amid luxuriant flowering plants. Over their coffee, Jessica handed Sam a letter in a neat, expensive-looking envelope.

Mrs. Jon Mason and Mr. Thomas Mason
request the honour of the presence of
Mr. and Mrs. Samuel Gordon and Miss Java Gordon
at the gala opening of Bina's.

Time, address, and date were given, and, in a disciplined handwriting, Misa Mason had added a personal note: *My dear Sam and Jessica. Tolo and I do hope that you can come. I think you'll enjoy the food and the entertainment. Please let me know, will you?*

"What is Bina's?" Jessica asked. "Or perhaps I should ask *who* is Bina?"

"I apologize, my dear," he said. "I guess I haven't been keeping you up-to-date on Sydney gossip. Actually, I'm a little surprised that you haven't heard. Bina Tyrell is that new singer who came down from Cloncurry—"

"A mining town, isn't it, in—?"

"Northern Queensland," Sam said. "She's quite good to look at, they say. She's gone into business for herself, and rumour has it that her new establishment, a bistro, really, is financed by Misa Mason. Since this invitation comes from Misa, I'd say that confirms her involvement in the enterprise."

"Well, we won't go," Jessica said firmly.

"Why not?"

"I don't think it's the right sort of place for Java."

"Lord, don't tell her that," he exclaimed, "or she'll be all over us, insisting we go, and take her, whether we want to or not. She's not a child any more, and if Misa thinks this Bina's place is all right—"

"I'm not sure I like the idea of Misa Mason deciding what's right and what's not right for my daughter," Jessica retorted.

Oh, ho, Sam thought, *now we're getting to it.* Aloud he said, "I think something *is* bothering you."

She shook her head and then, with a determined look on her face, said, "Well, yes. Haven't you noticed that Thomas Mason has been in our house twice in the last week?"

"I have. I find Tolo to be a solid-minded boy, quite sound."

"Would you want him for a son-in-law?"

Sam hid his shock. To his knowledge Jessica had never indicated in any way a distaste towards the wife of his dead friend because of her brown skin. He knew that she, like most Australians, considered the Aboriginals to be an inferior race, and she opposed an open-door policy for immigration of brown-skinned people into Australia. That last was just being practical. He himself would have voted to exclude mass importation of any nonwhite race, including cheap Kanaka labour. There were too few whites in Australia, and they could easily be bred into being a minority if, for example, the government opened the door to the Japanese or Chinese. He liked to think that these were all practical considerations, having nothing to do with prejudice.

He chose his words carefully and tried to treat the matter lightly. "Well, to be sure she'd never want for material things. Tolo is quite a rich young man, or will be when he comes into Jon's holdings."

"Money is hardly the issue," Jessica said.

"Aren't you looking for trouble?" Sam asked. "She's given me no indication that she's in any way interested in thinking about marriage to anyone. I think she's more involved in reforming Australia than in romance."

"She's seventeen, Samuel," Jessica said. "She's a woman in every way."

Sam rose and walked to stand behind Jessica's chair, putting his hands on her shoulders. "I think our little girl is a rather level-headed individual. Let's give her the benefit of the doubt. My guess is that her feelings for Tolo are nothing more than friendship. That's quite natural, since Jon and I were good friends."

"I'm frightened," Jessica said.

He pulled her to her feet, turned her, and put his arms around her. "Has she given you any reason to think that she feels more than friendship for Tolo?"

"Not overtly. It's just an instinct, a hunch."

"Far be it from me to knock woman's intuition," he said. "Tell you what. Let's go to this bistro. Let me see Java and Tolo together. Then perhaps I'll have a talk with her."

"And what would you say?" Jessica turned her face away. "I'm so ashamed of myself. I can't bring myself to say, 'Look, Java, he's half brown. He's rich, handsome, and he's quite pleasant, but to marry him would be cutting yourself off from most segments of Australian society. Do you want that?' I can't do that, because it would make me feel awful. It would make me the equivalent of Henry Lawson, condemning everyone whose skin colour is darker than mine. But, God help me, Sam, she's my daughter and I can't—"

"I know, I know," he said. "I still think that maybe you're looking for trouble. Let's give her a chance."

She looked up at him. "And you think we should accept the invitation?"

"I do, for a couple of reasons, one of which I've stated. The other reason is that I think it might be interesting."

Jessica was silent for a few moments. "Then you send the note of acceptance."

He nodded, but as he walked briskly back towards his office near the waterfront, he wondered if that last statement was Jessica's way of saying that she would not be responsible for anything that happened, that since he had made the decision to go, she washed her hands of any trouble that might arise. At the office he sat down at his desk and wrote out by hand a brief, formal acceptance of Misa's invitation. Then he gave it to his secretary, instructing her to have it delivered to the bank by messenger.

Although it was difficult to take Misa's attention away from last-minute emergencies at the bistro, Tolo managed to corner her and escort her to Price Vermillion's office.

At Misa's request and at the expense of the Mason Company, Vermillion had moved his family to Sydney, installing them in a pleasant house in one of the newer outlying districts. He had been given the task of overseeing all of the Mason businesses, including the sales of three of the five Queensland holdings. Slowly the

Mason business affairs were being consolidated into two areas: the bank in Sydney and the shipping company, which had offices in most Australian ports.

"Can we make this quick?" Misa asked.

"Mother," Tolo said with a tolerant smile, "you bought the bank, not I. You wanted to sell off scattered properties, not I." He put his arm around her. "You're like a child with a new toy, you and Bina and this bistro."

"Silly, isn't it?" she asked smiling.

"No, not silly," he said. "I'm pleased to see you so interested and enjoying yourself. There are, however, one or two little items I want you to consider with Price and me."

Price had fresh Sumatran coffee brewing in his office. The aroma filled the room and was so rich that Tolo waited until the brew was ready and Vermillion had poured before he said, "Mother, Mr. Vermillion has cash in hand from two of the Queensland sales. The third sale will be closing within days and the estate agents say there's strong interest in the other two properties."

"Fine," Misa said, trying to show appropriate interest.

"I'd like the money from the property sales to be put into a special fund to which I have access," Tolo said.

"I have no objection," Misa replied, "but isn't that going to be a rather large amount for pocket money, Tolo?"

He smiled indulgently at her.

Prince Vermillion cleared his throat. "Perhaps, Thomas, you need to tell your mother what you have in mind."

"I'm going to buy land," Tolo said.

"Whatever for?" Misa asked quickly.

"For a fraction of its true value," Tolo asked.

Price's doubt was evident in his voice when he said, "He's buying land in the drought area in the western part of New South Wales."

That was news to Misa. "When did this begin?"

"I started thinking about the possibilities when I went into the bush to check out those loan applicants for you," Tolo said. "There's a radical change under way out there, Mother. In many areas sheep and rabbits have joined with the drought to ruin the land. The smallholders and the squatters who try to stick to the old ways—sheep, cattle—are going to be beaten. Already many have simply walked off their land. Others will sell willingly."

"But if the land is ruined—" Misa began.

"Only temporarily ruined," Tolo corrected, "while there's no rain. But I'm not just counting on the rains coming again, nor on their regularity. One of the big changes that's going on can be summed up in two words: wheat and irrigation. We can irrigate wherever water is available."

Misa laughed unbelievingly. "You're going to be a wheat farmer?"

"I'm afraid not," Tolo said. "I'm going to bury my conscience and be a land speculator in a rather large way. I want to control as much land as I possibly can within the next two years. When federation comes, I would like to have at least two million acres of land available in the largest possible adjoining tracts. Then, when the government decides to subsidize smallholders—"

"I see," Misa said, frowning.

"You're involved in this, too, you and the bank," Tolo said. "You were the one who wanted to expand the bank's activity in smaller mortgages."

"I know that we're making a few loans," Misa said, looking towards Vermillion.

"They're sound loans," Vermillion said. "No examiner will question them. Any loan that is approved is well below the market value of the land used as security. In the event of foreclosure the bank will be protected, although it might take some time to turn the foreclosed land into liquid assets."

"I didn't go into the farm loan business to foreclose family farms," Misa said heatedly.

"No, but you knew that foreclosure was always a possibility," Tolo said. "And I'm afraid the drought has made it a stark reality. You must not have read my report when I returned from the field trip, Mother. In that report, if you'll check it, I stated my opinion that a number of the loans we've made will default."

"Yes, yes, I read it, every word of it," Misa said. She examined Tolo's face minutely. "Are you counting on the bank's foreclosures to create your wealth of landholdings?"

"No, not at all. I intend to purchase on my own as well. But I suggest that the bank hold any foreclosed land for accrual of value.

If that doesn't meet with your approval, then I'll buy your foreclosures," Tolo said.

"How sad," Misa said, "to think that I shall be responsible for taking people's homes."

"Nonsense," Vermillion said. "If you want to be a philanthropist with your own money, Misa, you may. But not with the bank's money, for the money that we lend is not ours. We have a legal trust, a duty."

"Oh, I know," she said. She thought for a moment, then shrugged in resignation. "All right, Mr. Vermillion, do as Tolo wishes." She rose, bent to kiss Tolo on the cheek. "The bank will hold any foreclosed lands for this boom you promise us, Tolo. And I won't make you take the foreclosures off my hands. You'll have enough to look after, making your own purchases."

Misa hurried out of the bank. Her driver was waiting. He was a short, thin lad of nineteen who spent a good portion of the day polishing and cleaning any mote of dust from the gleaming, painted surfaces of Misa's Daimler. The boy helped Misa into the vehicle, and as he drove grandly through the Sydney streets towards Bina's, Misa was thinking how odd it was that the drought had brought her the best friend she'd ever had, and how now it was going to involve Tolo in business. A sad business, true, capitalizing on the misfortune of others, but nevertheless an honest business. It was not up to the Mason family, she rationalized, those "inferior" beings, those brown-skinned outcasts of society, to give aid to every drought-stricken farmer or drover. There was no guarantee the money that Tolo was going to invest in the drought-ravaged lands in western New South Wales would ever be returned, much less with a profit. It could be argued, if one worked at it hard enough, that Tolo was bringing welcome relief to those landowners who wanted nothing more than to be freed of their drying land. At any rate, she would not let herself worry about it. The drought was an act of God. If God favoured the Mason family a bit and allowed them to make a profit as a result of the drought, so be it.

On the night of the opening Tolo arrived at Bina's early. His mother had been gone all day, helping Bina with last-minute

details. He went to the service door and was admitted by a Chinese
kitchen helper. Most of the kitchen staff was Chinese, except for
the excitable French chef whom Misa had lured out to Australia
from London with the promise of a huge salary and an opportunity to buy into a chain of bistros modelled on the new Bina's.
The waiters were white, but they were new chums, not yet truly
Australian. Service was not exactly in the Australian character,
and among the waiters there was a colourful chorus of various
European accents.

The main dining room, decorated in a tropical motif, was
spacious and airy. The tables had enough distance between them
to allow for a certain amount of privacy. Tolo walked to the left
front, near the little raised stage where the orchestra would play
and where Bina would perform, to check on the head table, which
had been set up for the Mason family and their guests. There were
ten places, four on each side and one at each end. Place cards were
set out. In addition to Misa and Bina, positioned at either end,
there were seats for Tolo, the Gordons, Magdalen Broome, Price
Vermillion, and the bank manager, Daniel Moore, and his wife.

The small orchestra arrived and began tuning up, the cacophony
of sound echoing in the empty room. Tolo prowled the room
restlessly. He had made his first large purchase of land the
previous week, a station of some two thousand acres with frontage
on the drought-starved Darling River. That thought turned his
mind easily to Java Gordon's face, the way she had looked when
she had been dreaming aloud of owning vast stretches of her
country.

When the doors opened at six P.M., a few people were already
waiting outside. The headwaiter courteously showed the diners to
tables, and soon waiters were streaming back and forth, their trays
laden first with beverages and then with food. The orchestra
played soft background music, saving the dance music for later.
Bina and Misa had not yet made their appearance. Tolo, hungry,
wandered into the kitchen again and wolfed down two very light,
fluffy rolls smeared with fresh butter. The French chef and his
assistants were not yet stretched. They went about filling the early
orders with calm efficiency.

The Gordon family arrived at seven. Java broke into a wide
smile when she saw Tolo across the dining room. He met them at

the table. "Good evening, sir," he said to Sam. "We're so pleased that you could come."

"Our pleasure, Tolo," Sam said. "Quite a place, eh?"

"It's beautiful, Tolo," Java said, moving ahead of her mother to examine the names on the place cards. "You're here, Mother," she said, "on the end next to Mrs. Mason." Next to Jessica was Sam, then Java and then Tolo, on the end next to Bina. Magdalen sat across from Tolo, to Bina Tyrell's left, with Price next to her and then the Moores.

Before everyone could be seated, Misa and Bina came sweeping across the floor, each resplendent in a new gown. Tolo sneaked a look around the dining room. Without exception every male eye was on the two women. Misa introduced Bina to others at the table, and there were the usual smiles and polite words.

The orchestra began a waltz, and Tolo asked Java to dance. Jessica, just getting seated next to Misa, did not see them leave the table; she looked around after taking her seat, saw the empty chairs and then glimpsed the two young people alone on the dance floor. Java wore a full-skirted dress of pristine white with powder-blue trimming at the cuff, waist, and neck to set off her pale red hair. She was looking up into Tolo's face as they waltzed, smiling, listening to him in rapt attention. There was a tug of pure panic in Jessica's chest and she looked at Sam quickly. He, too, was watching the dancers.

Waiters began to fill the table with the dishes that the British called "starters": pâté, caviar, tidbits, and appetizers that, Sam thought, would be costing a fortune if he were footing the bill.

"You've done such a beautiful job," Magdalen told Bina. "It's a lovely place." She nibbled a biscuit spread thick with pâté and said, "Ummm, how delicious."

"We're honoured that you and your family are here," Bina said.

"Darling girl," Magdalen said, "you and Mrs. Mason do us honour. And—" She laughed. "From all indications you're going to make me put another ten pounds on this slightly creaking frame of mine."

Bina laughed and proceeded to engage Magdalen in easy, pleasant talk, keeping a discreet eye on her other guests. Jessica, she saw, was hardly speaking at all, though Misa, seated next to her, tried several times to start a conversation. Instead, talk at that

end of the table flowed around Jessica, from Misa to Sam Gordon,
or across the table between Sam and Daniel Moore, the man he
had recommended to Misa as manager of her bank.

Java came back to take her seat, her face flushed, her eyes
radiant. Tolo bowed to Magdalen and said, "Mrs. Broome, would
you do me the honour of dancing with me?"

"Why, yes, Tolo, thank you," Magdalen said; then, to her granddaughter, "Did you put him up to this?" Her eyes sparkled with
amusement as she rose and took Tolo's arm.

Seated at the table, Java realized she was too excited to be
hungry. She loved being among the guests of honour at the
opening of a fancy place like Bina's. It was thrilling to see that as
the room filled, the cream of Sydney society was there. But those
things had not put the flush to her face. For, as they had danced,
Tolo had told her about the sheep station he had purchased on the
Darling.

"Oh, my," she had said. "Tell me about it."

"To tell the truth, I can't tell you much. I haven't seen it."

"You're joking."

"No, not at all. I know what it will look like. It will be barren
and sear. There may be a few trees here and there in low areas, but
the grass will be almost nonexistent, eaten by sheep and rabbits,
and the water holes will be dry, but—"

She was looking up into his face, hanging on every word.

"—it will be magnificent in its barrenness, and although the
earth will be powdery dry, there's a richness in it, and that richness
can be brought out by ditching water from the Darling, or by
pumping water from deep wells. I'm going to use some of it as my
demonstration wheat farm. I'll have several hundred acres ditched
and watered—"

"Oh, I'd love to see it," Java said. "How many acres?"

"Just over two thousand."

"I can't envisage just how large that is."

"A square mile is six hundred and forty acres," Tolo said. "This
plot is just over three square miles, but it's not in a square. It runs
long and narrow along the Darling for about five miles."

"Are there kangaroos?"

"I would imagine. There'll surely be rabbits. I'll have to repair the rabbit fences and gather a large number of men and boys and try to cut down on the rabbit population."

"Poor things."

"I'm not going to raise wheat to feed rabbits," he said. "After all, they're new chums, not real Australians."

She was silent for a while, giving herself over to the sway and swing of the waltz. "Tolo?"

"Yes?"

"Why did you buy the land? You told me not long ago that you were selling land in Queensland."

It was a casual enough question, but it stunned Tolo into a nervous silence, his brown furrowing as if choosing his words with care. Was he afraid of her? she wondered. It could not be, yet she felt his strong arms around her begin to tremble slightly. Finally he said, "Didn't you say you wanted to own huge tracts of land?"

Java felt the heat rush to her face, then felt a queer little flip of her heart. He was looking at her ever so seriously for approval, and she was not sure she was ready for seriousness with Tolo Mason or with anybody. His words seemed to hang in the air heavily, demanding some sort of an answer. It was obvious that he expected a reaction from her. All the thought and reaction rushed through her consciousness so quickly that it was only a short pause before she said, "Well, Tolo Mason, if it was intended to be a Christmas present for me, you're very late with it and far too early for my birthday." For she had decided that the only way to handle his query was with humour.

Tolo laughed, and she felt him relax instantly, his arms steadier and his step brisker and more confident as he spun her around in time to the music.

Bina sang twice that night. In her first performance she featured love songs and old songs from the home country. Sam Gordon enjoyed her playing and singing very much. He had allowed himself to try one of the featured "tropical" drinks from the bar, a concoction of several fruit juices and a startling amount of good rum. He was quite mellow.

Bina and Misa had requested that they be allowed to select the dishes that made up a meal that, Magdalen told Bina, had never been matched anywhere. They ate after Bina's first performance, and after a suitable time Jessica bent to Sam and said, "Don't you think it's time to go?"

"Bina's going to sing again soon," Sam objected.

Jessica said nothing further. She was watching her daughter, who was on the dance floor again with Tolo. Other couples were dancing now, but Jessica had to admit that Java and Tolo made the most handsome couple out there, and that was what was worrying her. As the young people came back to the table, Java breathing hard after a spirited reel, Jessica rose, took her hand, and said, "Keep me company, Java dear."

Java followed her mother to the lady's lounge, which was beautifully decorated. An Abo maid was there to do service, but Jessica dismissed her with thanks and a coin, which the maid accepted with an awkward curtsy before departing.

When Java and her mother were alone, standing before a large mirror pushing at their already immaculate hair, Jessica spoke in a pleasant, casual voice. "Don't you think you're overdoing the dancing just a little?" she asked.

Java, unaccustomed to criticism from her mother, flushed and looked at Jessica in puzzlement.

"I mean, should you dance every dance with the young man?"

Java had been enjoying herself thoroughly, and her mother's words brought shame—she would not have been able to explain why—and doubt, her ebullient mood affected as if she had been doused with iced water.

"I'm sorry," she said. "I didn't realize—" And then her anger flared. Didn't realize what? That she was young and having a very good time and enjoying dancing with a fine young man who was a family friend? She turned to Jessica and asked, "Why does it bother you?"

"Oh, it doesn't, really," Jessica said. "It's just that—"

And now the iced water seemed to run down Java's spine as she realized what was bothering her mother. "It's because he's half Samoan, isn't it? You're ashamed of me for dancing with a Samoan."

"No," Jessica said at once, but she then paused. "I mean, well—"

There were tremors of pain and sadness in Java's voice, tears in her eyes as she said, "Oh, Mother!" And then she turned away, put her face into her hands and let the great sobs come, for in that moment when she realized why her mother was criticizing her, she had also recognized one more truth.

She knew, and the knowledge knifed into her heart as she had a flashing vision of a troubled future, that Tolo was more than a friend.

God help me, she thought, as she foresaw the pain that she would bring others, *I'm in love with him.*

CHAPTER XXVIII

It was not odd, but natural, that most of the Australian correspondents in South Africa at one time or other sent back dispatches about horses. Banjo Patterson—who had ridden with the first column of Australian mounted infantry to enter Kimberley following relief of the city—wrote colourfully about how the people emerged from their shelters and from the twelve-hundred-foot mine shafts, where they had congregated to escape the shelling of the Boer's Long Tom cannon. But he reserved his finest passions for the horses, exhausted from heat and overwork, being shot as they fell, and starving Kaffirs—the white man's generic term for all South African blacks. He described them descending on the carcasses like vultures.

From Natal, Kelvin Broome, too, wrote about the horses, noting that Australian horses were too finely bred to withstand the rigours of African war; Kelvin, however, unlike Patterson, did not wax poetic over the fate of horses. Instead, he did a tongue-in-cheek piece on the famous steed of Lord Roberts, the supreme commander.

"This corresponent has not had the honour of meeting the war horse Vonolel," he wrote, "the Arab grey who was awarded more Afghan war medals than most men by Queen Victoria, nor has he had the pleasure of talking directly with Vonolel's companion in war, Lord Roberts. We can only assume, since the much-honoured Vonolel has carried Lord Roberts to victory in the ten terrible days of the Paardeberg campaign that broke the main Boer army in the west, that the fate of the empire rides a worthy mount.

"Furthermore," Kelvin added, "since British forces in South Africa stand at 180,000, outnumbering the entire Boer population, man, woman and child, there is optimism among the high command that this war will soon be ended. It is to be noted that colonial forces counted alone, chiefly Australians and Canadians, outnumber the entire British Army at Waterloo and almost equal the British forces that fought in the Crimea. This fact cannot go unnoticed in the halls of power in London."

Matt Van Buren had received orders to travel by rail and then by "available transportation" to rejoin the Queensland Mounted Infantry, which was now attached to the main force under Roberts and Kitchener. Both Matt and Kelvin Broome had arrived at the front near the Modder River in time to see Piet Cronje ride in to surrender after the Paardeberg campaign.

The Boer general wore an old green overcoat, battered *veldschoen* boots, worn frieze trousers, and a slouch hat of the type that more and more was being adopted by members of the enemy's forces. Cronje's old, grey, bony horse looked very tired. Four thousand Boers made a huge stack of their Mauser rifles.

Koos De La Rey did not take part in the surrender. With other Boer units, he was fighting a rearguard action as he moved east towards Bloemfontein, capital of the Orange Free State.

The Earl of Dundonald liked Australians. More than once he had heard from captured Boers that the Boers respected the Aussie troops above all. "They fight like we do," a Boer officer had told him. "They sneak into our lines and kill our pickets."

He had heard of Lieutenant Matt Van Buren, who had led a platoon of the Middlesex up Spion Kop, and he was about to request that Matt be reassigned to his own mounted brigade when someone informed him that Matt had sought and obtained transfer back to his original Queensland unit.

"Can't say I blame him," was the earl's reply.

Then he recalled the other Australian already serving under him: Lieutenant Slone Shannon. Slone was not a genuine bushman like Van Buren. In fact, since Slone had trained at Sandhurst, one might easily forget altogether that he was Australian. But Australian he was.

The earl sent for him. He thanked the young lieutenant for his valiant service at Spion Kop and then asked him about his other war experience. He was startled to learn that Slone had been one of Kitchener's boys in the Sudan.

Slone admitted that he had written to Kitchener around the first of the year, requesting assignment to a combat unit. Since then, he added, Spion Kop had more than fulfilled his appetite for action; he was entirely content to serve in Natal until ordered elsewhere. Nevertheless, the earl did not fail to catch the wistful tone in Slone's voice when the young man spoke of Kitchener.

Thus it was that Slone found himself once more on horseback with Dundonald's swift-moving mounted brigade.

The earl was but one of many who felt that Buller had hesitated long enough, that it was high time to move quickly to relieve Ladysmith. Dundonald and his men succeeded in taking high ground in the Tugela hills, causing consternation in the laagers of the Boers under the command of Louis Botha. Buller, however, failed to follow up this victory, and Dundonald fretted, wanting to move directly on Ladysmith. Buller, with his characteristic genius for complicating the simplest of operations, managed to get his army of twenty-five thousand men—five times the Boer force—strung out along the river so that it could not be brought to bear against the Boer positions. His first attempt to cross the Tugela led to disaster, as the British marched into devastating fire from the Boers in the hills above the river crossing.

It was not until February 27 that Buller, for the first time, deployed his huge army effectively. Attack after attack rolled over the hills, the British successfully crossing the river and advancing along a broad front, giving Louis Botha no chance to manoeuvre his outnumbered men to meet the British regulars. In six hours, the months of bumbling, of unnecessary casualties, ended in a wave of triumphant colonial khaki.

Dr. Hans Van Reenen's mobile hospital had been moved to a point near Colenso, and for some days had been treating the wounded from the hills around the Tugela. On February 27— ordinarily a day on which the Boers commemorated the great Boer victory at Majuba in 1881 during the first Boer war—the casualties began to pour into the hospital tents at a rate not seen since the day of Spion Kop.

In a relatively short time Sianna De Hartog had acquired skills that would have been envied by many an experienced surgeon. Her time was divided between treating less serious wounds herself— she had a steady, gentle, and skilful hand for stitching up the horrible tears made by shrapnel—and in assisting Dr. Van Reenen in more serious cases. By late afternoon they were overwhelmed, buried under so many wounded men that it was impossible to keep up with them. Men died while waiting for simple medical attention. The word from the fighting front became more and more grim.

At twilight Sianna heard her name being called and looked up to see Dirk De Hartog standing in the open flap of the surgical tent.

"Dr. Van Reenen," Dirk said, "it is time for you to move."

"Impossible," Van Reenen replied, not even looking up from his effort to stitch back together a kidney almost severed by shrapnel from a pom-pom shell.

"I'm afraid that's an order, Doctor," Dirk said.

Van Reenen sputtered in anger, waving a bloody scalpel to indicate the wounded waiting for treatment.

"You are too valuable to lose, Doctor," Dirk commented. "You will leave the wounded who cannot be moved quickly and easily."

"God forgive us," Van Reenen sighed.

"The British will have surgeons," Dirk said, "and believe me they won't be long in getting here." He came to stand beside the girl he called his daughter. "Will you come with me?" he asked quietly.

She shook her head. "I'll stay with the hospital."

He nodded. He would not deny her the right. "You'll be needed," he said.

"How far do we move?" she asked. "To Ladysmith?"

"Beyond," he said.

She felt sadness rise in her throat, making her eyes sting. "It's almost over then?"

"Roberts and Kitchener will be in Johannesburg and Pretoria within weeks," he said.

"All this for nothing," she said, as she handed the doctor a sponge without having to be asked. It was a dizzying, nauseating thought.

Dirk kept his commando unit, reduced now to fewer than twenty men, as an escort for the mobile hospital. Sianna was weeping as she drove a wagon away from the tents that were being left behind, tents that so thinly sheltered the severely wounded men. Around them the Boer army was in headlong retreat, a chaotic tangle of men, horses, wagons, and guns. The track led downwards to a small stream, and there the Transvaaler commandos struggled with each other in their eagerness to escape the flood of British khaki that was so close behind them.

Dirk, seeing the confusion at the ford of the small stream from the top of the rise, detoured the hospital train to the east. There the ford was not as easy, the water coming up to the wagon beds, but the footing of the stream bed was solid and all of the wagons were soon across.

And then the thunder that had been rumbling in the sky since early evening caught them, closing over them in a natural bombardment of sound louder than a British cannonade and just as fearsome. Lightning glared on the rocks and lit the anxious faces of thousands of men, bedraggled and drenched as the sky opened in a cloudburst. Some were on horseback; many were on foot, having to dodge among the exhausted, staggering mules and bullocks, which struggled to pull the wagons.

"Oh, my God," Sianna said, as the lightning revealed a group of men caught in the swirling spate of water that came rushing down a dry gully. Men went down and were tossed like twigs by the force of the flood. A wagon overturned, and the eight oxen pulling it writhed about, becoming entangled in their harness as the water threw them off their feet.

A Boer officer spotted Dirk. The almost continuous lightning made it possible to identify a man by his face. "Colonel De Hartog," he shouted, "General Botha has ordered that we retire to Elandslaagte, there to rally. Will you pass the word?"

Dirk saluted. Elandslaagte was twenty miles beyond Ladysmith. He knew that Botha had had plans to try to rally men for a stand outside Ladysmith, and he wondered if, by some mischance, the British were already at Ladysmith.

To his right, fitfully visible in the lightning, a loose column of men panicked and began to run, throwing away their rifles, ridding themselves of any excess weight. This, Dirk knew, was a sign of incipient surrender.

Somehow the hospital wagons managed to stay together through that terrible night when it seemed that nature herself had conspired with the British to crush the Boers once and for all. With the morning, February 28, the hospital train was halted, fires built with some difficulty after the soaking rain, and the wounded fed a hot meal of porridge. As daylight arrived to dispel the night's gloom and terror, the men began to regain their equanimity.

The plain before Ladysmith was littered with abandoned weapons and stores and broken wagons. Dundonald's mounted brigade crossed the plain without opposition, moving as fast as the sodden ground allowed, the horses' hooves sinking into the mud and pulling out with a sucking sound. Behind them Buller was resting from his success of the previous day, having ordered Dundonald to keep an eye on the retreating Boers. Dundonald decided to do more than merely observe. He did not want to risk his entire brigade, for he had enough respect for Louis Botha to know that the general was capable of inflicting one last, lethal blow at the British in front of Ladysmith. Instead he called in his Australian.

"Lieutenant Shannon," the earl said, "take your men and have a look at the town, if you please."

Bloody hell, thought Slone as he fanned his eyebrow with a salute. *Here we go again. Take that bloody ten-thousand-foot mountain, lads, if you please.*

Slone led his formation forward swiftly, and by late afternoon he saw the town ahead. All Boer resistance in the surrounding area had fled during the night. He pulled the men into a smart, close column, set the colour bearer to the fore, and rode forward until he heard an English voice cry out, "Who goes there?"

"The Ladsymith relief column," Slone answered.

In the town, gaunt and sunken-eyed men emerged from their shelters with tears wetting their cheeks. There was, oddly enough, little cheering. The populace of Ladysmith turned out and looked at the healthy faces of the troopers and at the plump horses as if in disbelief. It was only when Slone's column rode up the main street to see the man who had held Ladysmith for so long, General White, standing tall with his staff around him, that the garrison of the town broke into cheers.

General Archibald Hunter, White's chief of staff, sought out Slone as the senior officer of the column. "We've got them," Hunter said. "They're running. The plain to the north and east is covered with their abandoned arms and equipment. All we have to do is put cavalry among them, fire one gun, and the whole mob will surrender."

"Sir, you see that I have only thirty men," Slone said.

"Where in blazes is Buller?" Hunter demanded.

"I suppose, sir," Slone said, "that General Buller is regrouping back at the Tugela."

The Boer retreat swept onward like a flood, carrying Sianna's hospital unit with it. There was no rallying of the troops at Elandslaagte. At Glencoe General Joubert was ill, no doubt his own body's response to defeat. There Paul Kruger, the Bible-quoting president of the Transvaal, joined Joubert and made a personal effort to stop the panic.

"*Huis-toe!*" the troops yelled to Oom Paul. "We're going home." The retreat continued northward to Newcastle before the citizen army could be persuaded to turn. There, near Newcastle, Dr. Van Reenen and Sianna were able at last to set up the hospital. This work was light. The seriously wounded had been left behind. Sianna took time to pray for them, even as she moved to her tasks in yet another bivouacked operating room.

Lord Dundonald called Lieutenant Slone Shannon into his tent outside Ladysmith. "Well, Australia," Dundonald said. "You seem to have powerful friends."

"Sir?" Slone said noncommittally.

"This just caught up with us," Dundonald said, handing Slone an official dispatch. "Actually I'm not all that surprised."

Slone read the dispatch. It was from Lord Kitchener himself, and it ordered Slone to report to Kitchener's headquarters, somewhere near or along the Port Elizabeth-Johannesburg railway, with all possible haste and by any means possible.

"I imagine, sir, that the general wants me to help rebuild or to extend the railway. I served in the engineers."

"I know," Dundonald said. "Well, I don't seem to have any luck keeping young Australian lieutenants under my command. God go with you. I think this war will be over by the time you take ship from Durban to Cape Town and then make your way north."

"Sir, I don't think I'd be sorry," Slone said.

"I know what you mean. Good luck, Shannon. "

The trip by rail to Durban was uneventful. Not all of Natal's Boers had risen up in war. Slone rode past peaceful fields, through rich lands, and then he was on board ship and his thoughts were going ahead of him, to Kit Streeter, in Cape Town. Since his orders from General Kitchener said "with all possible haste," he would not be able to linger in Cape Town, but he would give himself enough time to see Kit, to dazzle his eyes and warm his heart with her once more.

Evelyn Streeter was in constant pain. Her periods of lucidity were more and more rare. Quite often she confused her daughter with the nurse that Roland Streeter had hired to sit with his wife during the night, and, to Streeter's own heartbreak, she quite often did not recognize even him.

Kit was tired. It had been a long, long siege of work and of sadness, for the growth in her mother's head did odd things to the woman's functions. And yet Kit did not feel her love stretched or abused, as she cared for her mother as if she were a baby. For some unfathomable reason God was testing the Streeter family with a suffering that was terrible pain for the direct victim and mental agony for Kit and Roland Streeter. It was a time, Kit felt, for those who would survive afterwards to close ranks. She felt closer to her father during those weeks than she had felt since she was a child, and Streeter returned her affection.

On a pleasant morning early in April Colonel Streeter answered the telephone. He had taken a leave of absence, for the doctors had said that Evelyn Streeter's condition was critical. Streeter was having a better-than-average day, considering the fact that he was watching his wife die slowly, for Evelyn, responding to the disease's unpredictable course, was surprisingly coherent today, in little pain, and eager to talk with her husband and her daughter. Her moments of lucidity were so rare these days that Streeter resented the intrusion of the telephone. He answered, barking out his name. He listened. His face turned grim.

"Kit," he called. Kit came from her mother's bedroom. "It's that young Australian lieutenant," Streeter said. He worked his lips. He was not accustomed to asking, more to ordering, but he knew in this case that to give an order might rouse just the reaction he wanted to avoid. "I beg you," he said, his voice filled with pain. "This could be the last time she's—" He could not say it, could not admit that the woman he loved and knew might never again be fully with them. The doctors said that it was astounding that she had retained her memory thus long. "You might never be able to talk with her again," he said.

Kit, her face troubled, took the telephone. "Slone, is that you?"

"You can't imagine how good your voice sounds to me," Slone said. "Listen, I'm on orders. There's a train leaving for the north in just two and a half hours and I must be on it. But I have to see you. Can you come to—"

"Oh, Slone," she broke in, the tone of her voice halting him. "Oh, my darling," she whispered. "I can't. I just can't."

"Then I'll come to your house," he said.

"Oh, no," she said. Recently her father had become obsessive in his insistence that Evelyn's condition be hidden from the world. She did not quite understand why the colonel acted as if he were wildly ashamed of his wife's condition—actually it seemed disloyal for her to think the word, ashamed—but she had given him her word. It would be over soon. "No, you can't," she said. "Oh, God, Slone."

"Is there something wrong?" he asked.

She swallowed, forced her voice to be firm. "No, not at all. I can't explain, Slone. When will you be here again?"

"Ask the gods of war that question," Slone said. "Kit, I don't understand."

"Kit?" The voice was that of her mother, from the bedroom, weak, barely discernible.

"I have to go," Kit said. "Oh, Slone, please forgive me. Please understand."

"I don't understand," he said, and those were the last words she heard as she hung up to prevent him from hearing her sobs.

The British Army was at Bloemfontein. The Boers' final defence of their capital had been crushed by the second week in March, and the khaki-clad ranks of the Queen's troops had entered the city. While they paused to await reinforcements, their leaders, "Bobs and K," as the press had christened Roberts and Kitchener, were planning what they thought would be the last stage of the war—the march to Johannesburg and to Pretoria, capital of the Transvaal.

On a sunny day in April Kitchener took time to greet a young man who had travelled a long way to join him.

"Ah, Lieutenant," Kitchener said.

The South African climate seemed to agree with Kitchener, Slone thought. Kitchener's square face was more handsome, his great moustache healthier. His odd eyes, however, were still wide-set, blue, and glittering in their emotionless stare.

"Good to be here, sir," Slone said.

"Too bad we don't have *all* the boys here," Kitchener said. "Ah, well. What's your pleasure, Lieutenant?"

Kitchener sounded so off-hand and relaxed that Slone was startled. Since the general had ordered him to report quickly, he had assumed that Kitchener already had a specific assignment for him. "I'm not keen on building railways, sir," Slone answered.

"I suspected not," Kitchener said with a mirthless grin. "Well, pick your unit, my boy. Grab yourself a bit of glory if you can, because it will be over soon, and then there'll be nothing to do but sit around and go over how each penny was spent with the home-front accountants."

"Thank you, sir," Slone said. "I'd like very much to serve with an Australian unit, if it can be arranged."

"Mounted, of course," Kitchener commented.

"We Aussies really are poor walkers," Slone replied, "sir."

When he reported to the Queensland Mounted Infantry, one of the first faces he saw was a familiar one. "Well, bloody do," Matt Van Buren said. "G'day, Queensland."

"G'day to you, Queensland," Slone said, extending his hand to the other lieutenant.

CHAPTER XXIX

Several weeks after the opening of Bina's, Johnny Broome devoted his editorial to the charming newcomer to Sydney, Bina Tyrell. Bina's singing had so impressed Johnny that he wrote of her songs in flowery prose that would have done credit to either Banjo Patterson or Henry Lawson, and his words were read and discussed in almost every household in Sydney and in many outlying areas. Almost a week later the Royal Mail Coach reached Cloncurry with copies of the edition that carried Johnny's glowing praise for the owner of Sydney's newest and finest bistro. Two days after that, the chief constable, Clive Taylor, was idly turning the wrinkled, dog-eared pages of the paper while waiting his turn in the barbershop. Letting his eyes scan the page, he did a double take and went back to Johnny's column to identify the distinctive name, Tyrell.

"Well dog me," he said. The barber looked at him over the head of the current customer and raised one eyebrow.

"Reading here about an old friend," Clive said. He drew the paper a bit closer to his eyes and squinted at the small print. Bina, it seemed, was doing very well for herself, in direct contrast to her old friend Clive.

At first, as the proprietor of the "boardinghouse" in which Ellie, Dolly, Nancy and the other girls toiled nightly, with matinées on Saturday, Clive had lived a great life. As Bina had predicted, the girls seemed to enjoy having a strong man around to protect them, and there had been no limit to the new owner's right to sample the merchandise. Law enforcement, luckily, had not been badly needed during those weeks, and Clive's constables took care of the occasional too-exuberant drunk and broke up the inevitable fist fights in the pubs. But it seemed that Clive Taylor was not a man who could stand prosperity. He lost the house in a poker game several weeks after he had purchased it from Bina, and there he was, with nothing to depend on but the modest salary of his sheriff's job plus a bit of pay under the table from the gambling houses and the boardinghouse, which was now prospering under the management of a slick gambler from Canberra.

For Clive—who had known the good life, with women at his beck and call, plenty of food and drink, and a decent income as a businessman—going back to working for a living was a bitter pill. He thought about striking out for the gold fields in Western Australia, even though he had tried looking for gold once and had found it to be dirty, hot, and unrewarding work. Seeing the glowing description of Bina's new place and her success in Sydney changed his mind about a possible direction of travel. He mulled things over while the barber trimmed his hair and doused it with a tonic that smelled like vanilla. He still had not decided fully the next morning when he found himself walking towards city hall, but as he entered the building and halted before the door to the mayor's office, he nodded his head vigorously as if in conversation with himself, removed his hat, opened the door and entered, his step quickening, a look of decision on his face.

He told the mayor that he wanted some time off, a sort of sabbatical, and that he might or might not be coming back but would notify the city as soon as he decided. The mayor was dubious but consented.

Clive arrived in Sydney with only a pound or two left to spend. He had no idea where Bina might be living, but the newspaper had given the address of the establishment which was apparently making her rich. He arrived there a bit tired, dusty, a week overdue for a bath, in the clothes he had worn while riding various forms of transportation ranging from horseback to tramp steamer.

The place was closed. He pounded on the door and heard silence from within. Finally he found a very small plaque on the door, stating the hours of business. He was damned hungry, and the place didn't open until six. He walked around, found a working-man's café, and had a bowl of soup and a hunk of cheese. He was at the door of Bina's place before six, and when at last he heard the interior locks being turned, he opened the door. A fay-looking man in a waiter's uniform stared at him in shock and said, "I'm sorry, sir, gentlemen are required to be properly attired."

"M'arse is covered, isn't it?" Clive replied, starting to push past him.

"Is there a problem here?" asked another man in a waiter's suit.

"Not unless you poofters want a problem," Clive said. "I'm here to see my old friend Bina."

"I'm sorry, sir," said the first waiter, "Miss Tyrell isn't in yet."

"I'll wait, then," Clived insisted.

The second waiter hesitated. "Where, might I ask, did you make Miss Tyrell's acquaintance?"

"Let's just say we did business together up Cloncurry way. Now why don't you get me something to eat?"

The two waiters exchanged doubtful glances, but Clive's size and growing anger obviously impressed them.

"Very well, sir," said the first waiter. "Since you are an old friend of Miss Tyrell's, please follow me, and I'll see that you're fed."

Clive followed him through a fancy-looking room with a little stage at one end on which sat a piano. Bina did play well, and he loved the songs she belted out, especially the one about the professional girl who wanted to become a virgin. He decided not to rock the boat. He followed meekly into the kitchen, sat down at a little table in the corner, and quite soon had forgotten his impatience as he ate a huge slab of the finest standing rib roast he had ever tasted. Finished, he crooked a finger at one of the Chinese kitchen helpers who came over, smiling and bobbing.

"When Missy Tyrell come?" he asked.

"Miss Tyrell usually comes in just before her first perfor-mance," the Chinaman said in perfect English.

"When that?" Clive asked, tapping his watch.

"Just before eight, sir. Occasionally she comes earlier. We never know until she gets here."

Hell, it was just a few minutes past six. "Do you know where Miss Tyrell lives?" he asked.

The kitchen worker had seen the big bushman being given preferential treatment, prime rib and all. He saw no reason why he should not give the man the boss lady's home address, which was at any rate posted in the kitchen in the event of emergency.

With Misa's help and the blessings of Price Vermillion, Bina had selected a manager for the business who, it turned out, had been sent from heaven. He was French, and he knew every aspect of restaurant management; he was scrupulously honest and, since he had fallen in love with the very attractive owner for whom he worked, totally dependable. In the weeks since the opening Bina had learned that she could leave all the details to Arnaud—who insisted that his name be pronounced in the English way, "Arnold". He was constantly annoyed by the effete pretensions of the waiters—of the type Henry Lawson would have called cheap European paupers—who persisted in addressing him as "Ar*NO*".

Thus, unless Bina had special guests who wanted to dine early, she often delayed going to the restaurant until just before her first set of musical numbers. She had finished applying her makeup and was removing the cloth protecting her new mauve and silver gown when she heard the knocker on the front door of her little cottage. Someone was using it with a force that could only be masculine. She frowned. Since she had become a public figure, there had been several "gentlemen" who had made pressing efforts to become better acquainted, but she had fended them off. She was courteous to all, warm to none, and so far there had been no trouble.

She chose to live alone, without servants. It was a luxurious change after the time spent in the house in Cloncurry amid the clutter of several other women, some of whom were not quite as fastidious as she in their housekeeping. So she had to open the door herself, and a frown deepened for moment before she said, "Well, g'day, Clive."

He brushed her aside with his shoulder, entered the front parlour of the little cottage, and looked around. "Small," he said.

She ignored his remark. "I'm surprised to see you."

He looked down into her face with a smile. He smelled of tobacco and stale sweat. "You're a sight, girl," he said. He reached out and fingered the material of her gown. "Doing all right, eh?"

"Clive," she said, "I'm working, and I'm due at the job. So if you'll excuse me—" She held the door and looked at him expectantly.

"Now, don't be in such a hurry," he said. "When you own the place, you can be late if you want to."

"It happens that I don't want to be late," she said. "Now, if you'll please go—"

He shook his head smilingly. "No, I don't please to go, mate. That's not why I've come."

"Then make yourself at home," she said, walking out of the door and closing it behind her.

He caught her on the small step and jerked her arm painfully as he turned her to face him. "Now you just get down off that high horse," he said. "You can go to work in a few minutes, after we have a little talk." He pulled her back into the house and pushed her roughly towards the centre of the room. "It's small," he repeated, indicating the cottage with spread hands, "but cozy. I think we can be comfortable here."

"I don't know what you're thinking," Bina said, "but my plans do not include having you move into this house or into any other area of my life." From the first moment she had seen him, she had felt fear for herself and dread for the women she had left behind in Cloncurry. She had received only one monthly payment on the money that Clive owed her, and now he stood before her—big, roughly handsome, all bushman and a yard wide.

"What has happened in Cloncurry?" she asked.

"A bit of bad luck," he said. He laughed. "A full house bumping head on into a small straight. Me? I was holding the straight."

"You gambled away the house?"

He shrugged.

"It wasn't even yours to lose," she said.

"Well, he won mortgage and all," he said with a wry grin. "I hope he's man enough to live up to his obligations and send you your payments." He lifted a hand. "Oh, you don't have to worry about the girls. They like him fine, and he knows how to treat them."

"Clive, get out!" she said, astonished and angry.

"Now, is that any way to treat an old mate?" he asked, stepping towards her and reaching for her. "We had us some fine times, didn't we girl?"

Bina backed away, moving towards her bedroom, where, behind the door, Lester Caldwell's old shotgun leaned, shells in the chambers of both barrels. It gave her a feeling of security, living alone as she did.

"Ah," he said, "you've missed your old friend, eh?"

She turned and moved swiftly into the bedroom, and when he

entered confidently, ready to take what he had come for, she was standing at the foot of the bed, the shotgun pointed at his middle. He halted, his face going slack. There were two heavy, metallic clicks as she cocked the hammers of both barrels.

"As I said, Clive, I have no intention of having you move back into my life. Now please go."

He chuckled. "Killing and burying a man in the bush is a bit different from killing a man here in Sydney. Be hard to explain, dearie."

"I have friends," she said.

"And you're being very damned selfish," he said unsteadily. "Here's an old mate, down and out—"

Suddenly he lunged towards her, fear and anger on his face. He went in fast and low, and the gun went off, the shot whizzing past his ears, making his squawk like a dying seagull. She had pulled both triggers at once. The shot blasted into the wall of the parlour, and there was the smell of burned powder in the air. Clive, visibly shaken, hit the discharged gun so hard that it flew up and smashed into Bina's face. Stunned, she let the weapon drop.

"You bloody bitch," he hissed, striking her first on the left cheek with the back of his rough hand and then on the right with considerable force, bruising force. She fell backwards over the low footboard of the bed, skirts awry, and he leapt around, his arm raised to strike her again. His slaps seemed to clear her head. There was a great numbness in her face, and she could feel warm blood pouring from her nose. She lashed out with her high-heeled, high-buttoned shoes and caught him directly in the groin. He yelped and bent double, and she scrambled for the other side of the bed, planning to run out of the house and scream for help. He caught her by one foot and jerked her back, and as she tried to scream, he began to pummel her, this time with his clenched fists, the thudding, jarring blows rocking her head, sending spasms of pain into her chest and stomach. He was gasping in perverse satisfaction, his face contorted.

As her senses faded, she became convinced of an irreversible fact: she was going to die; Clive was going to beat to her death. She was aware of only two feelings before the blackness came. First, hope—Lester would be waiting for her—and then regret, for she was not ready to leave a life that was just becoming rewarding and truly colourful.

Misa dined at Bina's three or four times a week, often alone, sometimes with Price Vermillion, sometimes with Tolo. On the night that Clive Taylor went to Bina's house, Misa was with the glum, often silent old accountant. They were discussing the status of Tolo's land-buying efforts. The sugarcane plantations in Queensland had sold and sold well and that money, too, had gone into the baked and dusty plains of western New South Wales.

"The boy is by no means the largest landholder in the state," Vermillion said, "but he's built a parcel of adjoining lands along the Darling that's now in the vicinity of half a million acres. He's working now on a corridor of land to join the Darling lands with a parcel he's been accumulating to the east of the river."

"And the loans that the bank has made to smallholders?"

"Shaky," he said. "We'll have to take the first foreclosure action in less than sixty days."

Misa frowned.

"No alternative," Price said warningly.

"I know," she said. "But sometimes I feel so guilty, Price. We have so much, and there are people out there who are losing everything."

Price shrugged. He had no patience with such bleeding-heart sentiments. "So split up your fortune among all those who are in trouble because of the drought," he said. "And while we're at it, let's include all the other unfortunates. Each family will be able to buy a square meal and then they'll be paupers again, and you'll be a pauper, too, and the world will not even notice that there's one more unfortunate."

"I know," she replied impatiently.

"The best thing you can do, my dear, is to continue the course you're on. Perhaps our loans will salvage a few of them. If Tolo's right, then when the government gets ready to subsidize land for smallholders, there's going to be a very large amount of land available. The shipping business is growing and making more jobs. We have two new reefer ships under construction. That gives men work in the building, and when the ships are completed, there will be jobs for two complete crews."

"Thank you for the lesson in economics," she said, smiling ruefully. "But many people would not see me as a representative of the useful rich, creating jobs and expanding the economy. I'm afraid they'd consider me a parasite, living off the sweat of those who build my ships and sail them. And they'd see Tolo as a greedy land speculator, hoping to get even richer at the expense of the workingmen who pay their taxes—and the government."

Price snorted. "The only jobs such people have created are jobs for labour-union officers and bureaucrats to supervise the governmental charity programmes," he said. He looked at his watch. "Now, where's our charming hostess?"

Misa leaned over and he held his watch for her to see. It was ten minutes past the hour of Bina's first scheduled appearance.

"It's getting on time for an old man like me to be going home," Price said, "but I did want to hear at least part of her performance."

Misa summoned a waiter and sent him to inquire. The waiter came back and said, "Miss Bina has not come in yet, madam. They're ringing her home now."

"Excuse me, Price," Misa said. She went to the office where Arnaud was talking excitedly and loudly into the mouthpiece of the telephone. When Arnaud was agitated, his English deteriorated. Misa tapped him on the shoulder and took the receiver from him.

"You, there," she said, as a man's voice came to her in incomprehensible yells, "this is Mrs. Misa Mason. Will you please tell me what is going on?"

"Madam, this is Constable—" She didn't catch the name. "May I ask what business this is of yours?"

"I am a friend of Miss Bina Tyrell's," Misa said. "Is something wrong with her?"

"Is Miss Tyrell a woman about five feet tall, youthful figure, with black hair?"

"Yes, yes," Misa said. "Tell me—"

"Your name?"

"Mason, I told you. Mrs. Misa Mason."

"Your connection with Miss Tyrell?"

"Friend and business partner."

"Do you know a man named Clive Taylor?"

Misa started to say no, but then she remembered Taylor as the name of the man who had been a law officer in Cloncurry, the man who had blackmailed Bina for money and for herself. "I don't know him personally. I know of him."

"Where may we contact you, Mrs. Mason?" the constable asked.

"During business hours at the Merchantman's and Marine Bank."

"Work there, do you?"

"Yes." She paused; then, since she wanted information, she added, "I am the owner of the Merchantman's and Marine Bank. Now if you'll please tell me what has happened to Miss Tyrell."

There was a new tone of cautious respect in the constable's voice now. "Perhaps, Mrs. Mason, you'd best inquire for Miss Tyrell at the Sisters of Mercy Hospital."

"What has happened?" Misa asked. "Is she ill?"

"I think it's best, madam, that you inquire for her at the hospital. Perhaps you can help us with our inquiry later?"

"Yes, yes," Misa said to placate him. "I insist, Constable, that you tell me what has happened."

"We're trying to determine that at the moment. We were called to investigate the sound of a gunshot in Miss Tyrell's cottage. We found her in the company of this man, Clive Taylor, who claims that he is the chief constable of Cloncurry. Mr. Taylor told us that Miss Tyrell had a bad fall."

"Thank you," Misa said. "Please call me at the bank if there's any way I can help." She hung up, ran back to the table. "Bina's been hurt," she said.

Price was just finishing his dessert. He took one last bite, wiped his mouth deliberately, and rose to follow Misa's immediate, swift exit.

If she was dead, death hurt. Her nose hurt. Her face hurt. Her chest and stomach hurt. There was something wrong with her eyes. She could not open them far; she could see only a slit of light, strain though she might. And she felt quite removed from herself. She heard voices and felt hands on her. The hands probed her torso, and she moaned when the pain from her ribs was great. At some moment during that timeless period when she hovered between blackness and awareness, she heard Misa's voice, soft, low, close to her ear, saying things of encouragement and comfort. She went to sleep with Misa's soothing words in her ear and awoke with a scream, tried to fight as she relived those moments when Clive's fists were killing her. There were restraining hands on her arms, a voice saying. "There, there, it's all right. You're all right." .

When she awoke again, she heard Misa saying, "Thank you, nurse, for staying with her. If you'd like to go for a cup of tea, I'll be here for a while."

"Misa?" Bina tried to say, but the sound came out funny and hurt her lips. They seemed to be swollen.

"Don't try to talk," Misa said.

"Where—" Bina managed.

"You're in the hospital," Misa said. "You're going to be all right."

Bina dozed, and as Misa stood over her, she had to struggle to keep the tears out of her voice, for her friend's face was terribly swollen and livid with coarse bruises. Her puffy eyes were weirdly colourful, laced purple and red through black with yellow touches. Her nose had been broken and was misshapen and huge. Her chest was taped to immobilize two broken ribs.

Presently Bina awoke again. "I'm alive?" she asked uncertainly.

"Yes, dear, you're very much alive," Misa replied.

"That's you, Misa?" The voice was faint.

"Yes."

"Promise?"

"Promise what?"

"Promise?"

"Yes, I promise."

"Kill—sumbitch."

"Yes," Misa said, merely to placate Bina, who seemed quite agitated.

"Help me—kill."

"Hush now," Misa said.

"Promise?"

"I do," Misa said. "Rest now. You're going to be all right. The doctors say that your ribs are broken, but you're young and strong and they'll heal rapidly."

"Face," Bina said.

"It's rather horrible," Misa said, forcing a laugh, "but it's nothing more than bruises, my dear. You'll be back at Bina's within two weeks."

"Nose?"

Misa did not answer immediately.

"Bad?" Bina asked.

"Not bad. It's going to have a little bump in the middle." she laughed. "It will give character to your face."

Bina's hand stretched out, and Misa took it. Bina squeezed, hard, and said, "Thank you." Then she slept again.

Price Vermillion met Misa in the hospital waiting area. He had just returned from police headquarters. "They're holding this Clive Taylor for the moment," Price said. "There is no doubt in the minds of the police that Bina's injuries were not the result of a fall, but of a severe beating at the hands of Taylor. He is claiming that he's being framed, that he is the chief constable of Cloncurry. He's changed his story, however. At first he told the constables that Bina had fallen down the steps. Then he said that he arrived to find her in her severely beaten condition and that she told him she had fallen down the stairs. He swears that he didn't beat her, but he has blood on his shirt and his knuckles are abraded."

"Price, I just promised Bina that I'd help her kill him," Misa said calmly.

Price took this radical notion calmly. "An understandable sentiment, but impractical," he said. "I think, as she recovers, she'll settle for sending him to prison for a few years."

Indeed, Bina did not mention again her desire to kill Clive. Her broken ribs did begin to heal rapidly. On the third day after she had been brought to the hospital she was sitting up, if rather painfully, squinting at Misa through the slit of one eye. "Misa, I want you to tell the police that I'm not preferring charges against Clive."

"You can't do that," Misa said, shocked.

"On the condition that he leaves Sydney immediately," Bina said.

Misa was silent for a moment. What Bina had said made sense. Clive Taylor was most probably not a forgiving man, and if Bina had him put in prison, she would be making a dangerous enemy, for Clive would be free in a few short years.

"Are you sure that's what you want?" Misa asked.

"Yes," Bina said. "One more thing. I want to see him before he leaves the city."

"All right. If you're sure that's what you want."

"And, dear Misa, there is one thing more. They allowed me to have a mirror today. It's going to be more than a mere week or two before I can appear in public, before I can come back to the club. I want to be alone, somewhere away from people until I look human again. Can you understand that?"

"Of course. Tell you what. You and I will go on a sea voyage. The sea air will—"

Bina was shaking her head. "Please, Misa. You know how fond I am of you, but please?"

"You mean, you want to be alone," Misa said.

"Yes. Besides, someone here in Sydney will have to keep an eye on the bistro," Bina said.

"Arnaud is quite capable of running it," Misa said. "But I'll be glad to do whatever else is needed."

"I heard Tolo talking about a sheep station he purchased on the Darling," Bina said. "I remember how he said it was a lonely place, miles from the nearest neighbour. Do you think he'd let me go there for a few weeks?"

"It would be a long trip," Misa said dubiously.

"Ask him, please."

"Well, yes, if you insist. As a matter of fact, he's due back from the bush now," Misa said. "You'll have to wait until your ribs are healed better. I'll see to it that a driver is hired to take you, a housekeeper, too. You must permit me to do that much, Bina. I won't have it any other way."

When Clive Taylor came into Bina's hospital room, his clothing had been washed and ironed, and he had taken the trouble to get a haircut. He stood at the foot of the bed, looking at her uneasily. She squinted at him from the one still-blurry eye with which she could see and waited for him to speak.

"Damn, Bina," he said. "I didn't mean—"

She remained silent.

"I mean, if you hadn't kicked me in the ballocks—"

She was seeing him dead, seeing his eyes glazed and staring, the way Steve Wells had stared after she had shot him in the bush for beating her friends.

"It was bad enough that you scared the life out of me by almost killing me with the bloody shotgun."

Her words were still altered slightly by her swollen lips. "It wasn't all your fault, Clive."

"Well, it's bloody decent of you to lift the charges, mate. I'm grateful to you."

"How grateful?" she asked.

He grinned, a silly grin it was, and it made her feel slightly ill. She could see him growing more sure of himself, reverting to type now that he was out of danger. The incident had shaken him; the police had probably given him a good going over. But he was the sort of man who quickly recovered confidence in his own brute strength, the sort who told himself that a little bit of judicious pounding can do wonders for a recalcitrant female. "How grateful do you want me to be?" he asked her finally.

"I want you to take care of me while I'm healing," she replied. "I can't be seen in public like this."

"You *are* a right sight," he agreed.

"But we will keep it between you and me," she went on. "My friends advise me to have you prosecuted and sent to prison. I don't want that."

"As I said, very decent of you."

"There's a place in the bush," she said. "A house, with good water from a well. Very secluded. We'd be all alone, you and I."

"You'd like that, eh?" he asked, grinning.

"Yes," she whispered. "I know I'm not much to look at now—"

"Maybe we'll put a bag over your head, eh?" he asked, chuckling,

She laughed with him. "Maybe. The bindings come off the ribs soon." She arched her body upwards under the sheet, making her breasts tent the material.

"How do you want to work it?" he asked.

Misa had arranged for a comfortable coach and a driver, as well as the housekeeper whom she had hired from an agency. She provisioned the coach with food for three—Bina, the driver, and the housekeeper. Tolo had given the driver complete travel directions.

When Bina was released from the hospital, her ribs still bound, her face hidden by a dark veil, she said good-bye to Misa and then, alone, she began to make her own preparations. Lester's old shotgun and a box of shells went into her packing. She withdrew a healthy sum of money from the bank. She rode in the coach out of Sydney, stopping only to pick up the housekeeper on the way. They passed through the outlying districts, and when they were several miles out of town, she instructed the driver to stop at a country inn. Clive would meet her there.

She gave the hired driver a goodly sum of money, enough to see him off to the Western Australian gold fields, on condition that he did not inform the woman who had hired him. The housekeeper turned out to be a flighty, undependable lass who had recently emigrated to Australia, had no ties in Sydney, and was easily persuaded both by hard cash and the driver's masculine appeal to go off with him.

Then Clive arrived, and it was just the two of them, travelling through the bush in the big, soft-sprung coach.

At night they camped in the open. Bina slept in the coach, Clive on blankets on the ground. She did not have to pretend pain and soreness to discourage his amorous advances, but with her smiles and words she promised him much when she had recovered.

Clive said once that it was foolish to travel so far just to hide away while a few bruises healed, but he did not press Bina on that point. He knew an opportunity when he saw it. He knew how much money Bina's was taking in, and how Bina and her rich friend, Misa Mason, were planning to open more bistros. He could live with it—Bina and her money. She wasn't such a bad sheila when she was in decent shape. And if she ever gave him problems, a bit of pounding, without doing any damage, would set her right. If that did not work, a casual hint that he would tell her decent friends, especially the prim Misa Mason, that she had worked alongside her girls in that whorehouse in Cloncurry would keep her in line.

Clive got a little out of sorts when at last they came to the empty house at the sheep station to find the doors blown open, the inside of the house heaped with dirt. Outside, branches and other debris littered the yard. The previous occupants might have been tidy enough in their habits, but their absence had allowed the bush to creep back inexorably. There would be some hard physical work for Clive to do, to make the place habitable.

They settled in, and Clive went out with an axe to fetch wood for the big old stove in the kitchen. Bina explored the upstairs rooms and hid the shotgun and shells.

CHAPTER XXX

When it became evident that Clive Taylor was going to do exactly as she wanted, Bina began to savour her scheme for revenge. Oddly enough, she didn't really hate Clive. There were even times she did not have to act to be pleasant to him. Still, she could cause the smouldering fire that was her need for revenge to burst into flames just by looking at herself in a mirror. She would examine her nose, which would always have a bump, gingerly touch the still sensitive, yellow-purple bruises, and then she would look at Clive and see him dead, his eyes still wide. Often she would awaken from sleep in a cold sweat as she dreamed of that moment when she had been sure that she was going to die under his blows.

After arriving at the deserted house, she began to finalise her plans. It would be necessary to wait until her ribs were healed completely, for what she had in mind required some strenuous work. She walked the sear land near the house through the groves of trees, the parched, dead grass making rustling noises underfoot. The land was different from that of Queensland, but the feeling was the same as when she and Lester were battling to hold on to their small parcel of land. She felt death in the air, although there were no dying sheep, no gaunt cattle, for the animals had long since been sold off or had died. There were only the birds and the rabbits, and down towards the dry water hole the nest of a lyrebird. The male bird was a bold one, perching himself on a dead limb to eye Bina arrogantly when she walked past.

There was something about the waterless, dying land that touched her, sent her into hour-long reveries as she relived her life from the time that she had first come to Australia with Lester. She could look at the lyrebird with pure hatred, fully expecting him to begin to imitate the weak, hearbreaking sound of the cry of a dying baby. But the bird was only a symbol. The thing that had altered her life was all around her: the land, Australia, a cruel, hard place that produced cruel and hard men.

She would never be able to prove it, never know for sure, but in her own mind she had become convinced that Joseph Van Buren had killed her husband, or had ordered others to do so. He had done it because the land rendered men brutal and grasping, and because wealth and power in an isolated land allowed arrogant men like Van Buren to hold themselves above society's laws. And so it was the land that had taken her husband, and also her child, starving the boy by refusing to produce any nourishment.

The land had also produced Clive Taylor. He too had come to Australia with high hopes and had spent long, hard years digging for gold in the unyielding earth. The land had shaped him, making him as much a predator as the hungry dingoes that lurked near the house in hopes of edible garbage.

So it was that she came to look upon the death of Clive Taylor as another blow against the land that had taken so much from her. The taking of a human life is a heavy thing, Bina knew that; unless the killer is totally perverse, the act requires dire provocation, or at least temporary madness. Bina was not mad. She told herself that she was fighting for survival. Her fight had begun on the sheep station, and it had been against the land and drought. It had continued during her journey away from the station after Lester's disappearance, and her adversary had taken animate form in the person of Steve Wells.

For a time, in Cloncurry, she had battled Australia to a draw, but a guarded truce with a deadly enemy is not conducive to happiness and security. She had lost a round or two in Cloncurry, being forced to give herself to Clive Taylor, a predator of women. After she made that compromise, the next step—into prostitution, highly paid though it was—was a victory for Australia. Leaving Cloncurry was not retreat, but a tactical manoeuvre, a seeking of the high ground in her continuing battle. In Sydney, for sweet, happy months, she had known the satisfaction of temporary peace.

When Australia struck back, as Bina's heart always knew it would—sending its instrument, Clive Taylor, demanding surrender with hard, brutal fists—Bina had been left with two choices: either total capitulation to a life controlled by another, or a renewal of the struggle for her freedom, with no holds barred. Through Clive, Australia was again threatening to take away all her happiness. But as an instrument Clive had one drawback: he was flesh and blood, and he could bleed and die. Steve Wells had died.

She concealed from Clive the fact that she had removed the bindings of her ribs, that she now had full movement of arms, waist, and torso. She found a shovel and a pickaxe in an outbuilding, chose the spot which she would use. This was not madness, Bina told herself, but she knew anyone watching her plans develop would name it for what it was, premeditation pure and simple.

Clive had a gift that some would have envied, the ability to avoid tedium by sleep. He could sleep all night, get up, have breakfast, and then enjoy a midmorning nap. The midday meal was a signal to him to sleep away the hot afternoon. In the evening, if she reminded him, he would split wood for the cookstove in the kitchen. He was not much of a conversationalist. His approaches to her were usually self-serving. "How are the ribs?" he would ask. Or, seizing her, kissing her on the neck and cheeks: "Lips still sore?"

The place she had picked was between the house and the main outbuilding. The soil there was dry and hard but would be softer, she felt, once she had dug through the dusty, hard crust.

She chose an evening made just a bit less hot by a high, hazy cloud cover that had sapped the strength of the afternoon sun. She reminded him that there was no wood for the cookstove; he responded with a groan, but soon he was at the back of the house, stripped of his shirt, swinging an axe with an ease that spoke of the strength in the rippling muscles of his back. She checked the loads in the shot gun and left the house by the front door, circled around, and came up behind him, being careful to stay about twenty feet away. She remembered well how his swiftness and daring had prevented her from hitting him when she had fired at him in her bedroom. This time she would not give him the opportunity to surprise her.

She stood there for a full minute, gun held at her waist, watching as he swung the axe, bent down to position the wood for the next blow, and then swung the axe again. He was a big man, and she had known the weight of his body, had embraced in passion the barrel chest, had felt the strong bearlike arms around her.

And she had felt the strength of his arms through his fists, with blows that had blotted out her senses and left her near death.

He straightened himself, put one hand on his back, and stretched, puffing out a sigh.

"Clive," she said.

He turned, a smile freezing half formed as he saw the gun pointed at his middle. His right arm twitched and the axe began to lift.

"Don't," she said, pulling back one hammer of the shotgun.

"What the blazes, Bina?"

"You told me back in Sydney that it was one thing to shoot and bury a man in the bush, another in a city. Since you are a man with some law enforcement experience, I considered that good advice."

"You're not going to shoot me," he said, but his eyes were darting from side to side as if looking for help, and he licked his lips nervously.

"I was fair with you in Cloncurry," she said. "More than fair. You were set for life with the house, and you gambled it away. And then you came to Sydney to spoil things for me for the second time. That I will not abide."

"Look, Bina," he said. He was shaking, persuaded by the steely look on her face that she meant to do away with him. "You're right. I shouldn't have come to Sydney. I shouldn't have hit you."

"Yes, the hitting is part of it," she said. "But the pain of childbirth was worse than the pain you caused me." Why didn't she pull the trigger? She was not a cat playing with a mouse before biting off its head. And yet she stood, the shotgun pointed, finger on the triggers.

"Bina, look, I'll go away. I've been thinking of going to the gold fields in Western Australia. I won't bother you. I can see that there's no place in your life for a bushranger like me. You've made yourself a fine little nest there in Sydney. Don't risk it by doing something you really don't want to do. You don't really want to kill me, now do you?"

She hesitated, and a hopeful look came into his face. He forced a laugh. "That beating, Bina. I know it was bad, but I've had worse myself. In Brisbane once I got mixed up with five Portuguese sailors. I put a knife into one, but the other four near killed me. I walked spraddle-legged for two months, and it was a month before anyone could recognize me."

Do it! she told herself. *He hurt you. He is the last threat to the good life you've built for yourself in Sydney.*

He saw her finger twitch. "Well," he said sadly, "I guess you're right. A man shouldn't pound a woman, least not to the point of damaging her. Go ahead, get it over with." He grinned. "Planned it well, didn't you? Not a soul knows I'm out here with you. You'll plant me in the ground, spend a week or so, take the coach back to civilization yourself, and no one will even ask about the man who drove you and the coach out here, because he was just a hired hand. The housekeeper, she was just a child newly out from England: they come and go all the time. If anyone should ask about them, you can say that they took off on their own."

"Yes, you see the plan quite clearly," she said.

"Bina, listen to me. Just listen. If you want to change your mind, I'll tell you what I'll do. I'll take a handful of food and I'll strike out south, on foot. There's a couple of bush towns down that way, and eventually I'll make my way into Adelaide and get a job and earn enough money for a fare to Western Australia." He grinned, but his face was pale, his eyes not smiling with his lips, for he had, he knew, never been so close to death. "That way I'll save you the trouble of digging a grave, Bina."

"Good-bye, Clive," she said, lifting the shotgun and sighting carefully along the barrels. She was aiming for his chest—in itself a change of plan, for her original intention had been to shoot him first in the groin and then in the stomach.

He closed his eyes. Her finger tightened on the trigger. Then, with a cry of frustration, she let the barrels drop. "You bloody bastard," she hissed. "I hate you, but . . ."

He opened his eyes.

"Go on," she said heatedly, "get out. Take the food and get out." She knew even as she spoke that she was opening herself to trouble, for there was no reason for her to trust his word. He could start south and turn back as soon as it was dark. She could not stay awake forever watching for him.

He turned a length of wood on end and sat on it. His hands were trembling. "Let me catch my breath," he said.

She backed away and leaned against the side of the house, still holding the gun, ready to raise it and shoot if he should move on her. "Clive, I mean it. Get out. Don't make me sorry I changed my mind."

"No, no," he said. He looked at her. "Funny. Looking down those barrels and into your face I realized that I've never had anyone seriously want me dead before. That time I got beat up in Brisbane I felt like I was going to die, and once I was seasick and wished I'd die, but—" He fell silent, lost in reflection.

He stood and took a deep breath. His knees were still a little weak. "All right. I'll just go into the kitchen and put a bit of tucker into a bag and be on my way."

She waited on the front porch, gun across her lap, careful to sit where she had a clear field of fire in any direction, her back protected as she leaned her wooden chair against the wall of the house. The sun was going down when he came out of the front door, a bag slung over his shoulder. He did not speak, but walked down the front steps carefully and took long strides across the barren yard. He stepped over the run-down rabbit fence and began to climb a slight slope leading towards the south. At the crest of the rise he halted and looked back.

He looked so small at a distance, and the land was so vast around him, swallowing him. It was the land, the harsh land, she thought, as she stood and walked to the edge of the porch, cupped a hand to her mouth, and called his name.

At first he seemed not to hear. He turned and was sinking out of sight behind the rise as she ran across the yard to the fence and shouted his name again. He stopped and turned. She motioned him to come back. He hesitated and, with a shrug visible even at that distance, came walking back down the rise.

"Bloody hell," she said as he approached. "It's not your fault. It's this bloody country. I've heard it said that there's a curse on all white people who come here because the land is sacred to the Aborigines and sometimes I can believe it."

He looked at her, his head cocked to one side. "Bina, you're as crazy as I am."

"Most probably," she said. For he was a victim as much as she. He, too, had been battered and mauled by the land and had fought for survival with tooth and nail just as she had. He had hurt her, but the hurt he had given her was so much more physical than anything else. The hurt left by the death of her son, by Lester's disappearance—those, now, those were hurts to the soul, indefensible and inexcusable hurts.

He stood before her, big and tall, looking at her questioningly. She had not been forced to take him into her bed back there in Cloncurry; she had chosen to accept him, for she had had a choice. She could have said no and faced the consequences. She could have left Cloncurry at that time with the money she had saved. She remembered how it felt to be one with him. When he had first made love to her, he had been only the second man to know her body, and he had been so different from Lester, who had been a small man.

"Darlin'," Clive said. "You're the champ. I've never known a woman like you."

"If you ever hit me again, you—" she said.

"No," he said. "I won't."

"I *am* crazy," she said, scanning the empty horizon for affirmation. "Come along, then, I'll sort out some dinner."

In the kitchen he tried to help, and she finally laughed and said, "Get out of here. You're nothing but a nuisance." He sat at the kitchen table and watched her. There was something new in his face, a softness, a yearning. Her awareness began to grow, and in the end she went to him and sat in his lap. Dinner waited for some time.

CHAPTER XXXI

On May 21, 1900, Joseph Chamberlain, secretary of state for the colonies, introduced into the House of Commons a bill for an act to constitute the Commonwealth of Australia. Chamberlain cited Australia's wholehearted participation in the war against the Boers as evidence that Australia's federation would not weaken the empire, but would be a tribute to the wisdom and patriotism of the Britons' Australian kinsmen. Only a few members of the House of Commons bothered to deny kinship with a populace that was descended in part from common criminals, men and women transported from England to a land believed at that time to be fit only for ignorant black savages and the dregs of British society.

There was jubilation among the Australian delegation in London, the group of which Jon Mason had once been a member. They joined hands in a circle and danced around the centre of the room. Their celebration, however, was only a minor one compared with the orgy of gratified patriotism that had seized London two days earlier with the news that Mafeking and its hero, Baden-Powell, had at long last been relieved. The bulletin came to London via the Reuter's News Agency, and although Arthur Balfour rose in the House of Commons to state that the report had not yet been confirmed, newsboys rushed into the streets with special editions. The Prince of Wales and the King of Sweden were at the Covent Garden Opera House, where the report of the relief of the last of the besieged South African cities was shouted out as the curtain went down on the second act of *Lohengrin*. Cheers broke out. The audience broke into "Rule Britannia," and the prince beat time on the edge of his box with his fist.

The wild euphoria spread to the far-flung reaches of Queen Victoria's empire, and soon a new word was added to the English language: to "maffick," meaning to celebrate with boisterous rejoicing and hilarious behaviour.

Mafeking fever reached Sydney on May 23. From the residential districts and from the countryside waves of people poured into the city by carriage, horse, train, and motorcar.

The Gordon family, including the matriarch, Magdalen Broome, gathered on their front porch to listen to the distant sounds of the bands, to the laughter and the cheering. Now and again a barrage of firecrackers would explode in the streets, the roar followed by the thunder of distant cheers.

Java was aching to be a part of it. She had pleaded with both her parents and with her grandmother to be taken down into the city streets. Magdalen had held up her hands in mock horror. "To be trampled underfoot is unpleasant, whether by an angry or a joyous mob," she had said.

As the day lengthened and the celebration became, if anything, more frenzied, Johnny Broome came trudging up the slope, paused at the gate to catch his breath, and then came up to the porch, hat in hand.

"And why are my kinsmen not joining in this glowing demonstration of the glory of Australia and the pride of the British race?" he demanded.

"I am as patriotic as any man," Sam said with a smile, "but to have to sing the national anthem more than twice in one day is above and beyond patriotic loyalty."

"Uncle Johnny," Java said, "my parents have no sense of adventure. Will you take me down there?"

"Mercy, child," Johnny wheezed. "I considered it my duty as a newsman to have one look, but I don't think I have the strength to survive another dive into that mass of humanity."

"Is it really terrible?" Jessica asked.

"It will only get worse," Johnny said. "Most of the male celebrants have brought their liquor with them. I observed one little incident that showed just how quickly a mob can turn nasty, even one bent on celebrating. For some reason a blighter didn't remove his hat when people around him began to sing the national anthem. I think perhaps he was just preoccupied or a bit drunk, but it didn't take the mob long to remove it for him, and not so gently, mind you."

"Well, I fear that it's home for the Gordons tonight," Jessica said. She did not let her secret satisfaction show in her voice: Today's events would cancel plans made a week earlier to join Tolo and Misa Mason at Bina's that evening, to celebrate Tolo's eighteenth birthday.

"You can't mean that, Mother," Java said incredulously.

"You heard your Uncle Johnny. It would be dangerous to go through the city streets," Jessica said.

Java, her face awash with disappointment, turned to her father. "Father—"

Sam reached out to pat her on the shoulder. "It's early yet. Let's withhold our decision for just a while."

"Tolo will be very disappointed if we don't go," Java said. And, as if the mere mention of his name had some magic in it, a neat little surrey came up the lane behind a trotting pair of bays, and Tolo Mason stepped down to stride strongly towards the porch. Behind him the roar of the crowd in the downtown streets seemed to swell. Out in the harbour a ship fired rockets into the air, which left trails of white smoke against a brilliant, blue evening sky.

Tolo stood on the lower step, smiling broadly. "The whole city has gone mad," he said.

Java moved down to stand on the step above him, putting her face on a level with his. He was taller than her father, she realized, and probably stronger. "Tell me all about it," she asked.

"In places, near the bands, they're packed so closely that they can hardly move," he said. "There are flags everywhere. In front of the city hall there was a group of art students who had put together a tableau depicting the brave stand of Baden-Powell and his men. The street hawkers are selling party horns and buzzers, and also these." He raised his hand and drew the tip of a peacock feather across Java's cheek. "They're calling the feathers Kruger's whiskers," he explained, "and everyone's tickling each other in the face with them."

"I shouldn't want strangers thrusting feathers into *my* face," Jessica said disapprovingly.

Tolo stepped past Java to the porch and stood before Sam. "I came primarily to scout out a route for you to Bina's tonight, sir," he said. "The crowds are concentrated in the main streets and near the public buildings. You can go by cab or carriage northward, swing around the outskirts, and come to Bina's by the Old Post

Road. You'll see hardly anyone that way, unless it's a few
latecomers from the countryside making their way into town."

"There, you see," Java said to her mother.

Jessica looked to Sam for support. Sam said, "Thank you, Tolo.
That was very considerate of you."

"I would feel that my birthday party was incomplete without
you and your family sir," Tolo said.

Java turned away quickly to hide a little smile. This great,
handsome boy-man knew how to flatter the adults. *There, Mother*,
she thought, *let's see you get out of that one.*

Sam looked at Jessica and winked, knowing when to give in.
"Wife," he said, "I think that you and I had best think about
getting ready to go to a birthday party."

"Shall I stay and be your guide?" Tolo asked.

"Thank you, Tolo," Sam said, "But I'm sure you, too, have
preparations to make."

"Just to change clothes," Tolo said.

"You go ahead," Sam said. "We'll make our way there in fine
shape."

Tolo knew, too, when to give in. He nodded. "I'll be looking
forward to seeing you all." He smiled at Magdalen. "And
especially you, Mrs. Broome, because your dancing makes me
look like an expert on the dance floor."

"Belay that talk, you honey-mouthed rascal," Magdalen said
smilingly.

"Father," Java said, "may I please go ahead with Tolo? I have
only to slip on my evening dress to be ready. And I do so want to
have just a glimpse of the celebration."

Jessica opened her mouth to say no, but before she could speak,
Sam caught her eye.

"I don't see why not," he said. "Just you be sure, Tolo, that you
keep your distance from the mobs."

"Yes, sir," Tolo said.

Java was ready in record time. Not ten minutes later, she had
joined Tolo and they had ridden off in the surrey. Watching them,
Jessica felt a surge of pure panic. It was as if she saw the future, and
it carried a knife meant for her heart. She made an audible gasp
and realized that her mother was looking at her with head cocked a

little, with her eyes squinted in speculation.

"I don't like the idea of her going out into that circus," Jessica said weakly.

"Well, I think she's in good hands," Magdalen commented. "After all, Jessica, she's much more involved in this war than we are. The lads who did the fighting in South Africa are of her generation. When the Smith boy was killed, we said, oh, isn't that horrible, and accepted the fact that young men die in wars. And then we got on with things. To her it was a personal blow. She had known Ian Smith from the time they were both in nappies. That's her country out there. Those are her people who are congregated in the streets and squares, making damned fools of themselves. We—your generation and mine—are colonials, don't you think, tinged with the pride of the British. But our Java, now. She is Australia."

"But—" Jessica protested weakly.

"Aren't you excited that the Commonwealth Bill is likely to be considered in Parliament soon?" Magdalen asked.

"Pleased, yes. But I can't say I'm excited," Jessica replied.

"Well, the juices run hotter in the young. When we get news that the bill has been passed, I expect Java and Tolo will want to dance in the streets again." Magdalen rose and took her daughter's hands. "Come, let's decide what we're going to wear to dazzle the eyes of every man at Bina's. And get the worry off your face. Tolo will take care of her."

Dressed, hair put up, little curls hanging to her ears, Jessica helped Sam fasten his studs. "Sam, do you realize that in all the trips we made aboard *Cutty Sark* we never visited the place where you were born?"

"Haven't missed much," Sam said.

"Speak for yourself. I want to see it. I want to know all there is to know about you."

He laughed. "After all these years, you tell me if I have any secrets left."

"But I want to see the town where you were born. I want to go to the British Museum. I want to see what they're growing at Kew Gardens."

"Filling huge greenhouses with plants from Australia, no doubt," he said.

"Please, Sam, I'm quite serious. I do want to make a trip, you and I and Java—and Mother, if she wants to go."

He lifted his chin and allowed her to adjust his cravat. "Has this anything to do with the way that Tolo Mason looks at Java?"

She was grimly silent as she gave the tie one last pat and lifted her eyes. "I'm relieved to know that you've noticed."

"I've noticed. My darling old girl, I think that we should bow to your mother's wisdom in this matter. I know what you're thinking, and I agree to a certain extent. Mixed marriages are not going to be accepted in this country in the near future. It is true that Tolo Mason has enough wealth to make any girl's life luxurious, but, as you have often pointed out to me, money isn't everything. However, Magdalen has a point when she says that we should let this situation play itself out, that she's only seventeen and will probably be in love half a dozen times before she makes her choice. To show our disapproval of Tolo—and, quite frankly, I think the boy has a lot of good qualities—would merely make him an object of sympathy and draw her to him artificially. Does that make sense?"

She nodded reluctantly. "Sam, I am *not* a bigot. It's just that—"

He nodded, took her in his arms. "I think it will work out," he said. "She's a wise young girl. Like her mother."

The wise young girl, sharing the pride of the empire's victory in South Africa, her blood singing with excitement, turned to her companion as the surrey moved smoothly along streets that were almost empty of people. "Tolo, turn towards the centre of town at the next corner," she instructed.

"I don't think that's in the approved plan," Tolo said dubiously.

"Tolo Mason," she said, "listen to them. That's Australia! That's not Sydney, or New South Wales, that's Australia singing and cheering. They're not cheering for Queensland boys or Victoria boys, they're cheering Australians, and I want to see them, to hear them close up."

"Well, I think we can just sneak down behind the city hall and have a look," he said, "without becoming too embroiled in the crowds."

He took the surrey up an alley. The crowd in front of city hall was singing "Soldiers of the Queen," the massed voices miraculously on key and to the beat, the inspiring words wafting over the crowd's other unruly noises. Before Tolo could stop her, Java was out of the surrey, scampering towards the end of the huge building to try to see the mobs in the streets. He secured the reins and leapt down to run after her.

She was among them, her fellow Australians, and now they were singing "The Absent-minded Beggar." Tolo, coming up beside her, trying to use his body to shield her from the pressing crowd, heard her voice lifted. He looked down and saw a look of joy and pride so fierce that he could not help but be touched. And when, as Java led them deeper and deeper into the mob, the voices started once again to sing "Rule Britannia," he himself felt a shiver of pride.

A man thrust a bottle into Tolo's face and cried, "Have a snort, mate." Tolo took the bottle, tilted it, touched it to his lips and made swallowing motions without taking a drop. The man whooped and clapped him on the back. Beside Java a tall man in khaki was kissing a girl. It was not a casual kiss. Java blushed and pressed closer to Tolo. Someone had climbed on the pedestal of a statue and was waving his arms in drunken oratory that no one could hear.

Tolo put his lips close to Java's ear and shouted, "We'd best go!"

She nodded but hesitated, wanting to oblige him yet still yearning to follow the crowd.

A band began to play, and the mob surged towards the sound, the people carrying Java and Tolo with their movement. Java was pressed tightly against Tolo, flank to flank. In an effort to resist the movement of the crowd, he put his arm around her shoulders. It was like swimming upstream against an almost irresistible current. The mood of the crowd was jovial. There was much shouting of cheerful greetings, many offerings of drink. A man who smelled of old sweat was pressed tightly against Java's back and to her horror he began to press his groin into her hip. She made a convulsive movement and slid directly in front of Tolo. The flow of the crowd packed them into a mass of humanity, and Java was having difficulty breathing. She squirmed in Tolo's arms, turned to face him, looked up, and said, "Please get me out of here."

He reached behind her to shove away a man's shoulder, his arm coming down to go around her. "Don't be frightened," he said, bending close.

"I'm not, really. But for just a moment—"

His face was close to hers. Their bodies were thrust against each other, beyond propriety, by the surge of people. Java, looking at Tolo's lips, felt a bit faint, seemed to be another person outside of herself as she stood on tiptoe, parted her lips, and pressed her mouth to his.

At first he tried to pull away. Although he loved this little Java girl more than his own life, there was the matter of propriety, of respect for the girl that, someday, he hoped to make his own. But he was only human; he was eighteen; the juices were flowing, and she tasted of heaven. He held her close, close, and his mouth savoured hers a second time, and his tongue had just a taste of hers.

Near his ear a male voice shouted, "Go to it, mate, lay it on her!"

His impulse was to hit the man, but others were cheering as well. He broke off the kiss and grinned.

Java's eyes were still closed. She knew that she would have sunk to the pavement had she not been supported by Tolo's strong arms.

"Get behind me," he told her.

She shifted around, put her arms around his waist, and snuggled herself to him, still reeling from his kiss, from the unexpected agony of wanting even more that it had kindled in her. Tolo was shouting, "Excuse me, mate. Great night, mate. Pardon me, mate," as he used his size and strength to swim through the mob. Java pressed her cheek to his back and closed her eyes and dreamed forbidden dreams until, suddenly, there was no more pressure from the mob and he was tugging at her arms around his waist to loosen them. They were among flowering shrubs in the garden at the city hall. Behind them the mob was doing yet another rendition of "Soldiers of the Queen."

"Java?" he asked. "Are you all right?"

"I think so," she said, but she was answering a question quite different from the one he was asking, for he was worried that she'd been hurt by the crush while she was still contemplating the impact of his kiss.

"Let's find the surrey," he said, taking her hand.

In the dark shadows near the alley she pulled him to a stop. He turned. "What's wrong?"

She stood on tiptoe and offered him her lips.

"I don't think we should," he whispered.

"Bloody hell, mate," she said hoarsely, laughing, "kiss the wench."

This time, without the press of the mob to hold her up, she sank willingly into his arms, her knees suddenly like butter.

CHAPTER XXXII

The citizens of Bloemfontein were surprisingly friendly. While waiting there for the army to move, members of Slone's troop bought home-baked bread, the first bread they'd had in over a month, and it was delicious. It was so good that even one cynical bushman suggested that it might be poisoned: "Revenge on the Boer home front."

Slone laughed, took the first bite, and replied, "Then we shall all die happy, with full bellies."

Many people felt that for all practical purposes the war was over. There remained only the formality of the three-hundred-mile march to Pretoria, capital of the Transvaal, there to singe Paul Kruger's whiskers once and for all and convince the Transvaalers that they, too, were defeated. Only a few men, Kelvin Broome among them, noticed that when Boer units surrendered, turned in their rifles, and made a solemn pledge not to fight again, that the proffered rifle was almost invariably old and uesless. Very few of the fine Mausers or Martini-Henrys were turned over. Cronje had surrendered and Louis Botha's forces around Ladysmith had retreated in disorder, but Koos De La Rey and a man whose name would soon become known to the world, General Christiaan De Wet, were undefeated both in fact and in spirit.

Slone Shannon and Matt Van Buren, fellow Queenslanders, had become fast friends. Each had a command in the ranks of the Queensland Mounted Infantry. During the advance on the capital of the Orange Free State, Herbert Kitchener, like the Boers, had come to appreciate the special abilities of the Australians. With the Aussies on board, things were never dull, not even as the army halted to catch its breath. Some had likened the campaign to Napoleon's march on Moscow, because the distances were great in both cases, and because Lord Roberts, like Napoloen, had taken the risky step of moving a large army away from established routes of supply. The advance had not been without its costs. The army-issue boots worn by the soldiers were hanging in shreds, and the fearful loss of horses left the army without adequate forces of mounted infantry or cavalry. Finally, as if on cue in this strategically critical situation, typhoid fever, that scourge of the battlefront, swept through the army.

Kelvin Broome, with no action to report during the seven weeks' halt as supply trains moved up additional equipment, horses, and men, wrote about the ill. His first visit to an army hospital was a blow to the gut. Men shivering with fever lay in sweaty, soiled cots, or on the ground, with only a blanket and a thin waterproof sheet. Food was scarce. Medicines of all types were in short supply. Private soldiers with no medical experience had been drafted to act as orderlies, and randomly, all over the hospital area, men died for sheer want of medical attention.

"Oddly enough," Kelvin wrote, and his dispatch to the Broome paper in Sydney was read widely throughout Australia, "there seems to be adequate transportation for weapons and supplies with which to continue this war, but none for the needs of the sick."

In a surprisingly short time the contents of Kelvin's story became known to Herbert Kitchener. When Kelvin received an imperious summons to meet with Kitchener in his headquarters, Slone winked and said, "Well, you're in for it now, mate."

Kitchener's contempt for all the gentlemen of the press was widely known. In the Sudan Kitchener's favourite comment, upon emerging from his headquarters to find the press waiting, had been, "Get out of the way, you drunken swabs."

When Kelvin reported to him, the man who was second-in-command of the largest British Army ever assembled was seated behind a table in his tent. Kitchener did not look up at first but continued to squint, his head tilted, his odd eye glittering, at a paper in his hand. When he did look up, there was only coldness in his square face. "So, Broome," he said. "How does it feel to give aid and comfort to the enemy?"

Kelvin had intended to walk softly, to say "Yes, sir," and "No, sir." The acid comment stung to the quick. "I resent that remark, sir. I resent it highly."

"As you should," Kitchener said. "Broome, when you accuse this command of neglecting the care of its sick, don't you realize that you're striking a blow at morale, at the ability of the command to conduct this war, and indeed at the empire itself?"

"Not at all, sir," Kelvin objected. "I see myself drawing attention to the fact that in the heat of the campaign, medical services have broken down."

"I could order you to be sent back," Kitchener said.

"You could, I imagine, and I'm sure you could enforce the order," Kelvin said. "I don't intend to threaten you, sir, but if you decided to do that, I would guess that there'd be headlines about it in every newspaper in the English-speaking world."

Kitchener tapped his fingers on the desk impatiently. "You write that the sick in hospital have only one blanket," he said. "My father, believing that blankets were unhealthy, never used so much as one. In fact, he knew the true value of the newspaper. By stitching newspapers together, he could regulate his comfort in sleep to the ultimate degree, gaining or losing warmth by varying the thickness of the papers. Perhaps instead of allowing your newspapers to stir up discontent on the home front, we might better use them to warm our ill."

Kelvin was at a loss to know whether or not Kitchener was pulling his leg. He chose to say nothing.

"Broome," Kitchener said, not at all in a pleading tone, "a bit more cooperation, please? The Australians are building a wonderful reputation, a great record in this campaign. Must you soil their achievement by writing of the minor things that can go wrong in war?"

Kelvin decided to counter-attack. "General, since I'm here, may I ask, sir, when the army is going to move again and how long you estimate it will take to march to Pretoria?"

"You may not," Kitchener said. "You are dismissed."

Kelvin made a mock salute. "Thank you, sir," he said.

"We will be in Pretoria, Broome, I assure you," Kitchener said to his back, "before you can write another tear-jerking story about something of which, evidently, you know nothing at all."

Don't—don't—don't—don't look at what's in front
of you.

(Boots—boots—boots—boots—movin' up and down
   again):
Men—men—men—men—men go mad with watchin' 'em.
An' there's no discharge in the war.

The army was moving. General French's cavalry, Australian units among them, swept the field before the marching infantry. Louis Botha, having moved his remaining forces to stand before Johannesburg, blew up the main bridge across the Vaal river. Johannesburg, with the richest gold mines in the world, was ripe for the plucking.

Dirk De Hartog had told himself more than once that it was time to go home, that the war was lost and it was appropriate now for sensible men to lay down their rifles, to make peace with the conquerors as best they could. Having lived under British colonial rule in Natal, Dirk did not see this accommodation as the end of all life. Nevertheless, he did not, for several reasons, follow the example of thousands of Boer citizen soldiers who were simply going home. He was reluctant to leave Sianna in the field with the hospital unit, and she was far from ready to admit that all was lost, though her idealistic optimism about winning the war had been slightly dampened by the chaotic, headlong retreat from Lady-smith. Even if she had wanted to leave, she would not have permitted herself to abandon her post; she was, after all, of the De Hartog blood, and she had decided that her duty lay in using her skills to treat wounded men. She would follow that duty to the bitter end.

Dirk had been given a few men from other commando units, so that his charges were back to the strength of a scout unit, thirty men, and he worked closely with Louis Botha. While Roberts and Kitchener refitted their army at Bloemfontein, Dirk and his men did a lot of riding, scouting out the advance positions of the British, acting as couriers to other Boer units. On one gruelling ride Dirk and three men dodged advance British cavalry patrols to make contact with General De La Rey.

De La Rey was pleased to see Dirk. "It's as if God has sent you," he told Dirk. "I have been praying for a man such as you, my friend."

"General, I'm answerable to General Botha now," Dirk said.

"It is to his rear that the mission I wish you to undertake will carry you." De La Rey, looking very much the Old Testament prophet, smoothed down his beard. "Dirk, once, early on, you and I agreed that this war was lost, is that not true?"

"That is true."

"And now you will probably say immediately that I am struck by the sun when I say that we can still salvage something worthwhile, that we can keep our independence from England."

"General, I'm learning how to sing 'God Save The Queen' and how to salute the Union Jack."

"My friend, why are we fighting?"

Dirk laughed. "Oh, no, sir, you're not going to get me started on that subject."

"Gold," De La Rey said, answering his own question.

"Yes, that is part of it."

"Where are the gold mines?"

Dirk nodded grimly. "Johannesburg." He waited, fearing what was to come. The mines, British-owned, were the major asset in the city.

"If we deprive the English of their gold," De La Rey went on, "we remove their primary incentive for continuing their advance into the Transvaal. First we destroy the gold mines, so that it will take years and perhaps more money than is now available to reopen them; then we can talk peace and compromise with the English. Only with the mines gone can we negotiate, keeping our independence. You, Colonel, will go into Johannesburg. There you will contact a Judge Johannes Kock, and you will give him all assistance in blowing up the mines."

"General," Dirk said, "with all respect, sir, I cannot accept that order without conferring with General Botha."

"Confer with him then," De La Rey thundered, "but be sure you understand—and make Botha understand—what is at stake. Tell him, if he does not know already, that we cannot win this war with arms or raw courage, but we can win with determination and imagination, and by denying to the British the one thing in Johannesburg they want above all."

Dirk nodded and took his leave without trying to explain his own belief: that the British would pursue the war to its end, regardless of what happened to the gold mines. He rode night and day to return to Botha's field headquarters where, tired, hungry, dusty, and bleary-eyed from lack of sleep, he reported to Botha on the state of De La Rey's command.

"No question that he will fight on, then?" Botha asked.

"If he has his way, sir, to the last man or boy."

"We pray that will not be necessary," Botha said.

"There is something else," Dirk said, proceeding to tell Botha of the plan to blow up the gold mines.

"Fools!" Botha burst out. "I thought that I had scotched that idiotic idea. Win or lose, the mines are the key to recovery for the Transvaal. Rest yourself for a few hours, Colonel, and then please ride with all haste into Johannesburg and tell the garrison commandos there that if much as one feeble attempt is made to blow up the mines, I shall at that moment lay down my command and surrender my forces to the British."

Johannesburg seemed calm as Dirk and ten of his commandos rode towards the city. On the outskirts they encountered a defence line manned by nervous old men and boys. Control of the defence line was in the hands of the Johannesburg police. Dirk sought out a senior officer for his inquiries.

"We have gathered here most of the armed men of the city," the policeman said. "We will stand here until General Botha comes."

"General Botha will be very appreciative," Dirk said. "Tell me, sir, what forces do you have guarding the mines?"

"The mines guarded?" The man shook his head. "Soon, I suspect, we will hear the explosions as the mines of the English are blown up."

Dirk did not want to take time to explain that it was not Louis Botha's desire to have the mines destroyed. "I understand," he said, "that it is a certain Judge Kock who is in charge of this operation?"

"Johannes Kock," the officer said, "yes, he whose father, the general, was killed at Elandslaagte. He has the dynamite."

"Where would I find the judge?"

The officer chuckled. "Last night he met with others, who stayed behind rather than join us here immediately, at the Grand Hotel. I suspect"—he looked at his watch—"that at this moment you will find him either at or headed toward the largest of the English gold mines."

Quickly Dirk got directions and led his men at a gallop towards the gold mine which was to be the first target of Kock's sappers. It was a ride of some miles, and he had to consider the condition of his horses, so that for the last two miles the horses were allowed to walk. Dirk rode with a certain tenseness, expecting at any time to hear the explosions, but when he came in sight of the odd, tall mechanical workings of the deep shaft mine, he knew that no explosion had occurred, at least not yet. He raised his hand and started the troop to loping, then came onto the ground of the mine through great heaps of slag to see a group of men busily unloading boxes from a wagon near the pithead machines. A young boy with a rifle stood between him and the wagon; he held the rifle at port arms and cried out, "Who goes?"

"Colonel De Hartog, of General Botha's staff," Dirk called back, not slowing. He rode to the wagon and looked around. Men had halted their work. Cases marked as dynamite were stacked on the ground, were being carried towards the pit workings. "Which of you is Judge Kock?"

A portly, sleek-looking man stepped forward.

"On direct orders from General Botha," Dirk said, "you will cease this activity. If you have planted any charges in this mine, or in others, you will remove them. You will not damage any part of the shaft or the works of any mine."

"I'll have to see that in writing, sir," Kock said, crossing his arms.

Dirk signalled to his men. Ten rifles rose simultaneously, and there was a little storm of clicks as the rifles were cocked. "Perhaps," Dirk said, "you can read this."

"Sir, you wouldn't—" Kock ceased talking, looked at the grim faces of the young commandos.

"Judge," said a young man in a shaky voice, "I think I can read this order very well." He put a case of dynamite back on the wagon. The other men began to do the same. Kock, sputtering, stood helplessly watching his own orders being contravened as the men loaded the wagon.

"There might be a use for the dynamite at the line of defence outside the city, boys," Dirk said. "You're welcome to tag along with me, for that is where I'm headed."

"It would be our honour, sir," said one of the men.

The battle for Johannesburg was anticlimactic. The British Army, having left Bloemfontein on May 3, marched into Johannesburg on the last day of the month. The Vierkleur, the flag of the Transvaal, was hauled down from the flagstaff at the courthouse and replaced by the Union Jack.

In Pretoria, Paul Kruger sent his young state attorney, Jan Smuts, to remove the remaining gold from the mint, and then, leaving his wife behind to receive the gentlemanly treatment of the occupying British, fled his capital.

Once again Sianna De Hartog witnessed retreat. Young and vital though she was, she was tired. The hospital unit had been steadily retreating since the fall of Ladysmith. Time and time again the advice had been given and received to move, to leave to the mercies of the British surgeons the wounded who could not be transported. Now Pretoria was going. Koos De La Rey, with less than two thousand men, was all that stood between the advancing hordes under Roberts and Kitchener and the capital of the Transvaal.

Sianna, her heart weeping, watched chaos come to the city. Government officials were leaving as fast as they could board trains heading eastward. As rumours flew about the proximity of the British, the streets filled with handcarts laden with private belongings and looted stores. Men pushed their possessions in wheelbarrows. By the time Botha's skimpy forces reached the city in their own retreat the town had been stripped bare, so that the Boers marched hungry and humiliated through their own capital.

Once again, when things looked hopeless, Dirk found the hospital and stood with his arm around Sianna. She stank of blood from the wounded. There were deep, dark circles under her eyes.

"Hasn't the time come to go home?" he asked her.

She put her cheek against his chest and allowed herself the luxury of a swift, violent spasm of sobs; then, with a shivering effort, she regained her composure. She looked at a Boer boy, not over fifteen, who had been shot through the shoulder. "Would you have me leave him to remove the bullet from his own flesh?"

"I understand," he said. He, like most Boers, knew that captives were treated correctly by the British, in accordance with the rules of warfare. The worst that could happen was that Sianna and the doctor might be interned in one of the camps for Boer refugees, where they would risk exposure to disease. They would be all right. "I can't stay with you this time, Sianna."

"Where will you go?" she asked.

"To De La Rey, most probably," he said.

"So you're asking me to give up while you fight on?"

"No," he said, brushing his lips against her cheek. "We've travelled a long way," he said. "I think that some of us will travel farther. For you, my dear, I say, when the time comes for you to decide between staying and surrendering or leaving the hospital and riding with the commandos, that you and the doctor should stay with the hospital. You'll be needed to treat not only our wounded men, but also the women and children who have been displaced."

Sianna nodded, but the thought of capitulation was bitter to her.

On the afternoon of June 4, 1900, Slone Shannon was leading a mounted patrol only two miles west of Pretoria. He saw no Boer opposition. As it happened, when he rode back towards the advancing army, he spotted the staff flags of Kitchener's headquarters unit, so he approached a group of horsemen standing atop a rise and reported. Kitchener himself questioned him closely.

"Well, Lieutenant Shannon," the commander said, "you Australians seem to like to be first. How would you like to take a solo ride and tell General Botha, there in Pretoria, that I'm looking forward to meeting him in person and that I think it highly advisable for him to surrender—unconditionally, of course?"

"My pleasure, General," Slone said. "I take it, sir, that it will be permissible to carry a flag of truce?"

"Unless, Lieutenant Shannon," Kitchener said with a trace of a smile, "you care to overwhelm General Botha single-handed." Kitchener was still fondly nostalgic about those who had been his boys in the desert, and it gave him pleasure to be able to give such a moment of glory to one of them.

With the white flag of truce flying, Slone rode alone into the capital of the Transvaal. He soon encountered Boer troops and shortly found himself standing before the infamous Louis Botha. At Botha's side stood a tall, ruggedly handsome Boer colonel, who nodded to Slone before Slone began to speak.

"And so," Botha said, when Slone had repeated Kitchener's message, "they still demand unconditional surrender."

"Yes sir," Slone said. "I have repeated the general's words as exactly as possible, sir."

"Go to Kitchener," Botha said, "and tell him that we will take his ultimatum under advisement."

When Slone was gone, the general turned to Dirk De Hartog. "This much is certain: we will not destroy Pretoria by continuing the fighting here," he said resignedly.

The main portion of the British Army entered Pretoria on June 5, 1900.

CHAPTER XXXIII

Sam Gordon was not wrong in believing that his only child was a strong-minded girl. Although on those rare occasions when Java was alone with Tolo she let herself be kissed—often insisted on being thoroughly kissed, and never failing to become weak-kneed and dizzy from the impact—she did not let her growing love for Thomas Mason distract her from other things that mattered. She had announced suddenly that she would like to study at the university during the coming term. Sam was delighted, and Jessica, too, welcomed her daughter's new line of interest. Entrance was relatively easily obtained following examinations, and so by the middle of June, Java was deep in her studies.

While keeping up with her work, where she was causing some wrinkled brows among the learned professors by asking insistently why more study had not been made of the Australian Aborigines, she did everything within her power to further the cause of federation. She wrote letters of support for unification to every newspaper in the various states. She spoke to fellow students at the university about federation, and to any voting-age man who came across her path and was even mildly willing to listen.

When she learned that at long last the main opponent against federation, John Forrest, premier of Western Australia, had introduced into his state's parliament a bill calling for a referendum in July, Java went into a state of suspense. She could hardly wait for the voice of the people of Western Australia to speak.

Tolo Mason was only mildly jealous of Java's vital interest in the unification question. His resentment of anything that distracted Java's attention from him was lovingly indulgent and often very proud whenever he happened to be with her as, with flashing eyes and well-chosen words, she argued heatedly with someone who criticized the idea of a unified Australian nation.

Java did not lie overtly to her parents, but she did take advantage of the fact that she had a certain amount of freedom of movement, as a university student living at home. She found time to be with Tolo, if not every day, almost never missing two days in a row. Since learning came easily to her, she could afford to miss certain classes, spending those hours walking arm in arm with her tall, handsome man, or sitting on the grass with him in some sheltered nook to dream the long, sweet dreams of the romantic young. She was endlessly curious about the land that Tolo continued to accumulate in the western portion of New South Wales.

"How I envy your being a man," she told him, "being able just to saddle up and go." She wanted very badly to see the Darling River, to see the drought-parched acres that Tolo was amassing by the thousands. She schemed and made up imaginary stories in which, somehow, she was allowed to travel into the bush with Tolo to camp under the big sky, to see the kangaroos and the birds of the hinterlands, and to be a part of the real Australia, the Australia outside the cities. In her real life she could not truly imagine a way to see Tolo's landholdings, so she merely listened as he talked about his latest purchase, sight unseen, of just over seven thousand acres of New South Wales bush.

With the coming of winter in the Southern Hemisphere, no definite talk of marriage had yet passed between Tolo and Java, although each knew that one day they, like the various Australian colonies, would carry out a unification programme of their own that would . . . There Java's imaginings floundered in her Victorian morality, for to think beyond standing before a preacher in a glowing white gown to say the sweet, old words of the marriage ceremony brought a flush to her features and strong, forbidden yearnings best left for the future. Ah, but for the kisses! The kisses led to a crisis.

Bina Tyrell came to the bistro early one afternoon, carrying a portfolio of sheet music that had just arrived from the United States aboard a Mason Line steamer.

It was several weeks since she had returned from the bush, without the marks of the beating, and with Clive.

There had been no instant and miraculous change in Clive to

make him a perfect gentleman, but after some serious and realistic thinking, Bina had decided that a man of Clive's talents had his uses. She had put him on the payroll and insisted that their relationship was one of business only. He was away this afternoon on a mission of special interest to her, and now she was alone in the big room, beginning to sample the musical selections.

As she was getting the feeling of a brand-new song from America called "Ma Blushin' Rosie," members of the kitchen staff came to stand inside the doors to listen. When Bina finished, they applauded, and she bowed her head towards them.

"How do you like this one?" she asked. Her right hand trilled sad, tremulous notes as she sang "A Bird In a Gilded Cage." She was watching the sheet music closely, since she was unfamiliar with the new song, and did not notice that Clive Taylor had entered the partially lit dining room from the office area. When she finished, she looked over at the members of the kitchen staff and saw that one of the female workers was wiping away a tear.

"That's me," Clive said, coming to stand beside her. "I sold my honour for gold, but to a woman instead of an old man."

"You're back," Bina said. She raised her eyebrows, asking a question without words.

"No worries," Clive said.

"They're willing to sell?" she asked, eyes sparkling with excitement.

Clive whipped a large envelope from behind his back and dropped it into her lap. "Signed, sealed, and delivered," he said with a grin.

She opened the envelope hurriedly and examined the sheets of paper within. Then she leapt to her feet and did a little dance step as Clive laughed. "We'll start immediately," she said. "First we must build the access road, but while that's being done we can start grading and filling the site—"

"Mind if I wait until I've had some tucker before I start?" Clive asked wryly.

She faced him with a smile. "Thank you, Clive, you've done well," she said.

He shrugged. "I'm still not one hundred percent convinced that it's smarter to build a hotel at the seashore than to open another place like this," he said.

"We've been over that," Bina said.

In fact, the matter had been discussed, not just once but many times. At first both Bina and Misa Mason had wanted to open a string of bistros. It had been Price Vermillion who, in his sour-faced, almost acidic way, had pointed out that Bina's was a success not only because of the good food, but because of Bina herself.

"You can't duplicate yourself," Price had said.

It had been Tolo who had suggested that Australia's growing interest in the shore was worthy of exploitation. The new hotel would be based solidly on private funds, with Bina and Misa putting up an equal share to provide enough equity to allow the Merchantman's and Marine Bank to lend Bina the balance needed to make the hotel a first-class establishment for affluent holiday makers.

Clive Taylor's participation in Bina's affairs had grown slowly from the time when they had returned to Sydney together from the bush. Australia was largely a man's world, and Clive moved well in some circles. When representatives of a labour union tried to organize Bina's relatively small staff, it was advantageous to have a man—a rather large man who could talk the lingo of the streets and the bush—to "discuss" the matter with the union leaders.

Clive enjoyed being at the bistro. He liked the music, Bina's performances, and the steady meals. "Good Lord," Bina had once remarked, "you'll waste away to a ton eating like that." But he had remained lean and hard.

They never mentioned the confrontation in the bush behind the deserted sheep station. Clive had not given up making hints—or, indeed, suggesting openly—that he wanted to come back into Bina's bed, but he accepted her firm refusals to go back to the relationship they had had in Cloncurry.

Clive had seen quickly that Bina had rich and powerful friends in Sydney. He had at first felt the true bushman's bigotry for Misa and Tolo; but Misa's calm, confident manner, her friendliness towards him simply because he was a friend of Bina's, soon made him realize that money and competence have nothing to do with the colour of one's skin. He came rather to like Tolo, too, especially after he had sat across from the boy during an idle afternoon and suggested a friendly little arm wrestle in which Tolo, without moving a muscle in his face, crushed the champion of Cloncurry with one quick burst of strength that banged Clive's hand against the tabletop.

"You've got a good thing going, mate," he told Bina, a couple of weeks after accepting her offer to work for her. "But you need a partner."

"I have a partner."

"I mean a male partner."

"I can hire men," she said.

"Hell, yes, including me," he said heatedly. "That you've done and for lack of anything better to do at the moment I'm glad to work for you for a while. But hiring me, mate, doesn't buy my loyalty."

"Oh? Does your loyalty not have a monetary value?"

"Bina, you can be so damned exasperating. You know what I mean. You're a woman in a man's world. Now I'll admit that you're doing fine so far, but there'll come a greedy shark of a man and he'll gobble you up. There's something unhealthy about a woman in business by herself."

Bina laughed scornfully. "Tell that to Misa. She's in the process of buying a bank in Melbourne now."

"She has Price Vermillion."

"He's an employee."

"What I'm saying, damn it, is that I'd be willing to marry you." She laughed scornfully. "How generous of you," she said.

After that conversation he had stomped away and had become so drunk that he had to hang onto the grass to stay on the world. But in three days he was back, and she accepted him—as an employee—without question.

As time went on, Clive seemed more steady in his character and behaviour, and when Bina asked him to go down to the seashore just to the south of Sydney to have a look at a piece of seaside property, he gave Bina a surprisingly astute appraisal of its value. He had an innate if unformed business sense born of shrewdness and opportunism. He could accurately estimate the pound value of almost anything. Now, with the land secured to build the seaside hotel, Clive was catching a touch of the capitalist disease that had so profitably infected both Bina and Misa, the desire to use money to earn more money, through the expansion of business holdings.

Bina was by no means rich, but the bistro was enormously

successful. She could live comfortably on the bistro alone, but she wanted more. For a time she had dreamed about seeking revenge against Joseph Van Buren, the squatter who, she was sure, had been responsible for the death of her Lester. Van Buren and his kind still had a bitter place in her memories, but she no longer thought about revenge against him alone. Instead he had come to represent the world that had been aligned against her from her early childhood, the powerful people who had made her life as difficult as possible. The only answer, she had decided, was to earn so much money that the world could not intrude through its insulating protection. Although they had never put such feelings into exact words, Bina felt that Misa's goals were much the same as hers, with a slightly different motivation. It was for her son that Misa was building an even bigger fortress on the financial holdings established by Marcus Fisher and expanded by Jon Mason.

Only once since Bina had come back from the bush with Clive Taylor in her employ had Misa questioned her about this alliance. She had been truly confused by Bina's willingness to have the man who had nearly beaten her to death near her at all, much less working for her.

"Misa," Bina had said, "you would have had to live it to understand. The long and the short of it is that I want him nearby. He's useful." She gave Misa a wink and a suggestive smile. "He'll not know it for a long time, but he's going to be even more useful—in a . . . personal way, shall we say."

Misa turned her head, embarrassed. Now and then Bina's background showed through in startling ways.

"You're blushing," Bina said. "Don't you ever wish that your bed was not so cold and empty, Misa?"

Misa hesitated before she answered. "I have too many sweet memories to allow room for another man in my life."

Bina patted Misa on the arm. "I know, dear, I do know. Lester Caldwell was small and a bit scrawny, and he wouldn't have won any prizes for attractiveness, but by God, he was a man, and if he could be alive again, I'd give up anything for it. God help me, I'd gladly go back to that bloody shack in the bush and fight squatters, drought, and the whole world. But he's dead. They took him from me. Now I'm still a young woman, alone, and I'm not interested in spending a lot of time looking for a man. Better the devil that I know, I suppose."

"Need I say, Bina, that this isn't Cloncurry? That the backbone of your business is formed of"—she frowned—"for lack of a better word, the decent people?"

"Don't worry," Bina said. "When I have the lout sufficiently housebroken, I'll invite you to the wedding."

Bina had decided that the building of the hotel would be Clive's testing. She could not afford to leave such a costly and important project in his care from the beginning. She and Misa would hire an experienced builder to supervise for them, but Clive would be given as much responsibility as he could handle. If he stuck with it, then perhaps there would be a financial share for him in the next project; after that—well, she would see. Until then, she could be as virgin as the professional girl who wanted to return to innocence.

Bina had bathed and was dressing in a comfortable apartment that was part of the bistro. She had learned through experience that personal contact with regular customers improved business, and so she now spent far more time in the restaurant than was required for her actual performances. For convenience, she had converted one wing of the building into an apartment with an adjoining office.

To Misa's shock and rather to her own surprise, Bina was allowing Clive to live in the apartment. Their bedrooms were strictly separate, but the bath was common territory, and as she stood in it, completing the application of her makeup, it smelled of the hair tonic he used and of the bracing lotion that he applied after shaving. Off the bathroom, just beyond a closed door, was the big bed where he slept. Bina glanced at the door and then left the bath; she finished dressing and went out of the apartment with a tickling, nagging desire in her, which she cooled by circulating among her early diners.

Nothing is more flattering to a diner's ego than personal attention from the restaurateur. To have the famous Bina know one by name was a mark of social success in Sydney. Sam and Jessica Gordon did not seem overly impressed when Bina stopped at their table, but Java knew that others were watching, measuring the length of time that Bina would spend there. The conversation was inconsequential until Bina moved up the table to speak to Magdalen Broome.

"I've heard that you're building a hotel on the seashore," Magdalen said. "I think that's wonderful."

"Book us a room for the opening," Java said.

"You shall be my guests," Bina said. This little Java girl had been the subject of many conversations between Bina and Misa, for around them Tolo made no effort to hide his feelings for Java. Bina and Misa both agreed that the young lovers were on a collision course with reality. Bina was genuinely fond of Tolo Mason, and she sometimes wished that she had a daughter like Java Gordon.

"That would be too kind," Magdalen said. "It would be bad luck at the outset to fill your rooms with nonpaying guests."

"Nevertheless," Bina said, "I can think of no one I'd rather have than the Gordon family." She looked at Sam and winked. "After all, you would put the stamp of approval on the place. All Sydney would follow."

"Oh, hardly," Jessica protested.

"Don't underestimate yourselves," Bina said.

Jessica smiled, but thinly. In truth, she knew that the steady patronage of the Broome-Gordon family members had helped Bina's, and their approval would be invaluable in launching the new hotel. And yet, if she had her way, that approval would never be given. Their regular visits to Bina's, where Tolo Mason always seemed to be at their table, had contributed to what had become Jessica's most persistent worry.

Although Sam had advised her to ignore the relationship, which he felt was cooling off, she believed this was the wrong tack. To her mother's eye, it was evident the feelings between Java and Tolo were becoming more intense. Sam did not seem even to notice that Tolo and Java danced almost every dance together, looking into each other's eyes and talking intimately.

Bina left the Gordon table. Tolo and Java went off to the dance floor. Java was back rather quickly, to ask her mother to look at her left eye. Something seemed to have got into it.

"I can't really see," Jessica said. "The light is rather dim."

Bina came back to stand beside Java as she bent over to let her mother look. "A problem?"

"Something in my eye," Java said.

"I can't see in this dim light," Jessica said.

"Come into my dressing room," Bina said. "There's good light there."

"Thank you," Java said.

"Let me go with you," Tolo said.

Tolo watched anxiously as Bina used the clean tip of her white handkerchief to remove a small, grainy mote from Java's eye. "There," Bina said.

Java's eye was watering. She dabbed at it with the handkerchief. Bina heard the small orchestra go into the number that preceded her first performance.

"You're on," Tolo said.

"Yes. Must go," Bina said.

"Do you mind if I stay here for a few minutes?" Java asked. "If I go out there weeping from one eye like this, people will wonder what's wrong with me."

"Not at all," Bina said. "You, Tolo, come with me."

"I'll stay with Java," he replied.

"Not in my dressing room you won't," Bina said.

"Oh, sorry," he answered. "I wasn't thinking."

"I'll bet you weren't," Bina said, not unkindly. He let her go out into the hallway first, then followed.

"I'll stand guard here," Tolo said. "We'll be there in time to hear your songs."

"Tolo—" She paused.

"It's all right." He smiled. "We'll be along in a moment."

She had barely disappeared around the corner when he turned and, with pounding heart, opened the door. Java was standing in the middle of the room, her back reflected in Bina's dressing mirror. Her eye was damp but no longer blinking. There was a look of aching longing on her face. Her full lips were parted slightly, parted further when he swept her into his arms and covered her mouth with his.

"You are a clever schemer," he whispered. "I can almost believe you put the mote into your own eye."

"No," she whispered through a gentle laugh, "but isn't it a pity I didn't think of it before?"

Jessica saw Bina returning from the office and apartment wing. She watched the handsome, small, dark-haired woman walk regally across the dining room, nodding and speaking to customers, then mount the little orchestra stand. Bina began with the new songs from the United States. Both were great hits.

Sam Gordon always enjoyed hearing Bina sing and play, so his attention was absorbed fully. Not so with Jessica. Java and Tolo had still not emerged from the shadows at the door leading to Bina's apartment. Bina had finished the two songs to great applause and was launching into the favourite "Good-bye Dolly Gray," when Jessica leaned across to Sam and said, "Would you please go and look for Java?"

"What?" Sam grunted, half listening.

"Java. She has not come out of the private wing as yet. Please go and see what is keeping her."

"Yes, fine. After Bina finishes."

Jessica's face was grim. She started to rise. Sam took her arm and pulled her gently back into her chair. "Are you that concerned?"

"Sam, It's time that someone became more concerned, and I hope it will be you. Will you go and find her, or shall I?"

"Jessica, she's seventeen—"

"So you and she keep telling me," Jessica said, "although, if you'll check your calendar closely, you'll see that her seventeenth birthday is still months away."

"All right," he conceded.

He tried to make himself unobtrusive as he crossed the room, but he had to pass quite a few tables, blocking people's view of the stage momentarily and causing a ripple of impatience here and there. He opened the door leading out of the dining room, walked down the hallway. He saw a door that was open just a crack, opened his mouth to call out Java's name, but heard whispering from behind the door. He took one step and the voice was discernibly Java's.

"In a few moments," she was saying.

"We'd better go now," Sam heard Tolo Mason whisper.

"Bina is singing," Java said. "They won't miss us at all as long as she's singing."

"Java—"

"Why do I always have to beg you to kiss me?" Java asked, with a low, throaty sigh that raised Sam's hackles.

His little girl! His little Java girl, *asking* a man to kiss her! For a split second he was poised to kick the door open violently, ready to yell out his shock. But there came a silence, and his violent jerk of forward movement had placed his eyes at just the right spot to see through the small split of opening. There, reflected in a large mirror, he saw his little girl standing on tiptoe, her arms thrown high around Tolo Mason's neck, one of Tolo's strong arms around her waist, the other at her shoulders pressing her close. Sam could hear their intense breathing.

"We're going now," Tolo said, breaking the kiss, pushing her away. She swayed and had to catch his arm for support. There was in her face a look of dazed, aroused womanhood. At that moment Sam Gordon knew that she was a woman, that she was no longer his little Java girl, and he felt a stab of pain as he turned and hurried up the hall. He was quick enough so that as the young couple came back into the dining room, he was already at the table. Even in the dim light he could see that Java was still flushed.

Sam waited until Jessica and he were in bed. He propped himself up on one elbow and looked down at her face. "It's summer in England," he said. "Still want to go?"

Her eyes, which had been half closed, opened wide as she came awake and smiled at him. "We'd see Rufus, wouldn't we," she said, as if seeking an additional pretext for the journey, though none was needed. Rufus was her brother Andrew, so called because of his red hair; a career naval officer, he was serving in England as an instructor of cadets aboard H.M.S. *Britannia* at Dartmouth.

"Naturally we'd see Rufus," Sam agreed. "And all the other places you said you wanted to visit. How soon can you be ready to sail?"

"In a day or two, a week at most."

"Speak to your mother. If she'd like to accompany us, fine."

"And Java?" Jessica asked.

"Leave that to me."

She sat up. "Sam, you saw something when you went back into Bina's apartment, didn't you?"

"No," he lied, but he had never been able to lie well, especially not to the woman he loved.

"Tell me," she insisted.

"A kiss, no more."

"Oh," she said, pain in the sound.

"I'll talk with her in the morning."

Jessica nodded. "She's an intelligent girl. She might be unhappy at first, but in a while she'll see that we're right."

The intelligent girl came down to breakfast in a lilac-coloured gown, her golden-red hair loose to her shoulders, a smile making her face sunny, her voice full of life and vibrancy when she called out a greeting to her parents. Magdalen, who had taken to staying in bed a while longer than the rest of the family, was not yet down. Jessica served Java breakfast from chafing dishes on the sideboard, finished her own meal, and disappeared.

Sam came to the table. "I have what I hope will be a pleasant surprise for you," he said to his daughter.

"You're going to buy a Daimler at last!" Java exclaimed.

Sam took inspiration from her eagerness. "As a matter of fact, yes," he replied.

She leapt from the chair, threw her arms around his neck, and rained kisses on his cheek. "Wonderful Father," she said.

"But it's not quite that simple," Sam said.

She went back to her chair and her food. She had a healthy morning appetite.

"We'll be picking out the car actually at the Daimler factory in England," Sam said.

Her spoon froze in mid air. She swallowed convulsively. "I don't understand," she said.

He smiled. "We're all going to England. E-n-g-l-a-n-d." he said, spelling out the word.

"No," she said; then quickly she dropped her head and put down her spoon. "I mean, why?"

"I need to go on business," he said. "I don't want to be away from my family. Therefore, since your mother has been wanting to visit England, my family goes with me."

"I'll stay here with Grandmother."

"Grandmother is most probably going with us."

"Isn't it rather sudden, this decision?"

"Not really. Your mother and I have discussed it. In fact, she's been asking to go for some time." That part was certainly true. Jessica had said she wanted to see the country where Sam was born; she had also begun to couple those requests with the idea of taking Java away. Unfortunately, Sam had not been wise enough to do as Jessica asked at an earlier time, when Java might not have protested so much.

"Please, Father, I do not want to go to England, or anywhere at this time. There are my classes—"

"The travel will be very educational."

"I just don't want to go," she said, her voice rising and tears coming to her eyes.

She looked at him with something that struck him as a cross between intense disappointment and anger. He wanted to take her in his arms, cuddle her, and hold her tightly, whisper soothing words to her the way he had done when she was a little girl with a hurt finger or a stubbed toe. But the look on her face now was not the look of a child.

"I'm sorry," he said, "but both your mother and I think that it's best. A little time away, time to think about the future. A chance to see something other than provincial little Sydney—" He paused, knowing that he was doing this badly. He ached for her as he watched the pain in her face.

"It's Tolo," she whispered. "It's because of Tolo, isn't it?"

"No," he said quickly.

"Liar!" she spat at him, and the passionate burst of anger cut him deeply.

"Java, you're not yet seventeen."

"What possible difference can a few months make?" she asked, fighting to keep back the tears and the sobs that, partially stifled, convulsed her. "Oh, Dad, Dad, I never thought that of you, too—I mean I knew that Mother—" She could not continue.

The subject was on the table, Sam thought, and he pushed ahead with it. "Dear, I think that Tolo Mason is a fine boy," Sam said. "I also think that my daughter is a fine girl and just a bit too young to be quite so serious about anyone."

"Bigot," she whispered.

"That's not fair, Java," he said. "You're jumping to conclusions. I would feel the same if I saw you being . . . so serious with any boy. I mean, there's plenty of time for that later, when you know your mind better."

Java's mind sorted the words, and her eyes widened. "So, you spied on us! You followed us to Bina's dressing room!"

Sam's face hardened. He, too, had the capacity to know hurt from someone he loved. "I came looking for you at the request of your mother, who was concerned about you. I heard you ask Tolo to kiss you—"

Jessica, who had been listening from behind the kitchen door, stepped into the room. "You heard her *asking* him to kiss her?" she gasped.

"Now *you're* spying from behind doors," Java said to her mother, "just as he did last night."

"Now you listen, young lady," Jessica retorted, taking a step forward.

Sam held up a hand. "We will have no family Armageddon over a kiss," he said.

"If that's all there has been," Jessica said.

"Mother!" Java gasped.

"Well," Jessica said defensively, "how can we know? I would not have believed that you would sneak away to that Tyrell woman's bedroom to—"

"Now, Jessica, please," Sam said.

Java was weeping openly now. "So that's your opinion of me," she whispered.

"Java, I'm so sorry," Jessica said, moving towards her daughter, arms outstretched. Java leapt from her chair and ran for the stairs. She halted at the top and turned, her face flushed, eyes already reddened. "You're not going to force me to go with you?"

"I would like to think that you would want to go with us," Sam said.

"I have told you that I don't want to go. Must I go in spite of that?"

"I'm afraid so," Sam said sadly.

"Well, then," Java said, running into her own room, slamming the door behind her.

Java went immediately to a large wardrobe and took out a small carpetbag. She threw into the bag her personal toilet articles and a few pieces of underwear. She would not take time to try to pack all her things. Tolo was rich, and he could buy her new dresses. She closed the bag, pulled on a hat, started towards the door, and then halted. If she left now, they would know exactly where to look for her. Thank God Tolo had not yet left on his next business trip into the western areas of the state. She put the bag away without unpacking it, removed the hat, and sat on her bed listening.

She heard her grandmother come out of her room and go downstairs, heard the front door open and close a bit later, and went to the window to see her father striding down the path.

Later she crept down the stairs. Her mother and her grandmother were at the breakfast table. Jessica was leaning forward, her face furrowed with concern, talking to Magdalen, who was shaking her head sadly. Java went into her father's study and spoke softly into the telephone.

"Tolo?"

"Yes, Java?"

"I must see you, immediately."

"I'll come right over."

"No," she said. "Not here. You have your surrey?"

"I can have it ready in a few minutes."

"It takes you a half hour to drive here?"

"Yes," he said.

"All right. In three quarters of an hour I will meet you at the corner, under the old eucalyptus tree two streets north of the house."

"I remember the spot," he said. Walking in the rain once, they had halted under the eucalyptus, and he had stolen a kiss. "Three quarters of an hour."

She went into the breakfast room. Jessica and Magdalen looked at her with much the same expression of concern.

"Do you feel better, dear?" Jessica asked, not unkindly.

"Yes," she said.

"Mother is quite excited about the prospect of seeing England again," Jessica said. "I do wish, darling that you could muster just a bit of interest in the trip."

"It will be quite interesting, I'm sure," Java said.

"Well," Jessica said, "at least that's an improvement."

"It came as a surprise to me, that's all," Java said. She sat down, looking at the clock on the shelf. Forty minutes.

"Java," Magdalen said, "we won't be gone forever, you know."

"I know, Grandmother," she replied. "Nothing is forever."

She listened for long, long minutes as Jessica and Magdalen talked about the coming voyage.

Twenty minutes. She rose. "It's such a lovely day out. I think I'll go for a walk."

"Give me time to change," Magdalen said, looking down at her dressing gown, "and I'll join you."

"If you don't mind, Grandmother," Java said, "not this time? I have some thinking to do."

"Of course," Magdalen said.

Tolo's surrey was already at the appointed spot when she turned the last corner. Java ran the last hundred feet. He leapt down and helped her into the surrey, then climbed in and clucked to the horses.

"They're going to take me away," she said.

He felt his heart sink.

"To England. My father heard me ask you to kiss me in Bina's dressing room last night."

"Bloody—" Tolo gasped.

"I will not go to England," she said with determination.

He looked at her profile. Her lips were set firmly. "How will you avoid it?"

She turned to face him, her green eyes flashing. "I should think you'd have some ideas about that."

He grinned. She was often fiery. He liked it, liked to see her eyes flash. He also enjoyed teasing her at times, so although his blood was beginning to surge with excitement as he sensed the meaning behind her words and her flashing eyes, he said, "Well . . . maybe."

"Tolo Mason!" she exclaimed. "What do you—"

He interrupted her with laughter. She clamped her mouth closed and tried to keep from smiling. "I have to ask you to kiss me," she said. "Do I have to ask you to run away and get married as well?"

He took her hand in his. "Someday, perhaps, I will tease you about that, too. But for now I am too overwhelmed with the mere thought of making you mine. But, my girl, my love, you must be very, very sure. They are your family, your mother, your father, your grandmother. Think it over. It would not kill either of us if you spent a few months in England." He lifted his finger and laid it across her full lips when she started to protest. "True, it would wound me severely, and I would limp and bleed for all the months, every day, until you returned, but we would live, both of us, and we would still love when you come back. Then maybe your parents—"

"No," she said. "Father, perhaps. Grandmother, yes. My mother, never. Tolo, I'd have to go against her wishes if we waited a hundred years. Now, I know that everyone would say, you're young, Java, you have plenty of time, but I don't want to waste months looking at stuffed animals in some old museum in London, or walking through some giant greenhouse to see a plant that I might dig up and toss out of my garden here in Australia. I want to be with you, and I want to see that land of yours—"

"Ours," he interjected.

"—in the west."

"They would know exactly where to find us if we went there," he said. "And you're only sixteen. They could have the marriage annulled."

"Help me?" she whispered, clinging to his arm.

He was thinking swiftly. Two or three transactions were under way for the purchase of land. Price Vermillion could complete them. This lovely girl, this little Java girl, was willing to leave her family out of her love of him. She was willing, she said, to go with him into the bush, where living conditions would be more primitive than anything she'd ever known. It made him think. Was she stronger than he? For his part, he had, on account of his own mother, put aside his own dreams regarding the long-planned journey to Western Australia and the deserts. Now . . .

"Would you go with me to Western Australia?" he asked suddenly.

"Oh, yes, yes!" she breathed.

"It won't be easy."

"It will be if we're together," she said.

Java wrote the letter in which she bid her parents good-bye in a cabin aboard a Mason freighter that was about to lift anchor for the run down to Melbourne. She finished it in time to send it ashore with the pilot, who left the ship at the mouth of the harbour. It joined a similar letter from Tolo to Misa, one that cost him considerable anguish to write. But he was his mother's son, he decided, in being bold and seizing an opportunity—his chance for happiness.

Once clear of the coast, Java and Tolo stood before the ship's captain and went through a ceremony of marriage. When they went into the cabin, which had twin bunks, she went into his arms and put her head against his chest and wept.

"If you want to change your mind," he said, "I own the ship. I can tell the captain to turn around."

"God, no," she said. "I'm weeping for what might have been, Tolo. I'm not sorry, mind you, it's just that I wish that *they* could have been present, that they—"

"I know," he said. "Perhaps someday we'll do it again, when they've accepted it and want to be part of it."

She lifted her lips to him. They tasted of salty tears, but soon her knees were weak and she was no longer weeping.

"Tolo?"

"Yes?"

"I'm a little bit frightened."

"Want to know the truth? So am I." He laughed nervously.

Her giggle joined his. "I feel as though every crewman on this ship were standing just outside, expectantly waiting to hear the virgin shriek when she's—"

"Lord, girl, how you talk," he said. "Where do you get such notions? I guess I know how you feel, though." He looked around the room. His face went firm. "This isn't the right place," he said finally. "Not now. We'll wait until we're at home. We'll have a proper church wedding. And then in my own home, in a house that I hope you can learn to like someday as well as I do, then—"

"You are a hopeless romantic, aren't you?" she asked. "But thank you, Tolo. Thank you ever so much." She tiptoed up and gave him her lips. He groaned, lifted her, placed her on the opposite bed, and went back to sit down on the other.

"I will need a bit of help, you know."

"I'll ask the captain for separate cabins," she said.

"Good idea."

"Do you really think so?"

"Bloody hell," he answered.

She rose, walked to him, put her arms around his neck and leaned on him, pushing him back down on the bunk.

Later, in the dark cabin that was aromatic with the scent of young love, she giggled. "I'm a terrible woman, a very bad woman," she said, caressing him.

"I don't think so."

"I mean morally."

"What you are doing right now is not the act of a moral woman, I agree," he replied.

"That's what I mean. Only bad women are supposed to enjoy. Good wives and mothers endure, and do their connubial duty."

Tolo laughed, remembering how she had been so wonderfully, joyfully astonished, and how her action had in turn astonished him. "You did enjoy, didn't you?"

CHAPTER XXXIV

General Louis Botha rode through a pleasant early June morning, answering a summons to meet with the political leaders of the Transvaal. He smiled wryly when he reached the appointed meeting place, for they had chosen a distillery as the place in which to gather and decide whether to end or to continue the war. He was greeted glumly when he entered to join a group of silent, discouraged men.

Johannesburg was gone. Pretoria was occupied by the British. The English generals were demanding unconditional surrender, sure that the war was finished; and for a gloomy hour, as the leaders of the Transvaal reviewed the long series of setbacks, it seemed that they also would agree that the war was over. Louis Botha was named to meet with Lord Roberts, and he was instructed to do his best to ease the harsh terms currently proposed. Fatefully, however, Botha, not at all eager to go to the British commander under a flag of truce to admit defeat, delayed leaving the distillery.

Dirk De Hartog arrived in a small swirl of dust, leapt from his lathered horse, and ran towards the entrance to the distillery office where the generals and the politicians still lingered. Louis Botha, looking out to discover the cause of the commotion, saw Dirk coming and stepped outside to meet him, closing the door behind him.

"I've been delegated to seek terms from Roberts," Botha said. "You have ridden hard. Is the news you are carrying going to affect that decision?"

For a moment Dirk did not answer. Certainly his news would affect the attitude of the men inside the building. He knew enough about his own people to fear that when he spoke to the leaders inside, they would change their instructions to Botha and the war would continue. He wrestled with himself. He had not expected Botha to be so willing and ready to give up. Had he suspected, he might have been tempted to ride slower, but now he was here, and he had sworn oaths, and he was, after all, a Boer.

"Yes, General, what I have to report might very well alter that decision," he said.

"Come in, then," Botha said. "We will all hear your news together."

Botha introduced Dirk quickly. Dirk stood before the small group of men. "I have been riding hard to the west and south," he said, "on orders from General Botha to determine the condition of Boer units in the Free State. In the past weeks my men and I have covered a lot of ground. I have this to report. The Free Staters are determined to continue the struggle for freedom, gentlemen. In fact, in the past weeks they've scored three spectacular successes. At Lindley they defeated a force under Colonel B. E. Spragge and captured five hundred prisoners. Four days later they seized a huge convoy of arms and supplies, along with its escort, near Heilbron."

Louis Botha was watching the faces of the politicians, seeing new hope being born, watching as imminent defeat transformed itself into renewed determination.

"General De Wet," Dirk continued—and in spite of himself he felt a shiver of pride—"has swept down upon the Central Railway. As you know, the railway is the lifeline of General Roberts's army. At Pretoria, Roberts is a long, long way from his base, and his supply line—the railway—has now been severed by De Wet in three places."

There was a burst of applause, a hearty cry of "Thank you good Lord."

"I have been told by members of General De Wet's staff that the British have suffered more casualties in a ten-day period in the Free State than they did during the entire march to Pretoria." He paused, looked around. He cast his eyes towards the dingy ceiling, seeing beyond it in his mind and praying silently that he was doing the right thing.

"Gentlemen, General De La Rey called my attention to some facts that I think bear repeating," he said. "Since the beginning of this war, last October, our own forces have lost fifteen hundred men killed, about ten percent of whom were foreign volunteers. By contrast, General De Wet's activities over a mere ten days have cost the British fifteen hundred dead. Now admittedly, thousands of our soldiers have gone home. Others have been captured. But the British have released many of the captives, and General De La Rey believes that a show of determination will induce the men who have gone home to rejoin their units."

Louis Botha thanked Dirk and rose to stand beside him, "Gentlemen," he said, "you are aware that we have sent delegations to the capitals of those nations who have some sympathy for our fight for freedom from British domination. We have men in Washington, Paris, Berlin, and St. Petersburg. There is a very good chance that these friendly nations will send aid, or will at least bring political pressure to bear on England to prevent the Transvaal and the Orange Free State from becoming mere political units in the relentlessly expanding British Empire. I myself will join those great men, General De La Rey and General De Wet, in continuing the struggle."

There were cheers.

Slone Shannon kicked his horse into greater effort and rode forward along a slow-moving column of mounted infantry riding towards the northwest after having crossed the Vaal River. He reined in beside Matt Van Buren, who had been detailed to lead the advance. Out front, scouting the veld, were battle-hardened veterans, bushmen with a sharp eye for the odd ambush or for the signs mounted Boers left on the baked earth.

"Seems to me we're going to a lot of trouble for a war that is all over," Slone said, repeating what had become a standing joke among the men of the huge, now-scattered British Army.

Matt grunted. He was hot, tired, dusty, and thirsty. Out here, beyond the border of the Orange Free State in the western Transvaal, the land was growing poorer and more desolate with each mile.

After the capture of Pretoria, when the war was supposed to have ended, the whole of South Africa had smouldered for a time. Then—with Botha in the east, Koos De La Rey in the west, and

Christiaan De Wet in the Free State—the curtain had risen on a new kind of war. De La Rey's commandos struck simultaneously at three British forces west of Pretoria. Behind British lines, in areas thought to have been pacified, spasmodic fighting flared. Across one hundred fifty thousand square miles, in the Free State, in the Transvaal, and even in the Cape Colony, small commando units of wandering Boers struck and faded away, unstoppable and uncapturable. No more than twenty-five thousand Boer men had discovered a method of paralyzing the huge British force of over two hundred thousand.

At first Lord Roberts concentrated on trying to destroy De Wet in the Orange Free State, for De Wet had been the first to strike quickly and then fade away, and thus to begin the British Empire's instruction in guerrilla warfare. As the season advanced, it became apparent to the British that new measures were in order. With Kitchener, Roberts planned to make at least seventy-five thousand men mobile, as mobile as the Boers themselves. The mounted Australian units, having shown their ability to match the Boers' tactics, became priority units. Thus it was that Slone Shannon and Matt Van Buren found themselves proceeding as rapidly as possible into that transition zone between veld and desert in the western Transvaal, where the man whom many thought to be the Boers' finest general, Koos De La Rey, was riding circles around the British Army.

The Van Reenen hospital unit, with nurse Sianna De Hartog, lingered in the vicinity of Pretoria for a few days before an officer rode in from the west with an urgent request from De La Rey himself. De La Rey had newly wounded men needing treatment, and he was short of surgeons and hospital facilities.

The news of the successes of De La Rey and De Wet had been filtering through to Dr. Van Reenen and Sianna. Sianna did not wait for Van Reenen to reply to the request that the hospital unit move west. "We *must* go, Doctor," she said.

"It is my impression, Sianna, that I am still running this hospital," Van Reenen commented, fatigue in his voice.

"But the fighting is to the west, with De La Rey," she insisted.

"You are needed badly, Doctor," the Boer officer put in.

"Already we are far from home," Van Reenen sighed, adding, when Sianna started to speak, "but apparently we are fated to travel even farther."

"How long will it take you to get ready, Doctor?" the Boer officer asked.

"We can leave tomorrow," Van Reenen said.

"Good," said the officer, "that will give me time to arrange an armed escort."

Van Reenen raised an eyebrow. "I thought that the area was controlled by General De La Rey."

The officer looked uncomfortable. "It is, as far as the British are concerned," he said. "It's the Kaffirs," he said. "Now and then they try to take advantage of the confusion."

"The tribesmen have attacked Boers?" Sianna asked, shocked. She had, of course, heard the stories of horror and sacrifice from the days of the Great Trek in the 1830s, when Boer newcomers to this land had had to fight for their lives against the blacks.

"On occasion they will attack," the officer said. "They will not, of course, disturb armed men in respectable numbers. The hospital will be safe."

Later, as they sat on the rocking, hard seat of a hospital wagon moving west, Dr. Van Reenen turned to Sianna. "So the tribesmen are out to settle old scores," he said. "They have never forgiven us for coming to their lands, and now they use our weakness to their advantage. To such depths have the British brought us."

On the veld to the west of Pretoria, Koos De La Rey found a natural haven for his small forces in a rugged, hilly wilderness called the Megaliesberg. After weeks of marching, the detached British force for which the Queensland Mounted Infantry were acting as cavalry and scouts were camped on the parched, brushy veld with the hills of the Megaliesberg forming a background to the east. The British force, under the command of Colonel James Westlake, consisted of less than two hundred mounted infantry and some twenty-five hundred foot soldiers. They had marched a long, long way and Westlake had decided to give them at least a day's rest.

The rest was interrupted at daylight when, out of a mist, Koos De La Rey's commandos charged. Fortunately for Westlake and his twenty-five hundred troops, the Boer force was very small—only three hundred men. The initial charge swept through the pickets and broke the outer defensive circle, and as the camp began to rouse and the battle hardened, British infantrymen seized rifles and began to fire at anything on a horse. The Boers withdrew, leaving behind only one dead, a boy of sixteen.

A dozen wagons of the supply train were blazing. Scattered shots from the pickets could still be heard. Colonel James Westlake called for a meeting of all officers.

It was a standard joke in the command that Westlake did his best to be a carbon copy of Kitchener. He bore a slight resemblance to Kitchener in the fact that he was a big man and wore a moustache like Kitchener's, but there the resemblance ended.

"The Boer thinks that he can strike wherever he pleases and without punishment," Westlake said. "But this time he has attacked the wrong unit, eh, men?"

"Right, sir," said a bored captain.

"We will chase the wily Boer to his lair," Westlake said. He pointed towards the hills of the Megaliesberg, purple in the morning light.

"Oh, Lord," Slone whispered to Matt, "take that mile-high hill, will you?"

"You have a comment, Lieutenant Shannon?" Westlake asked.

"No, sir," Slone said.

"Good. You Australians will, of course, lead the way," Westlake said.

"Of course," Matt whispered.

"Here is the plan," Westlake said, spreading a map. "You will note that there are two main passes into and through the Megaliesberg. Here at Zilikiat's Nek and here at Olifant's Nek. We will block both of the passes. I will be in Olifant's Nek with the main force. The Australians, with, ah, five hundred infantry, will go into Zilikiat's Nek."

"By all means," Slone whispered, "let's split our forces."

"Comment, Lieutenant Shannon?" Westlake asked.

"I was saying, sir, that you seem to be emulating General

Buller's brilliant strategy before Ladysmith. Splitting your forces to surround the Boers."

"Your sarcasm is noted, Lieutenant Shannon," Westlake said stiffly, "but not appreciated. Your remark will be entered into the record of this operation."

"Thank you, sir," Slone said.

Matt and Slone rode together at the head of the force headed towards Zilikiat's Nek. Matt was chuckling and, when Slone asked him to explain, he said, "Is it arrogance or stupidity with these Pommy officers?"

Slone shrugged. "A bit of both, perhaps."

Matt imitated Westlake's effete accent. "'Your remark will be entered into the record of this operation.' Good God, he's building evidence against himself in the event that old De La Rey is in there waiting for us."

"This is one time I feel fortunate to be with the smaller force," Slone said. "De La Rey, if he's in there, will want to destroy the main force. Maybe he won't bother with a mere six hundred men."

The mounted infantry, too, had been split by Westlake. Only one hundred Australians were riding with Matt and Slone.

The rocky, arid land rose towards the hills, and the scouts that Slone, as senior officer, had put out as they entered Zilikiat's Nek returned to report that they, at least, could not see any Boers.

"Matt," Slone said, "you go on back and stay with the infantry. That Pom captain might need some advice if things get choppy."

"Come on," Matt protested.

"I remind you, Queensland, that I am senior," Slone said, winking.

"Bugger you, *sir*," Matt said, grinning. "All right. Fine. Be a hero all by yourself."

But as Matt turned his horse, a great roar of small arms fire broke out from the west. Matt's horse reared as he tried to stop the turn. "Westlake's found 'em," he shouted.

"Tell that Pom captain that we're moving out, fast," Slone said. "Maybe we can take some of the pressure off him."

The morning calm now was torn asunder by the pulsing sound of pom-pom guns. Westlake's force had no pom-poms. "He must be catching hell," Matt said. Then he was off.

As the mounted infantry felt their way cautiously into the Nek, all was silent. The Boers did not reveal themselves until the infantry, too, had entered the pass. Then, from two sides, from the rear and from the front, the Boer sharpshooters opened up. A Maxim machine gun sputtered.

At the first volley, Slone shouted out an order to turn. Mounted infantry was of no value against Boers hidden away, high in the rocks and shooting downwards. Fortunately, shooting downwards had always seemed to be the Boers' one weakness. It was always difficult to be accurate under such circumstances. The casualties were light as the mounted infantry swept back towards the foot soldiers, who had taken cover and were firing at rifle flashes on the hills and slopes above them.

Slone saw Matt Van Buren, dismounted, firing upwards from behind a protective rock. Near him the British infantry captain was crouched behind a boulder, looking around with a pale face. Slone gave Matt a hand order to withdraw back down the Nek towards the open slopes. The British officer saw Slone and leapt to his feet to run towards him.

"Get into cover, sir," Slone shouted.

"I saw you!" the captain yelled. "I saw you give your lieutenant the order to withdraw. I remind you that I am the senior officer here. I have given my men orders to advance, to root out those bloody bastards on the slopes."

"Goodonyer," Slone said. "Lead on." He spurred his horse, riding to the rear, yelling and waving to the mounted infantry to follow. Matt caught up with him and shouted at him.

"I'm going to clear a way out of here," Slone said.

"Good idea," Matt shouted back.

A horse screamed in pain as a Boer bullet burned through its belly. A horseman fell, sliding on the hard, gravelly earth. And from the rear, as Slone led the Queenslanders in withdrawal, came the deadly swift pounding of a pom-pom gun. From every rock in the nek, at ground level and above, protruded a Boer rifle.

"The whole bloody Boer army is in here," Slone shouted, turning his horse just as a bullet impacted into one of his mount's eyes, splashing blood and brain matter into his face. Slone leapt free as the horse fell and ran for cover. He was within a few feet of a large boulder with good shelter behind it when a bullet smashed through his sun helmet.

Matt, himself running for cover, saw the life go out of Slone Shannon's legs. He had seen it happen before. When a man was shot in the head, it often appeared as if the man were an electrical light, burning with life one moment but, in the next instant, with the flip of switch, darkness. The quickness and limpness with which Slone fell left Matt with little hope.

Matt had to think fast. Once again the Poms had put an Australian unit at peril. Westlake had, indeed, split his force, but overall the action reminded Matt more of Kitchener than Buller. At Paardeberg Kitchener had launched a suicidal attack on General Cronje's forces, squandering eleven hundred men in the process. He had then personally ordered a small group of tired and exhausted New South Wales infantrymen to attack entrenched Boers on a kopje. Later, when Kitchener had to send in three thousand men to do what he had asked one hundred Australians to accomplish, the surviving Australians, separated from their supply weapons, were refused food by British units.

So the Poms had done it again, Matt concluded, and it was up to him to get as many of his men as possible out of the ambush. Bullets flew, making dust puffs around him, as he ran to the boulder where the Pom captain was hidden.

"I'm taking my men out," Matt said. "If you choose to come, we'll do our best to give you covering fire."

The Englishman's face was white. Matt saw a fleck of blood at his lips and then looked down to see that the man had been shot in the chest. "It is hopeless," the captain whispered. "This must be De La Rey's main force. I will instruct my men to surrender to prevent further needless bloodshed."

"Fine," Matt answered. "I'm getting out." He ran back to his horse. The animal, mostly protected by the huge boulder, was pawing the ground and whinnying in fear.

"Queensland!" Matt roared, mounting, sending his horse thundering down the nek. "With me, Queensland!"

Miraculously, only half a dozen men had been left behind in the nek, although the toll of horses had been much higher. About a quarter of the command was riding double.

The firing in the nek behind them gradually diminished and

then faded into silence. Westlake's infantry, Matt knew, had surrendered.

And one of the Queenslanders left ignominiously among the fallen was Lieutenant Slone Vincent Shannon.

CHAPTER XXXV

Matt Van Buren's battered group of mounted infantry rejoined the main body before Olifant's Nek. Westlake had suffered only a few casualties, mainly from hidden Boer sharpshooters and two of their pom-pom guns, which had been pulled quickly when the colonel ordered an advance. The main force had been waiting for Slone and Matt at Zilikiat's Nek.

"You ran?" Westlake sputtered. "You deserted the infantry under fire?"

Matt was not standing at attention. Perhaps the uniform that Westlake wore deserved to be shown respect, but the man did not. "I obeyed the orders of my superiors," he said coldly, "in salvaging what I could from a hopeless situation. The infantry was cut off and surrounded. They had no choice but to surrender. I simply chose not to join them in a Boer prison laager."

"You are relieved of command, Lieutenant Van Buren," Westlake shouted. "You will face court-martial as quickly as it can be arranged."

"I think I shall enjoy the chance, sir, to voice my opinion of the manner in which you conducted this operation," Matt replied.

Westlake's face was dangerously red. He almost choked on his anger; words sputtered, spittle flew. "To your quarters—you—you—"

Matt came to attention. "There is one thing, *sir*. We have bodies on the field back there in the nek. Before I am confined to quarters, I request permission to take a force and claim the dead before the scavengers go to work on them."

Westlake swallowed convulsively. "So, you've suddenly regained your courage?"

"Sir, not too long ago, I might have had the satisfaction of giving you a chance to test my courage personally. Since that is not possible any more, I can only repeat my request. The Boers will have withdrawn by now."

"Lieutenant, you go to your tent. I don't need you to tell me how to handle British dead," Westlake said.

Matt saluted and turned on his heel. He stood outside his tent and watched as a force was mustered to march to Zilikiat's Nek. The Queensland Mounted Infantry was the main component of the force. Matt located the Australian colonel in command and said, "Sir, Slone Shannon's out there."

"So I've heard, Matt," the colonel said. "Don't worry, mate, we'll see to him." He frowned. "Shouldn't have been so impertinent with the commanding officer, son."

"Sir, these bloody Poms—"

"That's enough," the colonel said. "Now you go to your tent and stay there until we get back. It's going to be hard enough as it is to keep that Po— that good colonel from delivering you to the court-martial he promised."

The brief fight in Zilikiat's Nek had had an audience: a small group of warriors of the Sekukini, one of the numerous South African tribes known collectively to white men as "Kaffirs." They had been on the heights when the Boers began to lay their ambush on the slopes, and they had lingered, blending invisibly with the dry grasses and the piled boulders. They watched wide-eyed as the storm of fire blew down on the unsuspecting British soldiers, then watched as the Boers gathered all of the weapons left on the field by the dead and the weapons of the infantry who surrendered. Lumbering wagons drawn by oxen were brought down to the valley to carry away the rifles and the wounded. Then the Boers marched off, and only the sound of the wind could be heard in the pass.

The tribesmen crept slowly to the floor of the nek and began systematically to loot the British dead. Nothing was left behind. The dead were stripped even of their underwear. A Sekukini used the tip of his spear to pry out a gold tooth from a dead man's mouth. Soon the blacks, too, were gone and the wind sighed through the pass as the afternoon sun blazed down on the naked dead.

The Van Reenen field hospital was camped in a dry valley of the Megaliesberg, no more than two miles from the site of the battle in Zilikiat's Nek. A handful of Boers came in early from the battle, mainly with head and hand wounds, as they had been hiding behind rocks.

Usually when a man was hit in the head, very little medical treatment was possible or required. The wound was either fatal or it was a superficial crease easily treated with a simple cleansing and bandaging. Hands were a different thing, and in some cases, when the multitude of small bones were badly smashed, Dr. Van Reenen amputated the hand as quickly as possible. Within days such handless men would be returning to their homes, their fighting over.

The British casualties arrived later, carried in by their comrades whom the Boers had captured. Van Reenen and Sianna laboured far into the night with the enemy wounded.

As the British prisoners were marched at a fast pace up the nek, over the rise and into the wilderness of the Megaliesberg, a Boer colonel in charge of the rear guard decided to have one last look at the scene of battle, the better to write his report for his general, Koos De La Rey. He led a small party back down into the nek. As the horsemen approached, the colonel thought he saw motion on the slope, but close examination revealed nothing.

"Colonel," called out a man, "the bedamned Kaffirs have been there."

The colonel rode slowly through the twisted and widely strewn British dead. The sun was already beginning to blister their white, naked skin. He shook his head in sadness. Death was indignity enough; to have the black savages dishonour them further by stripping them was indefensible.

A rider came pounding up the nek from below, a scout, his beard encrusted with sweat-moistened dust. "They're coming, the British, to claim their dead."

"How many?"

"Two hundred horse, perhaps three hundred foot."

The colonel pondered. This was good ground. The British had been hurt severely on this spot once; were they seriously intent on marching into the same potential trap? It was not credible.

"All right," the colonel shouted. "We go."

Perhaps, with the men he had, he could hurt the British again, but the main body of Boer fighting men was withdrawing, burdened with the many British pensioners. If the British were coming in force to collect their dead, it was better to let them have them. He himself would not drain the energies of his few men trying to dig graves in that dry and rocky soil.

"Colonel," a man called from the foot of the slope.

The colonel rode over, guiding his horse among the boulders and the dead.

"A live one," the man said, almost stunned.

The colonel dismounted and squatted beside a naked body. Dark, close-cropped hair was matted with blood.

"Head wound," the colonel grunted.

"But he breathes strongly."

The colonel looked up at the hot, burning sun. It would be hours before the slow-moving British column arrived. On the rocks above perched the vultures. The thought of them was abhorrent. "Rig a litter," he ordered. "Take this man to the hospital."

Sianna awoke slowly, fighting against exhaustion. A voice outside was calling, "Dr. Van Reenen! Doctor!"

She pulled on a heavy robe and poked her head out of the tent. "Hush," she whispered harshly.

The Boer who had been calling for the doctor came to her. "The doctor is needed," he said.

"The doctor is not made of steel," she hissed. "He is exhausted. What is the matter?"

"One shot in the head," the man said. "A prisoner, I'm told."

"I will come," Sianna said resignedly. A head wound would not take her long. She dressed quickly and went to the hospital tent. Inside, lanterns were burning, and the wounded man was lying on his stomach on a treatment table, a blanket spread over him. She adjusted a lantern for better light and peered down. Dark hair and much blood. She prepared a pan of water, began to clean away the dried blood. She had little hope for the man, judging from the quantity of blood and from the colour of his face—ashen under a new sunburn. When she lifted an eyelid, the eye was rolled far back, and there was no reaction to the light.

Soon she could see the point of impact of the bullet. It had not penetrated the skull. It had struck just above the temple and chewed out a ragged trench through the scalp towards the back of the head. The wound by itself would not kill the man. However, she had learned much from Dr. Van Reenen in the months since she had said goodbye to her Aunt Anna at the farm in Natal. As she worked automatically to cleanse, disinfect, and bandage the wound, she could almost hear Dr. Van Reenen's words.

"We know so little about the brain, you know. We think that consciousness is located in the brain stem, in the deep centre of the brain. When a man's head is struck by a bullet, the blow is powerful, even if the bullet does not penetrate. The brain is moved inside its protective shell, and if the movement is serious enough, the motor system fails."

She had seen some men who had stopped breathing after a bullet merely grazed their skulls, for the force of the impact had been so severe that the brain stem had been permanently traumatized. And she had also seen men who bled profusely after a head wound, but were able to keep on fighting and then, after the battle, walk to the hospital tent, their clothes saturated with their own blood.

Saddest of all, she had seen men regain consciousness after being hit in the head, appearing perfectly normal until they lapsed into a coma and died two or three days later. Dr. Van Reenen had explained that in these cases the brain had most probably been injured in some way that did not show up immediately. "Perhaps an internal swelling," he guessed.

The wound she was treating now was a wound to cause concern. The fact that the man was still unconscious did not bode well for him. She could only do her best. She possessed no magic with which to reach inside the skull and soothe the injury—Dr. Van Reenen called it "insult"—to vital tissue. She had no way to probe those mysterious masses of odd greyish formations that made up a man's brain and made him the person he was.

When she had finished, she had the hospital orderlies transfer the man to a bunk in the hospital. She followed along and supervised as the man was gently carried to the bunk, where he was laid out on his back. Now she saw his face for the first time and noted that it was a face that suggested upper-class breeding, a sharply angled, possibly aristocratic face that would have been, in normal times, quite handsome.

"Will he make it?" an orderly asked.

"That is in God's hands," Sianna said.

Colonel James Westlake's detached force was on the move. A runner had arrived from Kitchener's headquarters. The army was moving out from Pretoria. The detached units in the west would be the hammer, the main army under Kitchener would be the anvil. They would catch Koos De La Rey between them and smash him.

Matt Van Buren had talked with the burial party upon its return from Zilikiat's Nek and learned that no identifications could be made, since the blacks had stripped every body of any shred of cloth and any hint of identification; worse, they had also mutilated the bodies, cutting away ears, lips, and noses. He said a prayer for his friend and fellow Queenslander, Slone Shannon, and began to make notes of what he would say in his own defence when Colonel Westlake had him court-martialled.

In spite of confinement to quarters Matt was allowed to go to the mess tent, and it was there, on the morning after the burial party had returned, that he saw his own Australian commanding colonel. The colonel was grim faced about the previous day's losses, but he managed to wink and pull Matt aside.

"I want you to be a good boy, Van Buren," the colonel said flatly. "Don't tweak the Pom's whiskers any more."

"What, no court-martial?"

The colonel grinned broadly and looked around to be sure no one was observing this tête-à-tête. "I believe I've convinced our Pommy friend that his own conduct of the Zilikiat's Nek affair might not shine like a star under close examination. So just go about your business, lad, and for God's sake keep your mouth shut."

"Yes, sir," Matt said. He made an effort to conceal a sigh of relief.

The Boer camp came awake before dawn. Sianna recognized the sounds and sighed with all-too-familiar fatigue as she once again crawled out of bed. They would be moving. "Oh, dear God," she whispered, as she tried to straighten her aching back with both hands pressed at her sides.

She found Dr. Van Reenen at breakfast. "They can't expect us to leave the wounded this time," she said. "Not here."

Around them was a desolation, a sun-blasted, drought-killed brownness. There was water in the little valley where the hospital was set up, but even that standing water hole was being rapidly used up.

"I think not," Van Reenen said. "For there is no guarantee that the British will come here, is there?"

"None at all," Sianna said. "Why would any man in his right mind want to come here?"

"Are you assuming that the British are all sane?" the doctor asked, and Sianna took note of his mordant wit.

"I'm not sure any of us are," she said.

"De La Rey himself rode in before dawn," Van Reenen said.

"And my father?" Sianna asked.

Van Reenen shrugged.

Sianna ate quickly, then went to the hospital tent. Boer casualties, most of them coming along nicely by now, greeted her with respect. She worked her way down the line of bunks. There was the head wound. The man was breathing evenly and strongly, but his eyes were still closed. She took his pulse. It was strong. "So, you," she whispered. "Now it is up to you. You will lie there and not come out of your coma or you will choose to live, eh?"

Van Reenen was not in the tent. She reported her observations to him.

"We are ordered to move," he said sadly.

"Actually, there is only one man who might be endangered by a move," she said. She led the doctor to the man with the head wound. He bent and lifted one of the man's eyelids. To Sianna's surprise the pupil of the eye was now visible, and it flickered as the light hit it.

"The skull wasn't broken?" Van Reenen asked.

"There was no movement under light pressure," she said.

Van Reenen shrugged. "Ah, the human brain, the poor brain."

Something stirred at the entrance to the tent, and there was Koos De La Rey, like prophetic Jeremiah or Moses returned from the mountains, his beard wilder, his hair longer. "Nurse De Hartog," he said, "your father sends his love. He is to the north, where we will be joining him rather soon."

"We're moving out, General?" the doctor asked.

"We bloodied the nose of a British unit that just about matches our numbers," De La Rey said. "They are moving through the hills in an effort to force us to withdraw towards the guns of Lord Roberts's main army. Our plan is to slip out of the trap by moving through Zilikiat's Nek, to gain the open country to the northwest. What is your position, Dr. Van Reenen?"

"I imagine, as usual, that the walking wounded will head for home," Van Reenen said. "We have only one man who should not be moved at this time, a British soldier, as it happens."

De La Rey raised the tactical issue. "If you move him?"

The doctor shrugged.

"We can't simply leave him here to die," De La Rey said.

"Sianna," Van Rennen said, "please prepare the patients for transport."

The lead elements of the small, mobile Boer force were already moving northwards. The supply wagons were rumbling up over the rise towards the top of the nek. As Van Reenen had predicted, Boers who were lightly wounded, including three whose hands had been amputated, elected to go it alone, heading for the southeast to skirt British lines and make their way home.

The hospital tents were loaded. Van Reenen and three wagons of the wounded went ahead with the main body, leaving Sianna behind. Dr. Van Reenen was so tired, and she had insisted on being the one to stay, to bring along the seriously wounded Englishman. Only a small rear guard was on the southern side of the nek when suddenly four hundred British Lancers, the advance force of the main army, charged down the narrow valley.

There had been no warning. this was how the British wanted it: to give the enemy a taste of its own guerrilla medicine. The Boer scouts were moving towards the north, with the rearguard scouts keeping track of Colonel Westlake's contingent to the southwest. The surprise was total. The cavalry charge burst among the men left to guard the rear elements of the hospital. Sianna, stunned, saw the Boer force crushed in minutes. A young Boer, unhorsed, ran alongside the horse of a friend and, with amazing agility, was lifted to sit behind his comrade. A charging Lancer pierced the chest of the man in the saddle, and the thrust, delivered at a gallop, was so powerful that the lance went all the way through the first

Boer to impale the man behind him, leaving them both lying on the dusty, dry earth, connected in death by a broken lance.

Now the Lancers were among the wagons. Oxen bellowed in terror. Rifles spoke. The big, plodding animals, yoked in pairs, panicked as the bullets dropped harness mates, so that within seconds the oxen trains were a chaos of writhing, struggling beasts. A wounded man leapt from one of the wagons and ran, only to be pierced in the back by a charging Lancer.

Fire broke out in the tinder-dry brush and roared towards the hospital wagon, where Sianna had intended to carry the man with the head wound. The new terror of fire caused oxen to break their harness. The Lancers were chasing down the last of the Boers. Flames raced closer now, directly in the path of Sianna's wagon. She saw a Boer raise his arms in surrender, only to be dropped by at least three rifle shots. And now the Lancers were turning towards her, charging in front of the raging fire that swept the brush.

There were no survivors within her view. All the Boers she could see were dead. There were no wounded, only fatalities. She ran. She smelled the smoke of the veld fire, the burned powder of the rifles, the blood of the oxen. She ran towards the lowest spot in the camp, the almost depleted water hole.

She felt as if she were running for her life, although no one really believed the tales that circulated of British atrocities. There was more evidence to suggest that the British treated their captives in strict accordance with the rules of "civilized" warfare—if such a contradiction could be said to exist; women and children were supposedly always treated with great respect. Nevertheless Sianna ran in panic, stopping only when she had sprinted around the muddy water hole and reached a sheltering area of tumbled boulders and dry, thorny growth.

Panting with exertion, she hid among the boulders and watched. She could see little; the campsite was hidden now behind a pall of smoke. The veld fire had gathered an inexorable momentum and was a roaring contagion, climbing the slope to the south. She heard a British sergeant bawling orders and peered from behind a boulder to see the Lancers form and ride away towards the north, following the trail of De La Rey's main army.

She stayed hidden behind the rock for a long, long time, until long after the Lancers were out of sight and out of hearing—until she had ceased to tremble and realized that she was terribly thirsty. Then she walked back towards the camp.

The fire had burned all around, and a smell of scorched flesh hung in the air. The wagons had been incinerated or overturned, their contents strewn, smashed, and scorched.

Finding a canteen of boiled water in the ruins of the last hospital wagon, she tilted it up and drank voraciously. When she lowered the canteen, her eyes fell on the man with the head wound. The bunk on which he had lain was overturned. He lay on his back, but his eyes were open and he was staring at her, his throat constricting as he swallowed convulsively.

"Oh, dear God," she whispered, rushing to kneel beside him. He moved his head, his eyes following the canteen in her hand. "You are thirsty, no?" She lifted his head, put the canteen to his lips. He spilled precious water, but managed to swallow.

"So, they did not see you, or at least if they did they did not kill you."

His eyes moved from her lips to her own eyes. His lips moved, but no sound came.

"There," she said. "Rest." She found a blanket that was only a bit scorched and covered his lower body with it, for he was wearing only a hospital gown.

"You can move your eyes," she said, forming her words slowly, speaking in careful English. "You can move your head a bit. Is that all?"

He blinked his eyes and moved his head as far as he could, wincing with pain.

"So we, you and I, are in a pretty fix," she said. "My friends are gone. Your friends are chasing my friends. We have only ourselves and them." She meant the vultures, that army of parasites gathering in great numbers, already beginning to rip and tear at the dead oxen and the dead men. "I think that the first thing I'd better do is to gather all the boiled water that is left, and then the food. You rest yourself."

His eyes followed her as she rose. She looked down at him and felt pity, for it appeared that the head wound had done great damage, that he was paralyzed from the neck down. She also felt a bit of resentment: he would die eventually, but in the meantime he would hold her to this sad spot, for so long as he lived she could not abandon him. She would give him food and drink, and if she could find clean bandages in the wreckage, she would change his dressing. But he would die nonetheless.

She found a few more canteens. One of them was filled with a potent brandy. She kept it. For food there was a case of captured British rations, the tinned meat known as bully beef. She then turned her mind to the question of protection. It might just be possible to form some sort of protection against the sun with the remains of the hospital tents, but there was another consideration: the Kaffirs.

She talked her thoughts aloud to the wounded man. "What will I do with you?" She looked at the sky. "It will be hot. Can't just stay out in the sun." She turned, scanning the valley on all sides. "Look, you," she said. "I'll be back, do you understand?"

He blinked his eyes.

She walked past the water hole and began to climb the slope, moving along the boulders with an eerily sure sense of just where to go. A hundred yards up the slope she saw a dark space under the overhang of a rock ledge. She walked into the shadows. It was cooler there; a breeze fanned her hair. Far back, in the dim shadows, she saw evidence that others had used this large, open cave before her. On the grey rock walls, stick men with long spears stalked horned animals. The old ones had left evidence in pictures that they had lived here, those who had hunted the veld before the Zulu and other tribes, even before the little Bushmen who had now been pushed into the Kalahari to the west. The brush would give a supply of firewood. She would have to find an axe somewhere in the wreckage of the hospital wagons.

Sianna walked back down the slope, seeking out the best pathway, for she would be heavily laden when she next came up the hill. The vultures were still arriving. Moving to the cave would serve another purpose, to get her away from the scene of carnage and from the stench which would grow with the heat of the day. She was quite near the point where she had left the wounded man when she realized that something was wrong. Vultures had come there, too; even as she broke into a run and shouted at the vile birds, two of them were fluttering and squawking right over his body.

Slone Shannon had known fear in his life. He had known the fear of the supernatural in his youth, when people gathered to tell ghost stories. He had known fear when he realized that a large force of dervishes had hidden themselves in the ravine in front of the charge of the Lancers in the Sudan. But he had never known the gut-twisting horror, the terror that came to him when the vultures came after him in a small, dry African valley. He was helpless. He could move his eyes. He could move his head only slightly. He could not speak or cry out. He could smell the birds, the filth, the carrion, the sick, the dirty stench of decaying death. He told himself that they never attacked a thing that was living.

For some time now, since he had first begun to believe that he was alive, that the pretty face that he saw was not an angel but a living person, he had passed his waking time holding coversations with himself.

Vultures do not attack the living. They wait until you are dead.

Who told you that? How do you know? How do you know that that filthy bugger right there–the big one–isn't going to leap into your face and rip out your eyeball with his beak?

The world, he knew, was full of many so-called facts that were not based on actual knowledge, but on popular fables. *That* was the terrible truth. The only fact he could see now was that the filthy bird with its stench of death was going to claw and dig out his eyeballs, and he could do nothing to prevent it.

He fought. By straining his neck, he managed to move his head back and forth until he was very tired. He closed his eyes. *If you keep them closed very tightly they will not see the eyeballs and–*

Fool, they'll think you're dead.

He opened his eyes. The birds had moved in closer. The big one cocked its ugly, bald head and peered at him with one red eye. He tried to scream, and only a hiss came.

Oh, God, give me the use of just one bloody arm!

You can do it.

I can move that arm. I will move that arm. I will use that arm to–

The big bird waddled closer. Behind him were others.

"Aggggg," came a sound from his throat. It was a small sound, but it caused the big bird to move back a foot or two.

"Aggggg. Arrrgggg," he moaned, tossing his head from side to side.

A flurry of motion. "Oh, God!" he whispered. But it was only two birds struggling for position.

"Arrrgggggg," he croaked again, He strained, willing his arm to move.

The two birds moved forward together. One of them stretched his neck and pecked at Slone's hand. He made a supreme effort, and miraculously the hand jerked back, the movement startling the vulture. There was a flapping retreat, which ended quickly. The birds advanced again. This time one of them struck his foot, which protruded from the charred blanket. He felt pain. That beak was sharp. And the big ones were moving towards his face, jockeying for position, he was sure, near his eyes.

He moaned again, louder, moving one finger on his right hand.

The biggest bird leapt forward. The smell of the grave was in Slone's nostrils, agonizing terror in his heart. His eyes were wide, watching as the bird positioned itself, the cruel, sharp beak coming closer, closer—

"Shoo, scat, get out of here!" Sianna shouted, swinging a stick lustily, knocking feathers from the big brute that had seemed so interested in Slone's eyeballs. Some of the birds flew off to battle for less lively meals. Others, including the big one, merely flapped to a safe distance and waited.

"Arrrr," he managed again, softly.

She knelt. "Oh, my God, I'm so sorry. I didn't think the birds would come after you, too—you're alive and getting stronger. Now listen to me. I've found a place for us to hide. It's far enough away from here so we will be away from birds and the smell of this place. We will have some difficulty getting there, but then we will be safe. I know you're not a giant, but you're not a Pygmy, either. I'm sure I won't be able to carry you. The best I can offer is a bumpy ride on the litter. You must hold on and be patient."

He nodded. The terrible fear had wrenched his head back into more mobility. He wiggled the fingers of his right hand, but she did not notice.

"You're willing to try it, then?"

He nodded. Anything to get away from that big bastard of a vulture.

"I think the best way is to rig a one-man litter," she said. "Don't worry, I won't go far enough to let the birds get at you again."

She found plenty of materials in the ravaged camp, as well as other things—blankets, spare bandages, and an axe that would be useful later for firewood. She fashioned the litter, then made neat bundles of the things she wanted to carry to the cave. She would come for them later.

Rolling Slone over onto the litter, she strapped him to it and picked up the handles at one end. The other ends of the poles dragged on the ground. "Now," she said, "this may take us a while, and it won't be a smooth ride, but we're going to get there."

Fortunately, Slone felt no pain, not even when Sianna's feet slipped out from under her and she let him drop heavily. The really difficult going came as she dragged the litter up the slope, having to detour around the boulders. She was soaked with sweat and covered with dust when, at last, she gained the large, open cave and put the litter down.

She sat where he could see her, her head down. Her blond hair had come partially loose. Her dun-grey uniform dress was filthy, wet to the skin, but he had never seen anything more beautiful than this angel of a woman.

"Well, my friend," she said, still breathing heavily, "there's nothing for it now but for me to leave you alone for a while."

His eyes opened wide as fear swept through him.

"No vultures will come up here, I'm quite sure," she said. "I saw only a few jackal tracks here when I first came up, and they won't bother you. You'll be all right. We do have to eat, and we do have to have water."

He nodded.

She had to make several trips to the ruined camp. In the end she was very tired, and there was still wood to gather for the fire, for it would be quite chilly with the coming of night.

Slone could hear her as she cut the dry brush. Once she sang softly, some song in Afrikaans. And then she was with him again, and a fire was burning, sending a clean, aromatic scent to the spot where Slone lay on a crude bed she had fashioned for him.

"Hungry?" she asked, as she heated a tin of bully beef.

He nodded.

When she came to feed him, she had not yet eaten. He wanted to protest, to tell her to eat first, then feed him, but he could not form the words. She smiled. "Open," she ordered, then stuffed his mouth with the tinned meat. "Courtesy of General Kitchener himself, British," she said. "Ambrosia."

Slone chewed and swallowed with difficulty, making a face.

"Perhaps you'd rather have your beef in a nice, moist roast, with Yorkshire pudding and gravy," she said.

"Un, un, un," he grunted, and to his pleasure he felt his lips move.

"Well, well," she said, "baby's first smile. There's hope for you yet, British."

He lifted both eyebrows and let his smile fade.

"You want to know what's wrong?" She put aside the beef tin. "You came quite close to death, British. A good Boer bullet took you here—" She indicated a spot above her temple. "It sort of glanced off your hard skull without penetrating it, and dug a trench all the way back to here through the scalp."

He nodded, lifting his brows again.

"I don't know," she said. "Head wounds are mysterious. According to what the doctor told me, I'm afraid there's a reasonable chance you'll be paralyzed from the neck down."

"Un, un, un," he grunted, looking down and up, down and up, with his eyes. She finally looked down. He wiggled the fingers on his right hand.

"Well, good for you," she said, reaching out to touch his hand. Her hand was so soft and warm. "Keep trying, British. I could use some help chopping wood."

He nodded.

"Now, if you don't mind, I'm very tired. You haven't been much help today, you know."

He shook his head and lifted one corner of his mouth.

"Are you ready to relieve yourself?" she asked.

Ready? Good God, he was more than ready. He felt his face glow with embarrassment; he wished for his strength but could do nothing.

"We have no spare clothing," she said, as she uncovered him, lifted his hospital gown. "Can't have you soiling what we have, can we?" She reached around, touched his rear end lightly. "This end?"

He shook his head.

"Good."

She used a stick to dig a hole near him, down at a level with his groin, rolled him over on his side. "Go," she said. You're no feather."

He felt intense relief as he emptied his bladder.

"Now, like the cat," she said, covering up the wet hole with dry dirt.

With the morning the Kaffirs came. Slone awoke in the mists of dawn and heard the sounds, twisted his neck—he seemed to have more freedom of movement—and looked down the slope. He saw dozens of blacks, men, women, and children. They were looting the wrecked camp, and thoroughly, too. A teenage boy threw a stone at a lurking jackal. The glutted vultures didn't even bother to fly unless directly threatened, but these men—they were of the Sekukini tribe—were not interested in vultures.

Opposite him, across the dead fire, the woman was stirring, her eyes barely open. "Un, un," he grunted. Then, "You, you." She raised her head to look about and silenced him with a "Hssss," like a snake, her eyes now darting back and forth warningly.

She turned and saw the Kaffirs. She sat up and reached for a rifle. "I see," she whispered. "I don't think we need worry. There's enough there to keep them busy."

They watched together as the Sekukini cut huge chunks of meat from a dead oxen and roasted it over open fires. "How can they eat with that stench?" Sianna asked, for even though the cave was over a hundred yards away and higher than the campsite, now and then the putrid smell of death reached them.

They remained in the cave all day, the presence of the Kaffirs restricting their movement. It was twilight before the last of them had gone, each individual laden with booty, much of it having little value. Two men carried away a broken wagon wheel that would be useless to them.

"I think we'd best do without a fire," she said.

He nodded.

"You seem to have more movement in your neck."

He noded vigorously and lifted his arm a few inches, wriggling his fingers happily.

"Ummm," she said.

He raised his eyebrows in question.

She could not tell him that the next two to three days would be a critical period for him. If, as she feared, the terrible blow of the bullet had irreparably damaged the brain matter . . . if some horrible area of swelling was, even now, crowding the grey matter of the brain up against the unyielding skull, or if the blow had caused internal bleeding to fill the brain gradually with blood, causing fatal pressure—

"How about a fresh meal of Victoria's finest, British?" she asked, coming to him with a tin of bully beef.

He made a face and grunted with distaste. "Blaaa!"

"I agree," she said, "but until we can get home to my kitchen where I shall ask Aunt Anna to make a fine roast duck and a great, huge cake—"

"Umm," he said.

"Well," she went on, "I'm not sure you're invited. You are, after all, the enemy."

He shook his head hard, in the negative.

"But you're British."

He shook his head.

"Oh, come now, don't lie."

He shook his head. He let his arm fall, trailed a finger in the dust beside his blankets. He could not see, but he drew a large A and then a U.

"A, U?" she read, a question in her voice.

He made two S marks.

"Auss—Aussie. You're Australian?"

He nodded vigorously.

"Even worse," she said. Sianna felt so strangely drawn to him, this "enemy." "For shame! The idea of one colonial coming to fight against another colonial!"

He shook his head. They were both smiling.

"You must be quiet now," she said. "Eat your food."

CHAPTER XXXVI

Although Emily Shannon, like her husband, Adam, had been born English, she was Australian through and through. Brought to Sydney by her parents, she had moved with Adam to Wellington, New Zealand, where she had spent many happy years. She thought that New Zealand was a beautiful country and that Wellington was a pleasant city, but upon Adam's retirement she had begun a gentle but persistent campaign to move the family to Australia. She had hoped to settle in or near Sydney, but when the late Claus Van Buren had told Adam of a sweet little place not far from Brisbane, and when Claus had described the house, she had fallen in love with the place without ever having seen it.

Emily had lived happily in Australia at The Shadows—the name she had chosen for the house, nestled in a stand of fine, tall trees—for several wonderful years. She now had only one concern: her son Slone.

Her husband, the retired general of the New Zealand militia, declared that she must be the leading Australian authority on the battles and skirmishes of the war that was being fought thousands of miles away on the southern tip of another continent. Emily had large maps of South Africa, and she had used coloured pins to chart the progress of Lord Roberts's march to Pretoria.

She did not complain about her son's choice of career. After all, she had married a military man, and she was familiar with the emptiness of waiting, with knowing from day to day that she might receive news of the death of a loved one. She did express some bitterness, briefly, when, with the enemy capitals in the hands of the British army and the war seemingly over, South Africa erupted yet again in the flames of battle in dozens of different areas.

"You'll need another set of coloured pins," Adam told her, as he began to realize, with some admiration for the Boer, what was happening. "What you're seeing, my dear, is a new kind of war. The Boer strikes quickly and then fades away into the wilderness."

"It's not fair," Emily said.

Adam laughed. "I suppose that would depend on one's point of view." He dug into a pile of magazines and newspapers beside his chair. It was evening at The Shadows, and he was pleasantly tired. Though retired, he was a vigorous, active man with no intention of stagnating. He had started to drove a few cattle, and droving cattle, he discovered, could keep the stiffness out of a man's bones.

When Adam found what he was looking for, he said, "Banjo Patterson has gained respect, if not admiration, for the Boer. Have you read this latest of his, called 'Johnny Boer'?"

Emily shook her head in the negative.

Adam read:

> "On rocks a goat could scarcely climb, steep as the walls of Troy,
> He wheels a four-point-seven about as easy as a toy;
> With bullocks yoked and drag-ropes manned, he lifts her up the rocks
> And shifts her every now and then, as cunning as a fox.
> At night you mark her right ahead, you see her clean and clear,
> Next day at dawn—'What, ho! she bumps'—from somewhere in the rear."

"Well, it seems to me that Johnny Boer should know when he's whipped," Emily said. "Would you like a cup of hot chocolate?"

"I would," Adam said.

When she returned with steaming mugs he said, before she could sit down again, "Em, I've been thinking. It's been a while since we were in the city. Care for a couple of days in Brisbane?"

"That would be lovely," she said. "I love our home, but it's good to get away now and again. Makes the coming home even sweeter."

"Been a long time since we've been down Sydney way," he said.

"Ah," she said. "You're curious about that grandson of yours, aren't you?"

"The lad writes an interesting letter," Adam said. "Here he is, only eighteen, and he tells me he's involved in building up a holding of several thousand acres in western New South Wales."

Emily mused for a moment. "It would be nice to see some old friends. I'm sure that if I wrote to Jessica Gordon, she'd invite us to stay with them. We could have some high old chats with Magdalen about old times." She came, sat on the arm of Adam's chair, and bent to kiss him. "Let's do go. You have your good Aboriginal foreman to look after the place. The house will be in excellent hands with Mama Toto." Mama Toto was a half-breed, Aboriginal and English, and a very dependable servant.

"Only if you'll pack for me," Adam said. Over the years of his military service he had found packing to be the most onerous of chores.

"You've struck a bargain," she said.

A few days later, when they were almost ready to travel, a cablegram came, at first terrifying Emily into a weakness that left her faint and breathless as Adam ripped it open.

"Is—it—Slone?" she gasped. Adam rattled the paper in his own nervousness. Bad news came by cablegram these days, for all too many Australian families. Bad news from South Africa.

"Oh, Adam, please—" she whispered.

"No, it's all right," he said, his face relaxing, his hand beginning to shake a bit in relief. "It's not about Slone at all."

She sank back. "Oh, my God," she said. "You must tell your business associates never, never to send a cable."

"It's my brother," Adam said.

She sat up. "I beg your pardon?"

He seldom mentioned his elder brother, the only other one who had survived their father; he had become the Earl of Cheviot upon the old earl's death.

He lowered the cablegram and a thin little smile came to his face. "My dear Countess," he said.

"Whatever are you talking about?"

His smile faded. "My brother, the Earl of Cheviot, is dead. This cablegram informs me that I am now the earl."

"Adam!"

"It's a bit ironic, isn't it?" he mused. "Here I am, a man with a past. I was drummed out of the Royal Navy. I was disowned by my father. I served as an ordinary soldier, then spent the rest of my life away from England. Now I'm a peer of the realm."

He sat down and tossed the cablegram on top of the stack of literature on his table.

Emily came to him. "I'd hardly call you an 'ordinary soldier,' my dear, or a 'man with a past.' After all, a man who rises like the Phoenix out of his so-called disgrace is hardly ordinary."

"You're just prejudiced on my behalf, my dear," he replied, sighing deeply. But she was right, of course. More than thirty years earlier, he had endured a naval court-martial, in which he had refused to defend himself rather than bring dishonour to Caroline Omerod—later Caroline Fisher—whose son he had sired. . . . His first Victoria Cross had been stripped from him, and he had left England, joining the army as a common soldier under the assumed name of Shannon. During the Maori Wars in New Zealand, he had brought honour to his new name, earning a field commission and a second Victoria Cross. Then his naval case had been reopened; a second court-martial had fully exonerated him, restoring to him his father's respect and love as well as his reputation, naval rank, and first VC. He could have lived comfortably in England, but he had met Emily in Australia and fallen in love with her; when he married her, he cast in his lot with the colonies of the Southern Hemisphere.

"I just can't believe it. I'm the last of my brothers; I'm glad my father did not live to see how few of his sons survived to old age. He wrote to me once that he had looked forward to having male grandchildren and regretted that not one of his sons produced any except me. So here we are. I have a title I never expected or wanted. It will be something for Slone, don't you think?"

Emily stirred. "I wonder how Jon would have felt, if he had lived to hear the news?"

He shook his head sadly. Though Adam's first son, Jon, born illegitimate, would not have been in line for the title, even if he had lived. "My guess is that Jon wouldn't have cared. Had the circumstances of his birth been . . . more propitious, he would have been the earl, and deserving of it, too. But I feel that fate has been kind in letting the title fall to the right son. Jon made his mark in a big way, after all, and he left his family better off than any of us. The Masons could buy us all five times over. No, Slone's the one who needs the advantage now, and I'd say it's a benign providence that put him in the way of it."

"Will you have to go to England?"

"I don't know, Em," he said. "Don't know what the proper form is. I'll write to Slone, of course. As heir to an earldom, he's a viscount now."

A thought occurred to her. "My God, if this had happened a bit sooner, Slone could have had at least the rank of major, perhaps colonel."

"I don't think that Slone would have wanted to buy his rank, any more than I would have wanted him to do so," Adam said.

"Well, they made the rules," Emily said. "My pride certainly won't stand in the way of Slone's gaining by playing with their own rules." She rose and paced the floor. "Yes, we will have to go to England. Now I know we're comfortable, and we're happy here, Adam, and once you have everything in hand we can come directly back here and you can play with your cattle or whatever. But we have to think of Slone. I think that this is news that he should have as quickly as possible."

"I think he'll be mildly interested," Adam said, a bit ironically.

"Oh, you!" She gave him a reproachful but loving nudge. She was thinking that Slone's new status would most certainly alter his military status, perhaps get him away from a field unit into a safe area.

"We won't stop in Sydney," she went on. "We'll go directly to Cape Town, and from there to England. Perhaps we can even take Slone with us. After all, he's done his share of fighting. If he were in Australian uniform, instead of British, he'd be due for home leave soon, anyhow."

"We can't tell Slone his duty, my dear," Adam said.

"But we'll *see* him," she said.

"South Africa is a big place," he said. "The last letter we had from him placed him up north, a long way from Cape Town."

"Please?" she begged.

"All right," he said, going to her to pat her on the shoulder.

"I'll have to repack everything," she said.

"Wait, wait," he said. "Don't try to take every piece of clothing in the house with you. After all, we've suddenly become quite rich. I think I'll be able to afford quite a little shopping spree for you once we're in London."

"I am going to enjoy this very much," she said, her face beaming.

On the third morning after being wounded Slone awoke with a raging headache. He had been moaning in his sleep, and when he opened his eyes the first thing he saw was the woman's face. She wore her professional look, an inexpressive smile.

"Are you in pain?" she asked.

"God, yes," he said, and his eyes widened, for the words had come from his lips with hardly any distortion. "Well, now," he whispered, grinning his lopsided grin in spite of the ache in his head.

"So," she said. "Where do you hurt?"

He lifted his right hand and once again he was amazed. He touched the soiled bandage. "There," he said.

"We'd better have a look."

She had salvaged some bandage and some disinfectant. She unwrapped his head carefully. The wound was scabbed over nicely. There was no sign of infection. She cleansed it and rebandaged it.

"Your name?" Slone asked.

"Sianna De Hartog."

"A nice name."

"It's a Boer name."

"I know. I'm the enemy."

She was silent as she opened yet another tin of bully beef for breakfast. "Can you move your legs?"

"I have more feeling in the legs," he said, straining. Only the toes of his right foot moved.

It was the third day, a time of crisis for head wound. He was in pain from a headache. Soon, perhaps, she would be alone, for if the brain was reacting to what Dr. Van Reenen called insult, he would go into a coma and soon his breathing would stop. She looked at his smiling, hopeful face and felt a surge of sympathy.

"Why am I able to talk so suddenly?" he asked.

She gave him a reassuring shrug. Her grey uniform was badly soiled and torn in several places. Her hair was tangled. There was a smudge of dirt on her face, but she was, he felt, a Madonna, an angel of mercy come out of nowhere. And he could tell there was a perfect beauty underneath the dirt and evidence of battle. "The brain is an odd thing," she said.

"Sianna."

"Yes?"

"You seem concerned."

"It's just that we are far from civilization." There was no need to worry him. He would live or he would die. It was in God's hands.

He slept, and when he awoke, she was coming back with an armload of firewood. He began to move his toes, willing his legs to work. She threw down the firewood, sighed, and sat down to rest.

From the north came the sound of running horses. She leapt to her feet, hoping, praying, that some of De La Rey's men were coming back.

Four white horsemen appeared, raising behind them a small cloud of dust out of which rode more than two dozen tribesmen in fast pursuit, many of them armed with captured Mausers. One of the white men was swaying in the saddle, possibly injured already, and as he did so, his mount fell behind. A black warrior drew back his arm and launched a spear. The spear overtook the trailing white, striking him in the back, and he toppled to the ground as his horse sped on.

In desperation the remaining three Boers halted, threw themselves off their horses, and sought the cover of a burned-out wagon. With rapid, accurate firing they knocked a half-dozen blacks from their saddles, but the other tribesmen rode in directly, leaping onto the Boers to bear them to the ground.

One of the Boers survived. He was seized, tied to a wagon tongue that had been planted upright in the ground, and then mercilessly tortured. His screams of pain came clearly to the cave throughout the long, hot afternoon.

"How can one human being do that to another?" Slone asked.

"Kaffirs are not really fully human," Sianna said. It was the Boer in her talking. "They are not fully developed, but lag far behind us in ability, intelligence, and morality."

Sianna was feeling tired and weak. She thought at first that her faintness was a reaction to being an unwilling witness to the torture of the man, but as the afternoon wore on, she realized that she was burning with fever. All she wanted to do was lie down on her bed and sleep, but she forced herself to move the stack of firewood close to Slone's bed, to place the food, the remaining canteens of water, and the blankets where he could reach them with his good arm.

"What are you doing?" he asked.

"I am coming down with fever," she said. "If it is typhoid fever, which is likely, you should know there's a good chance that I will die."

"What can I do?"

She placed medicines in a row up against the rock at the back of the cave where he could reach them. "I will need the white pill every four hours. We will have to estimate the time. If I should become comatose, bathing my face and torso with this alcohol might help."

"Yes," he said. "I can do that."

"I am very tired," she said. "I will help you to relieve yourself before I sleep."

She helped him, and when her hand touched his bare skin, it was burning hot. "You're like an oven," he said. She pushed him onto his back, arranged his cover, lay down beside him, and covered her lower body. He strained far over and put his right hand on her forehead. She felt almost hot enough to singe his skin.

By twilight the occasional pathetic screams of the Boer dying on the stake were weaker. Sianna lay in a stupor, not having moved since she had fallen asleep at mid-afternoon. Her fever raged. Slone tugged himself into position, opened the pill bottle with hand and teeth, poured out the prescribed two pills onto the edge of his blanket, and positioned the canteen before he put his hand on Sianna's shoulder and began to shake her gently while saying her name. Her eyes opened. She moaned but opened her mouth, took the pills, and drank greedily, spilling water down the neck of her uniform.

In the darkness the tortured Boer died. From where he lay, Slone saw, in the flaring red light of a huge bonfire, the tribesmen mutilate the body, remove inner organs, place oozy red things on spits, and roast them over the fire. He gagged when they started eating.

He slept and awoke with an inexplicable, unfocused feeling of guilt. He could see, below the overhang of the cave, a starry sky. The tribesmen's fire had burned out and no sounds came from the camp. He gave Sianna her pills by groping in the dark, and she drank greedily.

"How do you feel?" he whispered.

"I am so exhausted," she said, and was asleep again immediately.

With the dawn the tribesmen left the wrecked camp, leaving behind more food for the vultures. Sianna would not awaken for her pills. Slone shook her, spoke to her, begged her to wake up. She was limp, and she was consumed with inner fire. Her clothing was damp with sweat. It was time, he felt, to obey her instructions about the alcohol bath. He pulled himself closer with his right arm, which was gaining strength. He cursed his uncooperative legs, but managed to lift one of them so that he could be on his side. He found that today he had movement in his upper body.

It took him a long, long time to find the fasteners for her uniform and then to work the sodden garment down to her waist. The underthings were easier to manage. At first, he used the cooling, clean-smelling alcohol to swab away the sweat and accumulated dirt from her face, her forehead, her neck, taking care to avoid her eyes and mouth. Then he worked down to her upper chest, keeping her breasts covered. Her young, smooth skin was fair but flushed with fever; her breasts were rounded mounds under the soiled white linen of her underthings.

"Forgive me," he whispered, as he pushed the underthings down to expose her breasts. "You said to swab your torso, nurse." He tried to do the job without looking, but, handicapped as he was, it was impossible not to look. He saw pure white mounds, ruddy aureoles, sturdy nipples. He swabbed away the sweat, worked all around the white flesh of her breasts, swabbed across the nipples quickly and felt a surge of some strange, dark power, a shock, sympathy, or shame for her—for the manipulation of her nipples, innocent as it was, made them erect.

"I'm sorry, dear Sianna," he whispered. "I understand. It is not you that responds so."

When he had finished he was exhausted, fell back weakly after covering her with a blanket. He slept and woke to find that she had tossed the blanket off, exposing her nakedness from the waist up. Her skin still gleamed with perspiration. He managed to get her to swallow her pills, although she was not conscious, and began the hard work of the alcohol bath once more.

A strong odour told him that in her stupor she had wet her clothing. He thrust his hand down, felt the wetness. He knew desperation. He talked to his legs, cursed them, begged them, and struggled into a sitting position. He could move his left arm a bit, and the toes of his right foot would now give him leverage. Reduced to these circumstances, his mission in life was to be able to move enough to get Sianna out of her wet clothing. Nothing else mattered. Twice, three times, he fell back and had to struggle into the sitting position again. At last he had the sodden dress and undergarments removed, tucked a dry blanket beside her, and rolled her onto it. He swabbed her entire body with alcohol, keeping most of her covered as he worked. She had long, shapely, strong legs. There were scars on her right calf, two dimples on opposite sides of the fleshy, muscular part.

"Ah," he said, as he swabbed the leg with alcohol, "and what happens here, my nurse? Not a war wound. Too old. Not recent at all."

Exhausted, he sat looking down at her face. "Don't die, Sianna. Please don't die. It is not because of my own condition I beg you to live. You are so beautiful, so good. The world will be a far worse place without you, Sianna De Hartog. Live. Hang on. I will get you out of this wilderness if you'll fight, girl, if you'll just live!"

He exercised his toes, fought against the deadness in his legs. When he estimated that it was time for her to take her pills again, he could not get her to swallow them. He crushed them with a small rock in the lid of the canteen and dripped the mixture down her throat. She had wet the blanket again, but this time it was easier for him to put a fresh blanket under her. The wet ones had dried quickly in the dry, hot air of the afternoon. They smelled inevitably of smoke and urine, but they were dry and would do. He slept.

Her voice awoke him. She was tossing fretfully beside him, speaking in Afrikaans. He caught a few words. She was calling out to Aunt Anna. He recognized the word meaning cold, and put his hand on her shoulder. She still burned, but she was shaking. Her teeth started to chatter. He took his own blanket and put it over her, and still she shivered, calling out to Aunt Anna that she was so cold.

Slone dragged himself close and tucked the blankets around her. She began to shake so severely that it frightened him. In such convulsions men had broken bones. "Easy," he whispered. He put his arm across her, tried to hold back her severe jerkings and shakings.

"Cold," she kept repeating. "So cold, Aunt Anna."

He somehow found the strength to edge himself under the blanket with her. He struggled to drag his remaining blanket over both of them, then turned and pulled himself close, working his right arm under her so that he could lift and turn her to face him. Then he pressed his body to hers to give her his own warmth. She was shivering so violently that he could not hold her close to him for long, for his arms grew tired. With grunting difficulty he positioned her on her back and drew himself on top of her. He was panting with exhaustion when he had accomplished his purpose, which was to put his warmth and his weight on her, to try to keep her violent spasms under control.

After an indeterminate time her trembling began to subside, to his relief. He felt dizzy and weak from his exertions, and as she relaxed, her teeth no longer chattering, his strength failed completely. He slept with Sianna's body warm and quiet under him.

He awoke to a dream of youthful power, an erotic energy. The dream, he discovered, was quite real; a lovely, full-bodied woman lay under him. He jerked into wakefulness. His manhood, aroused, was pressed firmly into an astonishing softness. With a start he raised his head. Sianna slept. She did not seem so hot now. But there was dampness, warm moistness there, below, and to his shock he realized that in his sleep he had penetrated her and was lodged deeply inside her.

"Oh, my God," he whispered, struggling away, tossing aside blankets with guilt. He covered her and sat looking down at her face. Still unconscious, she was no longer sweating. "Oh my God, please forgive me. I didn't—I wouldn't. You saved my life. I wouldn't—"

It was time for her pills. He pulled down his hospital gown and set about the task. They were down to the last canteen of boiled water. She roused when he shook her shoulder and called her name, her eyes flickering open. He lifted her head and she swallowed the pills and drank eagerly.

"There now," he said, "you'll soon be much better."

She was staring into his eyes. "How long?" she whispered.

"One day, two nights," he said.

Her lips moved in the semblance of a smile. "You're sitting up."

"Yes."

"You will live now."

"Did you doubt it?"

"Very much," she said. "When the headache started on the third day. Head wound. Thought you would—"

She closed her eyes and slept, but her skin was cool. When he next awoke she was leaning back against the wall of the cave, a blanket clutched up around her chin. "So we have no secrets from each other now, you and I," she said, with a wry smile.

"Your clothes were wet," he said.

"Yes, I know. I see that you've spread them to dry."

"Yes, they're dry."

"May I have the chemise and the—ah—the lower garment, please."

He began to crawl.

"I'm sorry," she said. "Stupid of me to forget. I'll get them."

"No. Don't move," he said. "I too am getting much better. I can move the right leg now. I need the exercise."

He turned his back while she pulled on the chemise and put her legs into the bloomers. She was weak and spent when she told him he could turn around. She did not bother to hold the blanket up to her chin, and her breasts were pert and nubile under the chemise.

"Do you think you can eat?" he asked.

"How many horses?" she asked, smiling.

"For all I know it may be horsemeat," he said, as he served the bully beef cold. "We've often wondered."

"The last thing I remember is the screams of that poor man down there," she said.

"They're gone now. They ate him. At least his internal organs."

"Yes. His heart, to capture his courage, most probably."

"My God," he said.

"It's a lovely country, my country," she said.

"Sooner or later," he said, "we're going to have to cross a good portion of it on foot."

She nodded. "Presents a dilemma, doesn't it, British?"

"My name is Slone Shannon," he said. "And I am Australian."

"Yes, I remember. But the question is, Slone Shannon, when we are fit to move away from here, which way shall we travel? To the north or west, where we will no doubt find Boer commandos? To the south or east, where we will find the British?"

"Does it really matter, so long as we get you to a doctor who can treat you?" he asked.

"Oh, yes, it matters," she said. "If we find the British first, then I am for a concentration camp. That will not be too bad, for I can be of use there. If we find a Boer unit first, then you are for a prison laager, and although we treat our prisoners humanely, it will not be pleasant."

"We have time to talk about all of this. We needn't decide now," he said.

"Have you seen any sign of Kaffirs?" she asked, changing the subject.

"No."

"I think then that we might risk a fire tonight. I dreamed that I was so cold."

"You were. You were having severe chills."

She nodded. "Can you manage the fire?"

He managed. As darkness came he had a cheery little blaze going in the fire hole dug down into the soft sand of the cave floor. As always the temperature began to drop with nightfall. They had a meal of warmed bully beef. Neither of them had been talkative during the late afternoon. Sianna was still weak and craved water. She had stopped drinking, however, when she realized that they were down to their last canteen.

"Drink it," Slone said.

"You are not able to go to the water hole," she said. "Perhaps I will be tomorrow. Then I can drink my fill, after we find some container over there in which to boil it."

"All right," he said.

He had not moved his bed from its position near hers. They lay near each other, watching the fire as it burned low. From across the valley came the bark of a jackal. The moon was visible low on the horizon. She was talking quietly about her home, about her Aunt Anna, and about her father.

"He sounds like a good man," Slone said. "It's easy to see, with men like him, why the Boers give us such a fight in the field."

"He didn't want this war."

"Someday, Sianna, when this thing is over, I'd like to meet him."

"I think you'll like him."

"To have a daughter like you, he has to be a fine person."

She laughed. "My cheeks are burning."

He jerked his head towards her.

"Not with fever," she said, "with embarrassment at such compliments."

Clouds moved in, covering the moon. The rain came suddenly, with vast upheavals of thunder and lightning that lit the desolate camp on the other side of the water hole.

"This will put more water in the pool," Sianna said. "If only we had something right here to catch the rain—"

A chill came with the rain. The fire was burning low. Slone tugged the blanket up around his neck. Sianna had been quiet for a long time. The rain had slacked off to a chill drizzle.

"Slone."

"Yes."

"I'm cold."

He sat up, removed his top blanket and spread it over her.

"No, that won't do," she said. "Now you will be cold."

"That's all right. I can wrap up in this one."

"There is no reason for both of us to be shivering," she said. She raised the edge of her blankets, inviting him under. "Come."

He hesitated, remembering with burning guilt how his body had betrayed him, and her, in his sleep.

"Come," she repeated, "together two can be warm."

He edged himself under the covers with her, then put his remaining blanket over them. "There, that's better," she said, snuggling her flank against his.

"Much," he said. "Just don't tell that fierce Boer father of yours about this."

"Shall I not tell him, then, how you warmed me with your body when I was having chills?" she asked softly.

Startled, he turned towards her. He could see just the suggestion of her nose, the faint gleam of firelight off her cheek. "You remember?"

"Yes," she whispered, turning to press her softness against his side, her arm exploring across his chest, her lips close to his neck so that when she spoke he felt the caress of her breath. "I remember."

"Everything?"

She pulled herself on top of him. She was a sturdy girl, but slender through the waist. Her breasts were heaving softly as she pressed herself to him and her lips found his. With one hand she was pushing down at her lower garment, then, naked to him, mouth still fixed on his, she positioned herself, moved frantically, learning as she experimented until—

Feeling himself engulfed in her loveliness, enlivened by her heat, he whispered. "My God, Sianna!"

"It was not you," she whispered. "It was I. You were exhausted, I suppose, sound asleep. And you were so warm. I couldn't press myself close enough to you until—"

"I have been in love with you, I think, from the first time that I opened my eyes and saw your face."

"Thank the good God for that," she whispered. "And may God forgive us, for you were sleeping and I was burning with chills and fever."

He lay on his back. She sprawled across his chest, her cheek in the hollow of his neck and shoulder. "We will find a Boer unit," he said. "Actually, I think I've had enough of this war. We are very much like, aren't we, British and Boer?"

"Oh?"

"Obstinate, a bit self-righteous, and too proud for our own good."

"You have said that, not I," she said.

"But isn't it true?"

"I would say yes, that the heads of British men can be as hard as the heads of the most loyal Boer. Australians? I don't know. Maybe Australians can be more sensible. Some of our young men learned early. I hear them tell Louis Botha *huis-toe*, we are going home. Can you say it?"

"*Huis-toe,*" he said.

"Good. We will find neither side, Boer nor British. We will go to my home near Pietermaritzburg. I will tell my Aunt Anna that you have deflowered me, and she will take my father's old fowling piece down from the gun rack and force you to marry me."

"Pietermaritzburg? That's all the way—"

"I know, it's far," she said. "But together we will go there."

At that moment, being young, having her clinging to him, her lower body urging him to excitement, he could believe anything she told him. "Do you know what it's called in Australia when people do what you're going to have done to you if you don't quit wiggling yourself against me?"

"No, tell me."

"It's called to have a naughty."

She giggled. "Naughty, naughty," she whispered, as he used new-found strength and freedom of movement to turn her onto her back. She reached for him with open arms.

There came a time when it was necessary for Sianna to go down the slope, past the water hole, and into the ruins of the hospital train. The latest dead, the four Boers who had been chased into the valley by the tribesmen, were nothing more than scavenger-scattered bones, but the stench of death hung over the place. Luckily, she found a kettle almost immediately. Their water at the cave was gone. Now, with the kettle, she could boil the muddy, stinking water from the sump. To drink it without boiling would have been to invite a fatal onslaught of typhoid fever. She then turned her attention to clothing for Slone. The wreckage of the burned wagons had been well plundered by the blacks, and all she found were some scraps of canvas.

When he recovered enough to walk, Slone's most pressing need would be shoes. To try to make the trek without shoes from the Megaliesberg towards Pretoria, nearest point of civilization, would be foolhardy. But all footwear had been looted. She found well-gnawed pieces of oxhide, toughened in the sun, and carried them back to the cave with her. Together they cut the oxhide into shape, punched holes at the right places, and strung straps of oxhide to fashion a crude pair of sandals.

Slone went outside the cave for the first time, using a crutch that

Sianna had salvaged from the hospital wreckage. His movement was slow and painful, but he managed to get about. He felt better, more like a man, when he hobbled back with two sticks of firewood in his right hand.

Sianna laughed at him. "You look like Robinson Crusoe," she said. She had fashioned a sort of cape for his shoulders out of a piece of stiff canvas and a canvas kilt to cover his lower body. His hat was a piece of canvas sewn into a bowl.

They spent three days in preparation, making another trip to the ruined hospital to come away with a British service revolver that had been hidden under burned debris. Slone was doubtful that it would fire after being exposed to such heat, but it was a comfort nonetheless. Most of the time was spent gathering firewood to boil enough water to fill four canteens for each of them.

Slone was walking with only a slight limp when they left the water hole laden with the canteens, the remainder of the bully beef, their blankets, an axe, a sewing kit, and Sianna's medical bag. When they had climbed out of the bowl of the valley and reached the crest of the ridge, they halted and looked off to the east, each of them awed and discouraged by the vista that lay before them: an expanse of veld shimmering in the heat, distant kopjes, the huge raw sky, and the burning sun. Pretoria was over a hundred miles away. With a confidence that he did not truly feel Slone said, "Piece of cake, mate." He started walking.

They slept in a dry camp that night, arms entwined. From a distance a lion coughed, and Slone spent long, sleepless hours with the service revolver in his hand. The lions did not disturb them.

The next day fate favoured them. Vultures were circling ahead of them, and Sianna said that they could be marking the kill of the lion they had heard in the night. Slone approached warily, using a ridge for cover. He observed that within the past few days, a running skirmish had been fought on a little plain between two hills. The scavenger-picked bones of the dead showed the uniforms of a British cavalry outfit and the drab clothing of the Boers. Slone found a pair of good British boots that were only slightly too large for him, a Martini-Henry rifle with plenty of ammunition, and— blessing of blessings—horses grazing near a water hole. Horses! They were saddled and trained and perhaps a bit lonely for human company, for they made no effort to escape when Slone drew near to them. Soon Sianna and he were riding sturdy Boer mounts. It made a world of difference. Each of them admitted privately that now there really was hope; only desperation had driven them onwards before.

Slone, dressed now in a mixture of clothing—Boer homespun shirt and jacket, British trousers, and floppy Boer hat, looked as nondescript as any Boer burgher who had had enough of war and had decided to go home. Seeing him thus made Sianna begin to wonder if, after all, they could not reach home without having to surrender to either Boer or British fighting unit.

"If I bandaged you well, so that the lower part of your face was hidden, your mouth covered so that you could not speak, you could pass for a Boer."

"Sianna, I don't want to be captured and shot as a spy," he said. "Nor do I want to be picked up by my own side as a deserter."

"You said you would take me home," she said.

"I said that, Sianna, and I will. I think I'd still have some small influence with Kitchener. I'm one of his boys. I could—"

"They would not listen to you," she said. "They would send you to a hospital to see why you still limp slightly, and they would send me to a camp."

"Sianna, it's crazy."

"No, not at all. It's just a crazy war." She pointed. "There is Pretoria. Just to the south is Johannesburg. Both are in British hands. Many Boers surrendered during the battle for Johannesburg and for Pretoria. I know, because I saw. And when they surrendered, the British asked them to give up their rifles, to make a pledge that they would not fight again. Then they were told to go home, to work their crops, and keep the peace. You will be just another Boer who has surrendered. And I will be your sister—"

"My wife," he said, grinning. "My wife or I don't go."

"Your wife," she agreed. "Your wife who is taking you home to heal your horrible wound and put you back to work on the farm until your back aches and your hands have blisters."

"Am I to spend the rest of my life with such a cruel wench?" he bellowed to the cloudless sky.

"You say yes?"

"I could never say no to you." He sobered. "But once I get you home, Sianna, I will have to report to army headquarters, probably in Durban."

"We'll see," she said.

When they saw the first of several British units that they would pass before reaching the railroad south of Pretoria, Slone threw away the Martini-Henry. He was not keen on being seen by British soldiers carrying a British weapon, while partially dressed in Boer clothes. Men had been shot for less. They were questioned several times, and Sianna did the talking. He told her after the first questioning that she was the *slim* one, the word in Afrikaans meaning clever or sly. She told the British interrogators that Slone, her husband, had fought with De La Rey, had been wounded, captured, treated well enough by British surgeons, then paroled to go home in her company. She herself had been a cook for a Boer hospital unit. With her fine, shapely body hidden in a bulky hodgepodge of clothing, a mixture of men's and women's rags, with her hair tied inside a dirty cloth, a man would have had to examine her face closely to see that she was young and quite pretty.

When they reached the railway, they sold the horses, garnering just enough money to buy tickets to Pietermaritzburg. Trains were running regularly in the British-held territories. They also sent a cablegram to Slone's parents in Queensland. The cable said in couched terms that in spite of what his parents might have been told by the military authorities, their son was alive and well and would be in touch with them again soon. Slone had been worried over the possibility that his parents had been notified mistakenly that he was either missing or dead.

South of Johannesburg, as the train steamed along, the countryside seemed calm, but there was guerrilla war to the northeast, the southwest, and the northwest. Botha, De Wet, De La Rey.

They passed Volkrust, Dundee, Elandslaagte, and Ladysmith. The once-besieged city was passed in the night, with only a brief stop. Colenso, Frere. Was there still a war on? At last they reached Pietermaritzburg. It was only a few miles then from the city to the De Hartog farm. They walked it proudly hand in hand, ragged, dirty, smelly but lost in themselves, very much in love, and content together.

Anna De Hartog was called to the front door by a household servant. She saw two beggars, grimy and in tatters.

"Aunt Anna," the female beggar said, "I want you to meet the man I'm going to marry. His name is Slone Vincent Shannon."

CHAPTER XXXVII

In her younger days Jessica Gordon had survived the eruption of the volcano on Krakatoa in the Dutch East Indies; she had been washed about by a titanic tidal wave and had struggled through the ensuing ash storms with her lungs aching and with burns from the hot ash over much of her body. And she had lived to give birth to a healthy girl child, the child named for the place of her birth, Java. Jessica was not a fragile woman. Still, when she accepted the envelope from the hands of a messenger boy and opened it to see her daughter's handwriting, she read only a few sentences before the blood drained from her face and she crumpled on the carpet, senseless.

Sam found her there only moments later, lifted her to a sofa, patter her cheeks, and shouted to the servants for cool clothes and a doctor. When Jessica's eyes opened she said, "I had but one daughter, and now she is gone."

A desolation of fear froze Sam. He tore the letter from his wife's hand and read. His daughter was not dead, thank God.

Married! She was a few months short of seventeen years old and she was married to Tolo Mason. Sam read on.

By the time you receive this we will be aboard ship, travelling to a place where you can't reach us, for I cannot be sure that you would not use the laws that would allow you to have our marriage set aside. Since I could not accept such a decision, I therefore take myself reluctantly away from you for a period of time. How long, Mother, Father, might just depend on you. How I wish we could all be together happily. At some later date, when we are at a safe distance, I will communicate with you and tell you where you might write to me, should you care to do so. Know that you have my love, now and always.

"They are, of course, going to the Mason cattle station in
Victoria, near Melbourne," Jessica said. "I'm sure of it. We have
to go after them, Sam. We must hurry."

"No," Sam said softly. "No, we will not go after them, Jess."

Jessica tried to sit up. He put his hands on her shoulders and
eased her back down. "Rest for a few minutes," he said. "You have
said, Jess, that by marrying Tolo, Java would cut herself off from a
good portion of Australian society. Do you really want to pursue a
course of action that will cut her off from us, too, perhaps
forever?"

"But Sam—"

"Jessica, it's done. They're man and wife by now. Can't you
imagine the anguish she went through in making this decision?"

"It seems to me," Jessica retorted, "that she made it rather
lightly, in haste and without any thought for our pain."

"No," he insisted. "Read that letter again. You'll see her pain in
every line." He bent and put his arms around her. "Jess, we're old
folks at home now. Our one chick has tried her wings, found them
to be fully feathered, and has flown. I think, my dear, that the work
you've done so far towards packing for a trip should not be
wasted. I think Mr. and Mrs. Sam Gordon will leave as scheduled
for Scotland, London, and possibly points of interest on the
Continent, such as Paris."

"Sam, I couldn't leave, not knowing—"

"Even if we wanted to find her, Jess, I doubt if we could.
Australia's a big bloody chunk of earth. If we were standing at
Ayers Rock, it would be at least a thousand miles in any direction
to the sea."

"We could have the authorities stop them at Melbourne."

"If, indeed, they are going to Melbourne. Remember that young
Tolo has ready cash at his disposal. They could take ship for
anywhere in the world and live comfortably once there. Suppose
they did go to Melbourne. First of all, it's not at all certain that we
could cut through the intercolony red tape in time to stop them
before they disappeared into the interior or elsewhere on the
ocean. And are you certain, Jess, that you'd want to have them
hauled in by the law and held until we could get there?"

Jessica was weeping quietly. Sam held her hands, sure in his own
mind that Java and Tolo were going to one of two places. They

would go either to Tolo's new landholdings in the far west of New South Wales or to Western Australia. His best guess was Western Australia, for neither Tolo nor Java was stupid. They would be aware that their parents could take legal action against a marriage of underage children, and they would realize that to stay in New South Wales would make it simpler for family or the law to interfere. No, Sam thought, they were heading for Western Australia, and once they ventured away from the coastal cities— Perth, or one of the smaller Towns such as Geraldton, or, farther north, Roebourne—then the vastness of the outback would swallow them up. He did not voice his guess to Jessica, knowing that she would worry. It bothered him a bit, thinking of Java wandering about in the Great Sandy Desert.

"Tolo, my boy." He formed the words carefully in his mind, and his eyes squinted with the intensity of conviction. "Tolo, you'd better bloody well take care of her."

The new Earl of Cheviot and his lady were enjoying a luxurious crossing of the Indian Ocean aboard a new White Star liner, where the first-class service rivalled what one could expect in the finest London hotel. To the agent arranging their passage, Adam had given his name as General Adam Shannon, Retired, and that was enough to ensure the best treatment. But when Emily, with a twinkle in her eye, let it be known to the steward that the general was General Lord Cheviot, the bowing and scraping caused Adam to scowl and Emily to giggle.

There were no current newspapers aboard ship, of course, and although steam had cut the travel time between Australia and Cape Town, there was a stretch of days during which Adam and Emily were contentedly out of touch with the world and the war. Upon arrival in Cape Town they were rapidly settled into a hotel, and Adam had the recent newspapers brought up to their suite.

For an old military man like Adam, the Boer War had become quite an interesting campaign. He thought he detected some rather ominous hints in dispatches from the various British Army headquarters in the field, and he wanted to talk to someone in authority who was familiar with the policies that lay behind enigmatic statements from the commanders, Roberts and Kitchener. The huge British Army was able to move at will, of course, but Roberts's assertion that the Transvaal was now a British Colony seemed to have little effect on the hit-and-run tactics of the Boer leaders, Koos De La Rey and General De Wet.

First things first, however. Leaving Emily in the hotel to rest, he took a hansom cab to British Army headquarters in Cape Town, announced himself as General Adam Shannon, Retired, and was quite quickly admitted to the office of a stern-faced colonel. A retired general, even of colonial forces, was *always* shown the utmost courtesy by *any* serving officer above the rank of captain, for as sure as the earth turned, one day the serving officers, too, would be retired, hopefully as generals, and they would want to be treated with respect and some little partiality.

"General Shannon," said the tall, stern colonel, "welcome to South Africa and to headquarters, Cape Town. I am Roland Streeter. How can I serve you, sir?"

Adam smiled, nodded, and returned an honorary and informal salute. "Well, Colonel," he said, "I most certainly don't want to get underfoot and hold up the works of this headquarters. I'm on my way to London, with an indefinite stopover in Cape Town for the purpose of seeing my son. That's my primary reason for coming to you, sir, to ask you to locate my son and, if he's not too deep in the veld somewhere, to whisk him down here by train for a quick kiss on the cheek from his mother."

"I see no problem there, sir," Streeter said.

"I'm also bloody curious about the success of this new Boer tactic," Adam said. "Reading between the lines, Colonel, it apears that Johnny Boer has the British Army stumbling around the veld like a blind elephant chasing mice."

Streeter chuckled. "A good analogy, that," he conceded, "with a good deal of uncomfortable truth in it. The Boer knows the ground, General. He has certain advantages. He most probably lives quite near the target that he and the other members of his commando unit will strike. He unhitches his oxen from the plough, saddles his horse, rides a few miles and strikes in the night or in the grey light of dawn, and then he rides back and hitches up his oxen and does a day's ploughing. The hard-core cadre of Boers who march with De La Rey and De Wet are veterans of many battles. They can move fifty miles in a night. They know every cleft in the rocks, every hole large enough to conceal one man and a horse."

"And have Generals Roberts and Kitchener come up with a counter-strategy?" Adam asked.

"One of the problems, as I told you sir, is that the Boer can simply break off the fight at a time of his choosing and go home to give the appearance of a peaceful farmer. While he's fighting, the women and those too young to fight grow food for him, and they supply it to him. General Roberts has given orders to deprive the Boer of this easy source of support."

"He's going to burn the farms and destroy the crops?" Adam asked.

"Scorch the earth," Streeter replied.

"I see. How terrible," Adam said.

"But necessary. There are also plans being formulated to make the rail lines into barriers to break up the Boer's freedom of movement. Our engineers are erecting blockhouses along the lines. These will be impervious to rifle fire and fairly strong against artillery—which the Boer has less and less of these days, in any case. Interlocking fences and overlapping fields of fire will supply total protection."

Adam sighed. "Well, Colonel, it sounds as if this war is going to drag on for some time still. Perhaps I'd better see my son as soon as it can be arranged, for it looks as if he's going to be busy in South Africa for an indefinite time."

Streeter picked up a pen. "His name and rank?"

"Slone Vincent Shannon, Lieutenant," Adam said. "When I last had a letter from him, he was with the Queensland Mounted Infantry moving north into the Transvaal."

To that moment Streeter had not connected the retired general with the young man who had so persistently courted his daughter, though both were named Shannon. Colonel Streeter's face blanched as he wrote down the name.

Adam was instantly aware of the change in the colonel's attitude. When Streeter next spoke, his voice took on the distant, aloof tone of the British aristocracy. Even his accent had altered. "General Shannon, I imagine you are aware that South Africa is a vast area, and that our units are scattered over rather considerable distances."

"I am aware of the potential difficulties," Adam said. "And yet I would hope that the British Army, even in so broad an area of manoeuvre, has the facilities and the skill to keep its separated units in communication with one another." To his amusement, Adam had let the old Pom accent creep into his own voice, and he looked down his nose at Streeter just as haughtily as Streeter had looked down at him.

"I can only send out an inquiry through channels," Streeter said. "It will, of course, take some time. The regular business of this army will take priority over any such messages."

Adam was a bit puzzled. For some obscure reason this Pom colonel's eagerness to please a retired general had reversed itself to stiff antagonism.

"Perhaps," Streeter went on, "you will not want to wait in dreary Cape Town for the weeks, even months, that it will take to locate your son."

"Colonel," Adam said, going against his own inclinations, but thinking of Emily, who had so set her heart on seeing Slone, "far be it from me to ask you to set aside urgent army communications traffic." He smiled. "But you and I both know, Colonel, don't we, that the great bulk of communications traffic is bloody claptrap—"

Streeter's face was reddening. He began to rise from his chair, opening his mouth to interrupt.

"—and we both know that if you put on the communications network the fact that General Lord Cheviot, Adam Shannon, wants to see his son, the word will be sent to every unit in the British Army."

The words were sinking through to Streeter. "I say, excuse me, but you are Lord Cheviot, the Earl of Cheviot?"

"I don't like to have to throw my rank around, Colonel," Adam said.

"I can understand, sir."

Roland Streeter's mind was working furiously. *Bloody hell, why didn't that young fool, Slone, tell them that he was the son of a peer of the realm?* Until now, Streeter would not have mourned in the slightest had he seen Lieutenant Slone Shannon's name on the casualty lists. Now things were altogether different. If he had known that the lieutenant was of such illustrious stock . . . *Oh, God, what if, in my ignorance of the boy's parentage, I have lost a chance for Kit to be the wife of a future earl?*

But perhaps it was not too late. He smiled. "Lord Cheviot—"

"I prefer 'General Shannon', if you please."

"General Shannon, may I assure you that every effort will be made to locate your son, and to have him entrained immediately for Cape Town. In the meantime, sir, I would be honoured if you would have dinner tonight with me and my daughter."

"My wife, sir, is resting from the rigours of travel," Adam said. "I accept your kind invitation, but beg you to bring your daughter and join us as our guests in the hotel dining room."

"My pleasure," Streeter said quickly. He wondered why the earl had not mentioned Slone Shannon's interest in his daughter. A horrible fear entered his mind. Had Slone been merely toying with Kit? No, impossible. He had seen the hangdog look on his young face. He could recognize it when a young swain was in love.

But why hadn't the earl mentioned the fact that Slone wanted to marry Kit Streeter?

None of this became clear until that evening, when he walked into the hotel dining room with his daughter on his arm and joined Adam and Emily at table.

Kit wore black, for it went well with her large green eyes and her sunset hair. She was frightfully nervous.

As her father introduced her to the earl and countess, Kit felt her gloved hands taken in the countess's. "You are truly beautiful, child," Emily Shannon said. "I can see why my son is so much in love with you."

"I am so pleased to meet you," Kit whispered. She was still quaking inside as Adam Shannon came to her and put his lips within a quarter of an inch of the back of her hand.

"Forgive me, I didn't make the connection this morning, Colonel Streeter," Adam said as he helped Kit into her chair. "I knew that Slone has been raving about a young lady ever since he was in Egypt, but I had let the name slip my mind."

Kit heard her father breathe an audible sigh of relief. Astounded by the new turn of events, she felt a bit of resentment towards her father. He had been so much against her interest in Slone until he learned that Slone's father was the Earl of Cheviot. She knew that on some level his turnabout was shameful. And yet Kit knew she would have been willing to accept almost any event that made it possible for her to marry Slone. She watched Slone's parents as they spoke with her father. They were indeed a striking couple. Mrs. Shannon was a lovely woman, and Slone's father, like Slone, was so handsome, so dashing, so impressive. Kit felt sure now that God loved her and was rewarding her for her patience and her faith.

Kit went through an unnerving moment when, for the first time, she heard her father tell a comparative stranger the deep, dark secret, that his wife was slowly going mad because of a mysterious growth in her brain. "Apart from the war," Streeter said, "that is the main reason why the two young people are not already betrothed," he said.

Kit squirmed with seething anger. To see her father toady to an earl, offering her in marriage as if she were a gift wrapped in exchange not for Slone, the man who had beggered her to defy her parents, but for a mere title, for the favour of a man of position and power. She had an urge to run from the dining room, but Emily Shannon's attention held her there. Emily soothed her and began to draw out the little facts, the memories, the stories that gave an individual dimension and depth.

"When did you last hear from our Slone?" Emily asked.

"Oh, just two weeks ago. The mail service is actually quite good, unless the Boers have temporarily cut the railway line somewhere. He was pleased to be moving north with an Australian unit—"

"Yes, I know," Emily said. "The Queensland unit."

"—and he was telling me about his best friend, a Lieutenant Matt Van Buren."

"Joseph Van Buren's son?" Emily asked.

"I'm not sure," Kit put in. "But he's from a Queensland cattle ranch—or station as I think you Australians call them."

"Then I think it has to be Joseph's son," Emily replied. She turned to her husband. "Adam, listen to this. Slone is in the same unit with Joseph Van Buren's son, Matt."

"As I remember him, a fine boy," Adam said. "Sturdy little six-year-old when last I saw him."

It was a pleasant evening. When Emily asked Kit to spend the next afternoon with her, perhaps to take her on a shopping tour, Kit at first demurred, citing her obligations to her mother. But Streeter interrupted, assuring everyone that the nurse could be induced to come in early, and Emily said she would call for Kit in a carriage around two.

Colonel Roland Streeter left the hotel a happy man. He had never wanted a daughter; he had prayed, instead, for a son, because a son can be steered into the proper pathways. With a daughter, a man in Streeter's position had to spend more money than was readily available on education and training in the skills of society, the dance, and music. And if, as Streeter had done, a father sent his girl to a fine ladies' finishing school, the expenses called for considerable sacrifice of living standards at home. After all that he had done for his daughter, all this sacrifice, she had wanted—or so it seemed at the time—to throw it all away on a backwoodsman from the colonies. But, thank God, a diamond in the rough, the son of an earl!

Streeter was in his office early the next morning, and soon the communications systems leading out of Cape Town towards the various army groups in the north carried an "Urgent-Urgent" message to locate Lieutenant Slone Shannon of the Queensland Mounted Infantry, to implement travel orders for him, and to have him report to Cape Town headquarters as soon as possible.

As it happened, Colonel James Westlake's official account of the Megaliesberg campaign reached Colonel Streeter's desk at midmorning the next day. Streeter would have preferred news of Slone's return to Cape Town. He opened the envelope, noted that the report concerned the Queensland Mounted Infantry, and fearfully began to scan the alphabetical list of casualties and those who were assumed to have been captured by De La Rey's commandos.

Shannon, Slone Vincent, Lieutenant Royal Engineers, missing, feared dead.

For a long moment Streeter could not move. Then he began to read the attached operations report. He had read enough battle reports to be able to see through Westlake's verbosity, his self-serving explanations, to the ineradicable fact that once again a British officer had sent a goodly number of men into an untenable situation. Streeter initiated steps immediately to have Westlake's report deleted from the records lest the Earl of Cheviot examine them and discover a flagrant example of British incompetency in dealing with Australian troops.

At first Streeter thought that he himself would inform the earl and his wife of their son's heroic actions and his probable death. Further reflection led him to a different plan.

Streeter wanted to learn all there was to know about the action at Zilikiat's Nek, and he knew that he would have a devil of a time getting a straight story from Westlake. He was fully aware of the Australians' growing contempt for "Pommy" officers. Perhaps he would get down to the truth, even if somewhat biased, if he could talk with one of the colonials who had been involved in the action. And although it was now too late for his daughter to be a countess, perhaps he could do one last service for the earl and his wife. He would let them hear about their son's death from the lips of a friend of Slone's.

There was a bit of risk, to be sure, in letting the earl and countess talk directly with an Australian officer who had been present when Colonel Westlake sent their son into a death trap. Streeter believed he could control the situation by interrogating the Australian officer ahead of time; only if it seemed safe would the bereaved parents be given the opportunity to speak to him.

Lieutenant Matt Van Buren led a patrol of the Queensland Mounted Infantry into a pretty little glen dominated by a well-built Boer farmhouse. He was tautly alert as he dismounted and approached a Boer woman who had come to the porch of the house. He checked a list, confirmed the woman's name, and asked for the man of the house.

"He is away," the woman said.

"We have information that your husband fights with Koos De La Rey," Matt said.

"That is not true. My husband was captured in the battle before Pretoria, and given his parole. He is merely away hunting for game, for meat."

"Then you have no objections to our searching the property," Matt said. The woman was obviously nervous, and the careful search, which yielded three Mauser rifles, two British Martini-Henry rifles, and a quantity of ammunition, as well as foodstuffs commonly used by the Boers as field rations, sealed the fate of the pleasant house, its outbuildings, and the surrounding crops. When the mounted infantry rode away, the buildings were irreversibly ablaze; the crops, too, were burning, the oxen confiscated to be added to the herd at the British bivouac, and the woman and her children on their way to one of the internment camps where noncombatant Boers—women, children, and old people were being "concentrated".

The humane treatement the Boers received in the camps was made less than impressive by the fact that most of them were there as the result of the new scorched-earth policy. Few of these Boer civilians realized that they were being held there to prevent them from giving aid and comfort to the Boer commandos.

When Matt's scouting party returned to the main camp, he was summoned immediately to the tent of the commanding officer, where Colonel Westlake told him that he was ordered to Cape Town immediately to report directly to Colonel Roland Streeter at army headquarters.

Matt was ready for a change. He took no pleasure from burning farms. And a lot of the fun had gone out of matching wits with the crafty Boers after the death of Slone Shannon. He could not imagine what Colonel Streeter wanted with him, but it gave him the opportunity to get away from Colonel Westlake, a truly worthless Pommy officer.

It was only a short ride on horseback to the central railway. He smiled his way through comments from fellow officers that he would probably find himself stranded somewhere in the heart of the Free State when old De Wet cut the railway line again. Matt boarded the train and was lucky enough to find a seat, where he immediately lowered his Australian felt slouch hat over his eyes, dropped his head on his chest, and had the most comfortable sleep he had enjoyed in weeks.

CHAPTER XXXVIII

Slone Shannon's bout with fever was mercifully delayed until Sianna and he had arrived safely at the De Hartog farm in eastern Natal.

After Slone had had a hot bath and shaved, and was dressed in some of Dirk De Hartog's old clothes—the trousers just a bit too long in the legs, the shirt a bit baggy—Anna De Hartog noticed that his face showed a certain yellowish pallor.

"I'm just tired, I suppose," Slone said, when Anna asked him if he felt all right. Sianna, alerted, felt his brow and shook her head.

"It's bed for you, my good man," she said.

"No, no, I feel fine," Slone protested. "I must get into the city to report to army headquarters there."

"You will not be able to go anywhere for a while," Sianna replied.

Slone recalled how the fever had made Sianna comatose for a seemingly endless day and a half. "I will just ride into the city, report myself, and request convalescent leave."

Anna said, "If the gentleman insists, Sianna—" Sianna looked at her aunt, who winked.

"All right, if you must," Sianna agreed. She walked with Slone out of the house and down towards the stables. He was still limping noticeably, and for some reason the sun seemed to be hotter than usual. Sianna showed him a good solid horse and then led him to the tack room. She stood aside as he hoisted a saddle to his shoulder and started to walk to the pen, where the horse stood snuffling at the newcomer's scent. Halfway there he halted, swayed a bit. The world was spinning in motion around him.

"Sianna," he said, looking back over his shoulder for help just before he fell.

Anna, who had been watching, came running with two Kaffir

servants, and soon Slone was in bed, his cheeks flushed with the raging fever that swept rapidly through him. When he next awoke, feeling spent, he looked up to see the same angel he had seen once before when coming back from a long period of unconsciousness.

"This is not fair," he said.

"What is not fair?" Sianna asked.

"You did not treat my chills the same way I treated yours," he said, managing a grin.

"Ah?" she asked archly. "Are you sure? You were quite ill."

"If you had, I would have known, just as you knew."

"So," she said, nodding. "No, I treated your chills with hot bricks. After all, we are now in my home, and my aunt was here. We are no longer in the wilderness." She was smiling teasingly. "To borrow my body's warmth in this setting, Slone Shannon, you will have to marry me in a church."

"Call the preacher, then," he said.

"What's this talk about preachers?" Anna asked, coming in just as Slone spoke these last words.

"Miss De Hartog—"

"Heavens," Anna said. "Calling me that makes me feel like the old maid that I suppose I really am. Please call me Anna."

"Miss Anna," Slone said, "your niece has just told me that I must marry her."

"I did no such thing, Aunt Anna," Sianna said, her face flaming in a blush.

"Never mind the protests," Anna said. "I have known from the moment I saw you, dressed like beggars, at the front door."

"How could you possible know?" Sianna asked.

"There is a look about you," Anna answered. "About the both of you. With you, Australian soldier, the look is somewhat like that of a hungry puppy contemplating a big, chewy bone."

"Come over here then, wench," Slone said to Sianna, "and let the puppy chew his bone."

"Naughty, naughty," Sianna said and, realizing that the word had other implications for Australians, blushed again.

"So this one feels his oats again, eh?" Anna asked, but even as she spoke Slone's eyes became heavy and he lapsed back into sleep.

Anna turned to Sianna. "What happened, there in the veld?" she asked.

"The fever came to me," she said. "I suffered terrible chills. He was paralyzed from the waist down then, and he could do nothing to warm me except drag himself—"

"I see," Anna said. "It is not the first time, nor will it be the last, that someone has used his own body heat to fight the deadly chills of fever in a suffering comrade."

"I love him more than my own life, Aunt Anna."

"And it appears that he loves you. That I can see. Will you leave us then? Will you go with him to Australia?"

Even as Anna asked, she knew the answer, for if, long ago, Jon Fisher had asked her to do so, she would gladly have left her home and her family to follow him anywhere. He had not asked. She had been left with his weak declaration that he would come back for her someday. That day had never come, and she had not married. It was not that she had waited for him—for she never believed for a moment he would return; it was just that she had never met a man who was capable of taking his place in her heart.

"What *am* I to do?" Sianna asked.

"You will not have to ask when the time comes," Anna said. "Your heart will speak for you."

"And will my father say the same?"

For a moment Anna was silent. She knew that Sianna was referring as always to Dirk. She was twenty years old, this Sianna, old enough and now experienced enough by the rigours of war to know the truth—or at least a part of the truth. But how hard it would be for her to learn that the man she had called Father for twenty years was actually her uncle. No, Anna thought, it was not time to tell. Perhaps the right time would never come. Dear Lord, how she wished she could put her arms around this beautiful girl, who had done her duty to her country so well, and say finally, "My darling Sianna, for all your life you have called me Aunt Anna. Call me now the name that tells our true relationship. Call me Mother."

More than ever she felt this wish, for now it seemed almost a certainty that Sianna would leave her and go across a wide ocean to a new continent. Yet still she was silent.

After another day of discomfort, Slone quickly recovered from the effects of the fever. He had lost some weight since his wound, and was as slim as a boy. "This one will cause you much sadness," Anna teased Sianna in front of Slone. "Look at his baby face. When you are forty years old, Sianna, you will look forty and this one will look twenty and they will say, *mevreau*, you have such a handsome son."

"And I will say, 'Mother, may I go out and play with the pretty young girls?' " Slone teased.

"And I will say, 'Yes, son, go and play with the young girls, but enjoy it well for when you come back I will cut off your—'"

"Sianna!" Anna declared, bursting into outraged laughter.

In the dark of the night Sianna crept into Slone's room, waking him with her naked warmth as she crawled into bed with him, instantly transporting him into that world of passion and first love that was nothing less than earthly paradise. When their first appetite was blunted, she whispered, lips to lips, "We will have to be married soon, for if you have given me a child, we will not want the relatives counting the months."

"Right now," Slone said.

"The preacher would be cross if we awoke him in the middle of the night."

"Tomorrow, then."

"Aunt Anna will want to make some preparations."

"Soon I will have to go back, Sianna," he replied. "I want you to be my wife before I go."

The next day they approached Anna together and told her of their intentions. "I have been giving it some thought," Anna replied. "I have been expecting my brother to appear any day. I have no reason to believe that he will come soon; it is only a feeling. He was not in favour of this war in the beginning. I am sure he is not in favour of drawing it out, making it last on and on with no hope of winning, only the satisfaction of killing a few more British soldiers who have done nothing more wrong than follow orders. He will come, and it would be good, Sianna, to have him at your wedding."

"Yes," she said. "I would like to have my father here to give me away." She was looking at Slone.

He made a face at her and began to count on his fingers, "five, six, seven." She made a hush sign at him.

Slone knew that he should report his presence to army

headquarters. Then, too, he needed to have an army doctor take a look at him, because he could not get over his limp. Everything seemed to be normal except his left leg, which did not seem to want to take orders from his brain without some argument. But if he went into Pietermaritzburg and reported they would want to put him into the hospital immediately. He knew that there would be red tape, perhaps involving both the army and the civilian authorities, regarding a wartime marriage to a Boer woman. He did not know the law or army regulation in such matters, and he had no way of finding out, but he reasoned that it would be easier to take Sianna with him back to Australia if they were already legally married—under British jurisdiction and in Natal, a British colony. He decided to wait until Anna agreed to the wedding, with or without the presence of Dirk De Hartog.

When Colonel Roland Streeter received word that the Australian lieutenant who had been with Slone Shannon was on his way south by train, he was relieved. To have Van Buren, a friend of the Shannons, or at least the son of a friend of the family, might well ease the blow. As for Kit, well there was nothing he could do. She was a strong girl. She would just have to meet her sorrow head on, conquer it, and get on with her life which, at the moment, was centred on Evelyn Streeter.

Upon Matt's arrival, the colonel closeted himself with the lieutenant immediately. He listened with anxiety to Matt's account of the battle and its results. From Westlake's report it was obvious that the colonel had made serious mistakes. But when Matt had finished, Streeter felt better. Westlake, it appeared, had not done anything criminal, only stupid. And Australians tended to be troublemakers; they believed they knew more about warfare than the nation that had spawned them—the nation that had defeated Napoleon himself.

"Lieutenant Van Buren," Streeter said coldly, "I did not bring you all the way to Cape Town to criticize your superiors. I'm sure that when Colonel Westlake made his decisions, he was privy to intelligence that was not available to junior officers. He is by no means the first commander who has found it necessary to split his forces in the face of the enemy."

"By no means, sir," Matt said, his voice rising in anger.

"Chelmsford did it at Isandhlwana and lost half his command. Buller did it at Spion Kop and managed to score a single day's championship for losing men to the Boer."

"That's quite enough!" Streeter stormed. "I have brought you here, Van Buren, in the hope that you might soothe the feelings of Lieutenant Shannon's parents, the Earl and Countess of Cheviot."

"What? Old Slone was a bloody nob?" He laughed. "The sod. He didn't say so much as one word to me. Thought he was pure Australian all the way, like the rest of us. Yes, sir, I will gladly speak with Slone's parents."

"Good. I will arrange it." Streeter used the telephone. Matt was to meet with Adam Shannon within the hour.

"When did they first get the word that Slone was dead?" Matt asked as he got up to leave Streeter's office.

"Ah, well, as a matter of fact—"

"You've told them nothing?"

"Not as yet."

"Bloody hell, then you want me to . . . *Bloody hell!*" Matt said.

Roland Streeter took the easy way out with his daughter. He carried home a copy of the report of the battle of Zilikiat's Nek with the attached casualty list. Kit sensed from his serious mien that something was wrong, and as she began to read, fear came to her like a sudden cold rainstorm back home in England. She stopped reading and turned to the casualty lists and skipped to the S column.

"This isn't true," she said, quite calmly. "He can't be dead, father, for if he had been killed I would have known. I would have known it immediately. It would not be the same world without Slone in it."

"I'm sorry, Kit," Streeter said. "I'm afraid it's true. I've spoken with a man who was there. He saw Slone go down. It was a head wound."

"No," she said, still quite calm, staring off into space, "there's been some mistake."

General Herbert Kitchener, Kitchener of Khartoum, had spent some of the most frustrating months of his life in South Africa under the command of Lord Roberts. Although his title had been chief of staff, his duties had never been made totally clear by the commander-in-chief, the man who had been immortalized by Rudyard Kipling:

> There's a little red-faced man,
>   Which is Bobs,
> Rides the tallest 'orse 'e can—
>   Our Bobs.
> If it bucks or kicks or rears,
>   'E can sit for twenty years
> With a smile round both 'is ears—
>   Can't yer, Bobs?

And now, at last, the little red-faced man with the big horse was going home. Kitchener was to have his opportunity to end the bloody little war in South Africa.

As it became evident that Lord Roberts would soon be turning over command, Kitchener had quietly gathered a team, and to his great pleasure he had back with him Percy Girouard, the leader of the engineers who had built his railway in the Sudanese desert. Although Girouard was by no means the highest-ranking officer on Kitchener's staff, the cheerful young man was a man Kitchener could talk to—but only to, not with.

"I do not begrudge Lord Roberts the reception he received in Cape Town," Kitchener told Girouard, who had the good sense and the past knowledge of Kitchener's personality to confine his part of the conversation to such brilliant ripostes as "Ummm," and "Ummmm-huh."

"We can consider that the acclaim that the citizens of Cape Town gave him was an indirect tribute to the men of the army, the men who gave their blood and did the terrible work of killing and dying. But consider this, Percy, and mark it. Think about it again in, say, twenty years and see if I'm not right. I state without equivocation that no British general has ever been so overrated as Roberts."

Lord Roberts sailed to England, and word came back that the Prince of Wales had met him at Paddington Station amid clouds of flowers and bunting. He had been made a Knight of the Garter by Queen Victoria, and she was to bestow an earldom on him. Bands played "Hail The Conquering Hero Comes". The ride to Buckingham Palace with the prince was the equivalent of a state procession. Parliament was to vote Roberts an award of one hundred thousand pounds.

"No returning Caesar ever met with more acclaim," Herbert Kitchener complained to his junior aide one day in his office. "Consider, Percy, the actions for which Lord Roberts is being rewarded. He was sent out here to end the war in a satisfactory manner. He achieved exactly the opposite. In all fairness we cannot hold him totally responsible for the Boers' stubbornness, but we can say that he did nothing to prevent the start of this guerrilla war, a second and entirely new war. This new war will bring devastation and misery beyond all that we experienced on the march to Pretoria. Thousands of lives will be lost, and millions of pounds squandered in an unnecessary epilogue to a story that should, by rights, be over. Is this a prudent investment for the empire, when we all know that war, in the end, is the most wasteful of all human actions?"

Kitchener paused, put his hands behind his back, bent forward and rocked back and forth as he thought. "Do you know, Percy, that he defeated the enemy only once, at Paardeberg?"

"Yes, sir," Percy said.

"Only once, and then it was only because old Piet Cronje was pig-headed enough to make a stand, because there was a river in flood to prevent easy movement of the enemy, and, I might add, because I acted without the commander's direct order and insisted on attack. The commanding officer would have gone into trenches, Percy. Siege tactics. I sent men *forward*. I sent them into pitched battle. And even then, because the commander would not move, the Boer armies in the Cape Colony escaped. Because we sat so long in defensive positions, typhoid fever crippled the army so that we had to pause at Bloemfontein. This respite gave Koos De La Rey and De Wet the time and the freedom of movement to discover these new infernal guerrilla ways to prolong the war."

"Ummm," Percy said, as Kitchener stared at him obliquely out of his odd eye.

"He was content to push the enemy aside, like water from the bow of a ship," Kitchener went on, "and by pushing them aside he thought he was defeating them." He pounded his fist in his palm.

"You defeat the Boer only when you kill him," he said, his voice rising. "You defeat him when you not only capture him and take away one of his rifles, but when you deprive him of his *last* rifle and destroy the support system that provides him with food whenever he decides to leave his farm and fight."

Kitchener was up now and pacing, taking long strides, his voice low and pensive. "Roberts allowed the enemy to escape in front of Bloemfontein. He allowed them to withdraw when we were in a position to inflict a disastrous defeat, a defeat that would have left the Boer little strength to continue in this guerrilla fashion. He gave the enemy time to escape again at Johannesburg, and he failed to push the advantage at Diamond Hill. And still they praise him, because he moved an army a few hundred miles. Good Lord, he had nothing like the cataracts of the Nile and the Nubian Desert to contend with."

"Well, sir," Percy ventured. "It will be different now."

Kitchener smiled grimly. "It will be different," he said. "You see, Percy, Roberts had never fought white men. I believe that in his head he was still fighting the war in Afghanistan, marching out to chastise a few tribesmen by spanking them and then burning their huts. Why, on the day he captured Pretoria he was the most surprised man in the world when the Boers didn't immediately fall down on their knees and surrender. But his two biggest mistakes, Percy were, first, not sacking Buller after Spion Kop, and, second, announcing the scorched-earth policy. The first protracted the war by keeping a bungler in command. The second has stiffened the Boer's backbone more than anything that has gone before. And you and I, Percy, will pay for our former commander's decisions, you and I and those men out there in the army. We'll be here for a long time, Percy, because we're stuck with Lord Roberts's scorched-earth policy. And history will blame us for it, because we'll have to carry the policy to extremes to persuade Johnny Boer to lay down his guns and quit."

"I'm sure you're entirely right, sir," Percy said, nodding his head.

Kitchener sighed. "Well, so be it. I've never been a politician, just a simple soldier."

Percy had to lower his head to prevent Kitchener from seeing an astonished grin at so false and self-effacing a remark.

"Just a simple old soldier who does his duty," the general repeated. "Percy, we're going to have to do some railway building, and then we're going to construct the longest, most complex system of block houses the world has ever seen. We're going to fence Johnny Boer in. Then we'll go into the area where we have him confined, and we'll hunt him down as if he were a fox."

"Yes, sir," Percy said, himself giving a sigh, for he knew that when it came to building railways and blockhouses, Kitchener was speaking directly to him. His orders were now clear.

CHAPTER XXXIX

Dirk De Hartog was tossed into the air bodily by an exploding artillery shell. Little pieces of shrapnel lodged, of all places, in the fleshy, lower portions of his rump and he spent several uncomfortable days lying on his stomach in a hospital tent. His hearing had also been affected by the nearness of the explosion. The doctors said that he would gradually regain it, but Dirk was already walking, if a bit stiffly, and still, as the saying went, he was so deaf he couldn't hear it thunder.

"My friend," Koos De La Rey told him, "I think it is time for you to go home. The good Lord gave you a warning, and you must heed it. Go home, or next time the force of the shell will cut you in half instead of merely giving you a short ride through the air."

"General," Dirk replied, "isn't it time for all of us to go home, you included?"

De La Rey shook his bearded head sadly and put a finger to his temple. "In here it says, it is over, go home. In the seat of reason is the knowledge that we are beaten." He thumped his chest. "Here it says, oh, my God, the enemy is on our soil. He tramples our crops. He pens our women and children into prisons where they die of disease. Here in the heart is the anger, the desire to strike one more blow, and even the wild hope that something of our honour can be salvaged." He sighed. "I will still be fighting when your sister's loving care and good, home-cooked food have healed you. Come back then."

"I don't know, General," Dirk said. "My heart speaks to me in a voice that is different from yours."

"Well, since I fight for freedom against the English, I will not try to deprive you of your freedom of opinion," De La Rey said. "God go with you."

Dirk rode southeast into Pretoria, where he encountered the

English occupation forces. With their usual efficiency the British had the trains running on time. Botha, De Wet and De La Rey had been driven into the high veld. In Natal the British prevailed also, for there were no commandos to put down their hoes and take up their rifles and explosives to cut the rails leading to Durban.

There was hardly time for Dirk to adjust from his days in the saddle, to adjust from the dust and thirst and heat of battle to a gently rocking railway carriage moving at good speed towards his home, moving through a fertile, peaceful countryside. Yes, it was time to end the war. He would not go back. As far as it could be determined, his had been the first blow struck against the English in the war's beginning. Dirk would yield to another man the dubious honour of striking the last blow.

At the farm outside Pietermaritzburg, Dirk held Anna in his arms for a long, long time, tender and patient with her tears of happiness. Her first words to him made his world right again. "Sianna is here," she told him. "Now I have back all those I love. God is kind." She sniffed, wiped her eyes, and smiled broadly. "And is there a surprise for you!"

Sianna and Slone had been sitting in the cool shade of the veranda. Dirk stepped up, and Sianna, with a scream of joy, threw herself into his arms. Then, laughing, weeping, she pulled back and looked at Dirk. "Father, you're too thin," she said. "And you've been wounded."

"Only slightly," he said. "And I forbid either of you to ask me where."

"Well, we will know, won't we, Aunt Anna?" Sianna said. She turned as Slone approached. "Father, may I present Lieutenant Slone Vincent Shannon, of the British Army, the man I am going to marry."

Slone stepped forward and bowed. Dirk offered his hand, and Slone took it, gave a typically brief, almost embarrassed British handshake.

"I know you," Dirk said.

"If we came face to face in battle, sir, I am glad that neither of us succeeded in killing the other," Slone said.

"No, no, not battle." Dirk snapped his fingers. "You rode into the city to deliver General Roberts's demand for surrender."

"Ah, yes," Slone said. "You stood slightly behind him at those unfortunate ceremonies."

"It is a small war," Dirk said. He beamed at his two women. "And so, while I ride the veld, fighting to my last breath, you two harbour the enemy in my own home." But he was smiling. "The man you are going to marry?" he asked, turning to Sianna.

"Enemy no more, sir," Slone said. "Let us pray that soon all those who are still fighting will be in their homes, as well."

"Yes," Dirk replied sombrely. "But now what's this about marriage?"

"I was going to ask you properly, Colonel De Hartog," Slone said.

"Well, that was not necessary, after all," Sianna put in, "for I found this one abandoned, thrown away, in the veld, and I decided that I would keep him for a pet."

"I think I detect a story here," Dirk said. "I had assumed, Sianna, that you were safely confined in a British camp. You can't image my relief at finding you here."

"We came all the way, through the British lines, through everything," Sianna said.

Nothing would do but for Dirk to hear the whole story. When, after some hesitation, Sianna confessed how Slone had struggled against his own disability to care for her when she had the fever, Dirk looked at Slone with sympathetic speculation.

"Well, perhaps it will not be too shameful, having an Englishman in the family," was his comment.

"Australian," Sianna corrected him. "There's a difference."

"I know," Dirk said. "I just thank God that there were no more Australians in General Roberts's army."

Dirk's face turned a bit red when he realized that this man, this Slone Shannon, had probably been forced to remove Sianna's clothing, to swab her body with cooling alcohol, to warm her with his own body heat. In ordinary times Sianna would have been totally compromised by the intimacy that they had shared, and if the Australian had not wanted to marry her, Dirk would have had to insist on the wedding at the point of a gun.

Later that day, as Anna was preparing the evening meal and Slone had gone to his room to change, Dirk had a chance to talk with Sianna. She was a bit shy, at first, and she asked him if she had been too sudden, too quick in telling her father she had decided to marry Slone.

"No," Dirk reassured her. "Unless my eyes deceive me, you love this Slone Shannon very much."

"Oh, yes," she said.

"And you are certain that is not simply because you two have shared an adventure, hardship and danger, and have managed to survive by working together?"

"No," she said. "No, Father. I do love him." She came to embrace Dirk and look up into his face. "He will take me to Queensland, in Australia," she said. "My heart breaks to think of leaving you and Aunt Anna, but—"

"The Good Book says that it is God's plan that man and wife cleave together, leaving father and mother, to become one flesh." He kissed her on the forehead, wondering, as Anna had before him, if at last the time had come to tell her the truth about her parentage. Now she was a woman. The last vestige of childhood, of girlhood, had been burned away by the war. Did she not have the right to know? And did not Anna have the right to accept one final embrace as mother before her child was taken from her across great and watery distances?

There were four of them at the table, Slone and Sianna seated across from one another, eyes often meeting. It was good, Dirk felt, to see them thus. And it was ironic that this girl whom he had called daughter, this girl who was actually half Australian, would become the wife of an Australian. Odd, though, that in two different wars fate would bring an Australian soldier to the De Hartog house to win the love of a De Hartog woman. Twenty years ago the woman in love had been his sister. Looking back he felt no anger, no resentment. God had known what he was doing when he gave them Sianna, for she had been a joy for both of them. Thanks be to the frail girl who had become Dirk's wife and who had not lived to see in maturity the child that had been passed off as hers.

"So, in two wars now, De Hartog women have nursed Australian soldiers back to health," he said aloud.

Anna looked at him, raising one eybrow, but something drove him on. "I, too, Sianna, found a wounded Australian—two of them, in fact—in the veld. At the Buffalo River I found them.

Zulus everywhere. They'd just killed Chelmsford's army and they wanted more blood, but the Australians fought well, and I brought two of them back here with me for my sister to nurse. Harry Ryan and Jon Fisher were their names."

Anna was looking down at her plate, not eating. She sensed the earth moving under her feet.

"Pardon me, sir, did you say Jon Fisher?" Slone asked.

"I did," Dirk answered.

Slone laughed. "It's a smaller world than any of us suspected, sir," he said. "Jon Fisher was my half-brother. Couldn't be anyone else. He was in business for a while with a man named Harry Ryan, and I remember my father telling me—" He halted in consternation.

Dirk had dropped his fork. It clattered against his plate and fell to the floor. Anna's face had gone white.

"Father?" Sianna gasped. "Is something wrong?"

Dirk controlled himself with difficulty. He had suspected that Sianna's account of her ordeal with Slone in the veld had omitted a few intimate details. Now he prayed fervently that that was so. He forced himself to be calm. "There is nothing wrong," he said. But his voice was low, cold. "Anna, come with me."

Anna rose swiftly. Dirk strode from the room, his back straight and stiff. Anna cast a stricken look back at Sianna, biting her upper lip. It was a look that Sianna had seen before, and she gasped in fright to see it. It was worse than her father's enigmatic reaction.

"What did I say?" Slone queried.

"I have no idea," she replied.

Dirk led the way into his study and closed the door behind him. "It is God's punishment," he said. "They were alone in the veld, Anna, both of them, desperate and frightened. There is a look to her, a rose in the cheek, a secret in the way she looks at him."

"No, no," Anna protested.

"Incest," he whispered. "God help them, how could they know? How could they even suspect?"

Anna was having difficulty breathing. Her chest was heaving. Perhaps it was God's punishment, but if so she was to be punished for a sin that was not Dirk's but her own.

"There is nothing to do but tell them," Dirk said. "Who will drive the knife into her heart?"

"She is my daughter," Anna said.

He went to her and took her in his arms. "Ah, sister," he said, "how our old sins do follow us." He sighed. "The sooner we tell them, the better. It's a hard thing, to lose a lover and gain—what? An uncle? Half uncle? I don't think that she will consider that a fair exchange."

Although Dirk was not as severe in his religious beliefs as some, he was a Boer, and he had lived by the Bible all his life. The Bible said that fornication was a sin, but in his mind there were varying degrees of evil attached to that most universal of human activities. If the truth were known, he had always suspected many young couples had sampled the forbidden fruit while waiting for the church to bless their union.

Before Slone's chilling words at the dinner table, he would have said that if Sianna and Slone had indeed consoled each other, had given each other love and warmth in a way that went beyond the teachings of the Bible—all while they were in a desperate situation in the wilderness—then he was sure that God would understand and forgive, once they were married. But incest was a dark and unnatural sin, a sin to put a blot on the record of a man's, and a woman's, life forever. And what if Sianna had conceived? Dirk's mind raged against itself. *Please, God, do not let it happen.*

For Anna, the moment was torment. The old sins were catching up with her, but not exactly in the manner which Dirk so feared. "Brother," she said, "I have thought for some time now that Sianna should know the truth of her birth."

"What has that to do with—"

She put her soft hand on his lips to hush him. "It has everything to do with her love for Slone Shannon," she said. "Come." For she, too, had made up her mind. It would be difficult to tell the whole truth, but to withhold it meant not only sadness and loss, but also shame for her own daughter. "Come with me," she insisted, letting Dirk leave the room first.

"What is wrong with you two?" Sianna asked, as Dirk and Anna re-entered the dining room.

"Sianna, my dear child," Anna said, "there is something difficult that you must hear."

Slone, looking at Anna questioningly, started to rise to give the family some privacy. "No, Slone," Anna said. "What I have to say affects you, as well."

Dirk went to his place at the head of the table and sat down. A Kaffir serving maid entered and poured coffee as Anna took her own chair and waited for the maid to finish and leave. Then she lifted her head, and with chin high, a determined look on her face, she began.

"Dirk told you that I nursed an Australian soldier, Jon Fisher, back to health in this house. It is truly odd that it should happen again, that a woman of this house should bring a wounded Australian soldier here." She looked into Sianna's eyes. "You love this one," she said. "I fell in love with the other, twenty years ago."

"Oh," Sianna said softly, her eyes searching Dirk's for confirmation.

"He did not return that love," Anna said, "or at least not enough to stay with me or to ask me to go with him. He left me here. Nine months later, Sianna, you were born."

Sianna's eyes went wide. "Aunt Anna!"

"Yes," Anna said. "You are my own blood, Sianna, my daughter."

Sianna leapt to her feet, a little cry of surprise escaping her lips. "You know," she whispered, "I think I've always known, or suspected. There's always been something special between us."

"Sianna," Dirk said softly, "you are still missing one important aspect of Anna's revelation."

Slone Shannon had not missed it. He felt cold, felt a kind of fury begin to grow in him, for he had made the connection immediately. This girl, this blond angel whose love he had known, whose body he had shared, was incontrovertibly of his blood.

"Oh, God," Sianna said, falling back into her chair, looking at Slone helplessly.

"Wait," Anna said. "I have more to say."

Sianna was looking at Dirk, tears streaming. "Then you are not my father?"

Dirk shook his head and looked away, unable to speak lest he, too, break into tears.

"I am the daughter of—"

"Be silent," Anna said firmly. "Listen." She looked at Dirk and hesitated. What she had to say would hurt him, too, but it would be an old hurt and it was, after all, her daughter's happiness that was at stake. "Neither was Jon Fisher your father, Sianna. I told my brother that it was he, but it was not. Jon kissed me. He was a perfect gentleman. He was never in my bed."

"Anna?" Dirk said, puzzled.

"Perhaps he cared for me a bit," Anna said, "but he told me good-bye eagerly and went on his way with only a halfhearted statement that perhaps he might return someday. I knew that I would never see him again, and the need for his kiss, for his love, burned in me. I was young, and I was very much in love, and I was devastated when he left. I knew that the way I was thinking was a sin, but I would have gladly crawled into his bed in the dead of night had he not been gone. I had been deprived of even the opportunity to sin, and I was resentful. I blamed God, and I set out to punish him, and perhaps Jon Fisher, although he would never know. I would give to another man that which Jon Fisher disdained. I will not speak his name, not even to this day. He was Boer, Sianna. You are Boer. And the truth is you have none of the Fisher or the Shannon blood in you."

"Oh, Anna!" Sianna cried, running around the table. "Oh, dear Anna, I'm so sorry. How terribly you must have suffered."

"Anna," Dirk asked in a low voice. "Why did you lie? Why did you tell me that the father of the child was Jon Fisher?"

"Because he was far away," Anna said. "Because if I had told you that I had gone out in my grief to give myself to a Boer boy, you would have forced me to marry him, and I didn't love him."

"But you—" Dirk didn't finish.

"I used him," Anna said. "I used him to show God how angry I was that he had taken Jon Fisher from me, and to punish myself for not forcing Jon to make love to me."

"You're my own mother," Sianna said in wonder. She turned to Slone. "I have a mother after all, and she is so beautiful."

"Yes, she is," Slone agreed, his face beaming with gratitude.

Sianna's smile faded. "But how can I leave you now, Aunt . . . M-m-mother, just when I've found you?"

"No such talk," Anna said. "I have not gone through this agony of confession for nothing. I have already sewn your wedding gown. Now that Dirk is here we *will* have a wedding."

It was not an elaborate affair. No one wanted to have to explain to hordes of relative strangers why a good Boer woman was marrying one of the enemy. But it was a beautiful wedding, with the words intoned by the full-bearded minister in both Afrikaans and English, with Slone using a ring borrowed from Anna to place on Sianna's finger.

Two days later Slone and Sianna went down to Durban by train. Sianna was at his side when he reported in at army headquarters. He gave a bored-looking sergeant-clerk his name, rank, and last unit of service, adding that he would like his whereabouts to be made known to General Kitchener himself.

"By all means, sir," the sergeant said, with fine sarcasm. then he looked up sharply. "Lieutenant Slone Vincent Shannon, Queensland Mounted Infantry?"

"Yes, that's right, Sergeant," Slone replied.

"Please wait here, sir," the sergeant requested, disappearing into an inner office on the run. He came back with a cadaverous major who saluted Slone smartly even though Slone was the junior officer and not in uniform.

"You're supposed to be dead, Lieutenant," the major said. "Cape Town has been moving heaven and earth to locate your body."

"I am pleased to report, sir, that my body is here, and only slightly damaged and very much alive," Slone said.

"My telegraph operator is trying to reach Cape Town headquarters at this moment," the major said, and no sooner was it said than a clerk came hurrying out with a sheet of paper in his hand.

"From Colonel Streeter, army headquarters, Cape Town," the clerk said. "Lieutenant Shannon is to take the first available transportation to Cape Town and report personally to General Adam Shannon, at the Cape Hotel."

"My father? In Cape Town?" Slone asked, looking at Sianna. He turned back. "Well, thank you sir. I wonder if I might draw some fresh clothing from supply?"

Telling Adam and Emily Shannon that their son was dead, that he had seen him fall, was one of the hardest things that Matt Van Buren had ever done. He did it while standing stiffly at attention, his voice low, and when he had finished he added, "I am so very sorry to have to be the one to tell you."

"You saw him fall, shot in the head?" Adam asked, as Emily sobbed into her handkerchief.

"I did, sir."

"But you couldn't get to his side to see if he was dead?"

"I could not, sir. He had ordered me, only moments before, to try to extricate the troops from the ambush. When I saw him fall I began to implement those orders."

"As he would have wanted you to do," Adam said. "And you were not in the party that buried the dead, so you never actually saw him dead, you only saw him fall?"

Emily looked up, holding back her sobs. Adam put his arm around her. "Please don't get your hopes up, my dear," he said. "I was merely trying to be certain we had the entire story."

"Sir," Matt said, "if he had been taken by the Boers, I believe that he would have escaped by now. They're not too keen on feeding prisoners, the Boers, so they don't guard their prison laagers very closely."

Emily, however, was not easily placated. The news of her son's death was entirely too shocking, even though all through his military service some part of her—a part she did not like listening to—had told her again and again of that distinct possibility. And so she pressed Adam to agree with their staying on in Cape Town just a few more days, if only to let the reality of their sad loss sink in. Actually, she knew, it was to give luck enough time to reverse itself.

Thus it was that when the word came from Durban that Lieutenant Slone Vincent Shannon was very much alive, recovered from his wounds, and on his way by fast steamer to Cape Town, the earl and his lady were still in the Cape Hotel. After overcoming her tears of joy, Emily went immediately to the Streeter house to tell Kit the good news.

"I knew," Kit said, with a straight face. "I knew all along that he wasn't dead."

Emily was impressed by the girl's faith and resolution. "We'll give him a splendid welcome," she said. "We'll have a huge meal, a party at the hotel. You'll be there, his friend Matt Van Buren will be there, Adam and I will be there, and your father."

Kit was beaming, and Emily said. "You're very beautiful, my dear. I'm going to be pleased having you for a daughter-in-law."

"And I feel so fortunate to have you," Kit said sincerely.

Emily embraced her, kissed her on the forehead. "We'll have fun, you and I. The estate of the Earl of Cheviot is a large, rich one. We'll shop at the finest stores in London, spend money as if it were going to be outlawed next day."

"Then I think I shall feel almost wicked," Kit said with a giggle. "Mother and I have always had to skimp along on an army officer's salary."

Steamships, unlike sailing ships at the mercy of the wind and the elements, could keep a fairly close schedule. The ship on which Slone was a passenger arrived in Table Bay on the appointed day. As it was laid alongside a dock Slone kept looking for his parents, but did not see them. Instead he saw a young corporal holding a sign that read Lieutenant Shannon. When he and Sianna had disembarked he hailed the man and identified himself.

"There are men to take care of your luggage, sir," the corporal assured him. "I'm to take you to the Cape Hotel immediately."

"I suspect it's a bit of a surprise party," Slone told Sianna as they rode through the Cape Town streets in a carriage. He put his arm around her. "We'll have a bit of a surprise of our own for them, eh?"

"Oh, Slone, will they like me?"

"I've told you they will," he said. "How could they not? You're my wife. You're pretty, too, for an old Boer lady."

She elbowed him in the ribs. "You didn't call me an old Boer lady last night in our cabin."

"Nor the night before," he said. "What do you say, instead of joining my parents, we take a room and—"

She said a word in Afrikaans. He asked, "And what does that mean?"

"It means greedy-gut," she answered.

He tried to bite her ear, and she squealed and pulled away, causing the driver to turn around and look at them curiously.

At the hotel they were ushered quickly through to a private dining room. A bellman opened the door and motioned Sianna through, so that a pretty, blond girl was seen by those inside the room before Slone himself entered. There were banners and balloons. A sign suspended on the far wall read Welcome Home Shannon. Adam led a cheer as Slone, grinning, stood just inside the doorway, his hand on Sianna's arm proudly. And then he saw Kit Streeter. She was standing at the end of the table with her father, and her face was puzzled as she looked at him and the blond girl. Emily, unable to stand it any longer, started towards Slone.

He raised his hand and said, "Wait, Mother, listen. Before you begin to embarrass me with affection—"

"Back from the dead and he orders me about," Emily said, laughing.

"I want to introduce you to someone. Mother, Father, everyone"—he deliberately did not address Kit or Colonel Roland Streeter—"this is Sianna, *née* De Hartog, now Mrs. Slone Vincent Shannon."

Matt Van Buren, standing to Kit Streeter's right, saw out of the corner of his eye trouble on its way and, acting with the reflexes of the young, caught Kit before she hit the floor in a faint. Her eyes, were closed, her breathing rapid. He carried her to a couch and lay her down and began to fan her face with his hand. Heads in the small crowd turned this way and that. No one seemed sure what to do or say next.

PART THREE
1901

CHAPTER XL

As the year 1900 ended, soldiers began to return home to Australia from the South African war. When the New South Wales contingent arrived in Sydney, it was as if the Mafeking celebration, during which Java Gordon and Tolo Mason had first felt the true heat of youthful love, had been only a warm-up.

On the morning after, Johnny Broome's editorial fairly sizzled. "It would take the pencil of a Hogarth," he wrote, "or the pen of a Juvenal to do justice to the Saturnalia that occurred last evening on Sydney's streets."

Johnny was dining once again at the Broome house, which had become temporarily a Broome house in truth, since Sam and Jessica Gordon were in England. Magdalen presided as hostess, for without Java, the purpose for her accompanying the Gordons to England had vanished, and the elderly woman had chosen to remain behind in Sydney. Though she knew it would never happen, she secretly wished that Java would come back to her.

Other guests that evening included Sydney's two most eligible widows, the good friends Misa Mason and Bina Tyrell. Now that the Gordon family was tied to the Mason family by marriage, Misa had become a regular at Magdalen's table, and Bina was nearly always with her.

Misa had at first been shocked by her son's sudden marriage, but Bina had encouraged her to accept it. In the end Misa, like Tolo, came to see in his action something of herself: he had reached boldly for happiness, and she was secretly proud of him.

This evening Misa and Bina seemed to be intent on outdressing each other, so that they fairly glowed in the latest fashion, making it a pleasure for Johnny to look across the table to see them sitting side by side. He had taken to referring to the three women, Magdalen, Misa, and Bina, as the "TNT Threesome." They were an improbable but inseparable trio: the respectable Sydney matriarch, the ex-madam of a bawdy house, and the very rich Mrs. Mason were often in each other's company and could be seen three or more nights a week at their private table in Bina's place.

"The problem is," Johnny was saying, "that every man wants to be a swashbuckler." He laughed. "It might have been worse had not so many of the returning troops been too drunk to leave their barracks."

"They were having a high old time," said Clive Taylor, manager of the newest and most successful seaside hotel in Australia. He laughed. "You've never seen such stumbling and staggering. I'd say that our boys went off to South Africa and promptly forgot how to hold their booze."

"I'd say," Magdalen commented, "that Australian manhood has come to a sorry pass when they make such spectacles of themselves."

"Now Mrs. Broome," Clive said, "you must admit that the girls had something to do with egging them on."

Magdalen gave a ladylike snort through her nose. "Yes, I will agree."

"Made me wish I was a returning fighting man," Clive said. "Terrible way to go, to be smothered with kisses from dozens, hundreds of girls."

"The jails are full," Johnny said. "The courts will be packed for months trying the cases of assault, drunkenness and indecency."

"I suppose that all we need is Henry Lawson to write that the capitalists have debauched the people to distract their minds from the legitimate problems of society," Magdalen said. "Poor Henry. I wonder how he's doing out in London."

"Well, he swore he was not going to parade down the London streets in top hat, gloves, and spats," Johnny reminded them.

"If the people celebrate so wildly the homecoming of a relatively small number of troops from a war that has not yet been won," Misa asked, "what will they do when January first comes, both New Year's Day and Commonwealth Day?"

"God help us," Johnny said.

On January 1, 1901, to everyone's surprise, the crowds were orderly. Trams, trains, and ferry boats had carried people into town to jam the city, to cheer buxom ladies costumed as Britannia and Australia. Triumphal arches had been built across the streets. Marching on the avenues were the Shearers' Union and the Australian Workers' Union. Crowds cheered banners calling for an Eight-Hour Working Week. Prancing horses pulled gleaming fire engines. A banner reading One People One Destiny drew cheers wherever it was seen throughout the city. And throughout Australia there was jubilation. Silver miners from Broken Hill, gold miners from Western Australia, seamen, tin-miners, timber cutters, slaughterhouse workers, tailors, drovers and shearers, stockmen and bushmen, bank clerks and their ladies cried, "A continent for a nation and a nation for a continent!"

On that sultry January day the air in Sydney was heavy, and the thousands of flags were damp and limp from a shower early in the morning. Australian and imperial troops on parade added military gleam and glitter, and the sound of martial music competed with the crowd at Centennial Park singing the old hymn, "O God our help in ages past, our hope in years to come."

Magdalen accompanied Misa and Bina Tyrell, and Clive Taylor acted as escort for the ladies at what everyone knew was to be a momentous occasion. First they heard the Anglican Archbishop of Sydney, William Saumarez Smith, hold sway against the evils of gambling, drinking to excess, and the worship of the body. And then the governor-general-designate read the Queen's historic proclamation: "We do hereby declare that on and after the First Day of January One Thousand Nine Hundred and One, the people of New South Wales, Victoria, South Australia, Queensland, Tasmania, and Western Australia shall be united in a Federal Commonwealth under the name of Commonwealth of Australia."

Hearing the words, Magdalen wept quietly. She wept for her dead husband, Red, who would have been so pleased by these events. On January 26, it would be one hundred and thirteen years since his grandmother, Jenny Taggart, had landed in Sydney with the first fleet of convicts to arrive in New South Wales.

She wept, too, for her daughter, Jessica, far away in England and missing the grand day, and for her granddaughter, Java. Mostly for Java, for the day would have meant more to her than to any of them. She told herself that wherever Java and Tolo were— Java's most recent letters had come from Perth, in Western

Australia—they were sure to be celebrating the day. God, how she missed the girl. She let her thoughts stray, tried to picture Java in bush clothing, tramping through some desolate wilderness to see how the Aborigines lived in the wild, and she felt a hint of anger. Magdalen was not a young woman. She wanted her family about her. She wanted Sam and Jessica to come home from their holiday in Europe, and she wanted her granddaughter to come home from wherever.

All right, all of you, she said to herself, *you've all had your little tantrums, and you, Java, and you, Tolo, have had your way. I will grant you that much. But now it's time to come home.*

"Look, Magdalen," Misa Mason said, bringing the grand-mother out of her reverie. "The new flag, the flag of Australia."

A mighty roar from the huge crowd filled the square, echoed up and down the streets, reached to the heavy sky where, in the distance, thunder rumbled.

Thousands of miles away to the west, across the Indian Ocean, Matt Van Buren lifted his glass to his fellow officers on New Year's Day and said, "Gentlemen, I give you the Commonwealth of Australia."

"Hear, hear," they said, and they drank.

Matt had not gone home with those Australians being repatriated after having fought the wily Boer for over a year. He had had some little difficulty in finding a way to stay, but he had managed it, with the help of his friend Slone Shannon, the bloody heir to an earldom, before Slone went off to England with his blond Boer wife and his stunned but proud parents. Matt was attached to the staff of Colonel Roland Streeter, with the job of easing the integration of fresh contingents of Australian troops into the British Army. Old Johnny Boer was still fighting and giving a noble account of himself. Matt did not particularly want to rejoin the fighting, but he had a reason for wanting to stay in South Africa.

Her name was Kit Streeter. From the first time he had seen her he had thought that she was the most beautiful girl in the world. Ever since the day he had held her briefly, as he saved her from falling straight to the floor in a faint when Slone introduced his new wife, Matt had wanted to claim the right and the privilege of putting his arms around Kit Streeter whenever he wanted to.

As for Kit, one painful event had followed another. On the heels of her discovery that Slone Shannon had brought a bride down to Cape Town from Natal, she had to organize the funeral of her mother. It had been sad, but also a blessing, the end of terrible pain for Evelyn Streeter, a release from mortal bondage. Although Kit at first had been quite reserved with Matt Van Buren, his genuine interest in her, his sympathy when he appeared unexpectedly at her mother's funeral, could not help but make an impression on the young woman. When her father, in a kind of shock following her mother's death, said, "Good God, Kit, not another bloody Australian hanging around the house," she had looked at him calmly and spoken softly.

"I don't blame my dead mother for causing me to lose the man I loved very much," she said, "for she was ill and quite often did not know what she was saying or doing. I do blame you. I love you, Father, and I respect you, but I will never, never allow you to decide for me again whom I will see, or, eventually, whom I will marry."

If Matt Van Buren could have heard those words, he would have been greatly cheered.